Reviews of the book *Mobile as 7th of the Mass Media*

"Tomi instinctively knows that in the tumult of convergence between mobile and other media, there lies opportunity. In this book, building on his earlier themes, he presents his ideas with characteristic wit and charm, handily demystifying this new media landscape. A most enjoyable and remarkably practical book, his best yet!"

Daniel Appelquist, Senior Technology Strategist, **Vodafone Group** UK

"Tomi Ahonen has always been a visionary and lucid thinker about media in general, but especially ahead of the pack in his insight about the profound computing revolution that is being led by digital mobile phones. This book provides a solid foundation for how we got here, why, and what's next."

Trip Hawkins, Chairman & CEO **Digital Chocolate** USA
Founder of **Electronic Arts** USA

"Tomi's latest book continues his deep insights into the mobile industry and provides practical examples of advanced media concepts utilizing the unique benefits of mobile. I can warmly recommend this book for anyone who wants to deploy media concepts to mobile."

Jari Tammisto, CEO & President, **Mobile Monday Global**, Finland

"Tomi Ahonen's latest book adds to the wealth of insights he has given to the industry, and has useful perceptions of how the Japanese market is evolving as it adjusts to cellphones as a mass media channel."

Ted Matsumoto, Executive Vice President and Chief Strategy Officer, **Softbank** Japan

"Tomi's book takes us through the changes and opportunities in this new converged world of voice, data and broadcast media. With fascinating examples from around the world he lays out the potential for an industry that could become one of the largest in the world. Anyone who is interested in the future of mobile should read this book."

Colin Crawford, Executive VP Interactive, **IDG Communications** USA

"Tomi Ahonen is the most thoughtful commentator on the mobile industry: his theory that mobile is a new mass media is spot on."

Mark Curtis, CEO **Flirtomatic** UK
Author of ***Distraction: Being Human in a Digital Age***

"Tomi's latest book offers a deep comprehension into how advanced marketing and advertising concepts can be built using mobile phones. His style of mixing real world practical examples with the latest customer insights and sound commercial data makes his books so valuable in understanding mobile in leading markets today."

BJ Yang, CEO **AirCross** South Korea

"Tomi has built a compelling story not just of how the mobile platform will evolve, but how the other 6 media platforms will ultimately be part of the 7th mobile platform. In other words, he demonstrates the fundamental shift from 'mobile communications' to 'personalized communications' and in the long run, to 'all personalized transctions and interactions' and that this will encompass all elements of the value chain from research and awareness building to sales, marketing, production, service and lifecycle. Welcome to the world of the segment and segments of one customer. Bravo, Tomi."

Garrett Johnston, Chief Marketing Officer, **MTS** Russia

Tomi T Ahonen

Mobile as 7th of the Mass Media

Cellphone, cameraphone, iPhone, smartphone

By
Tomi T Ahonen

FUTURETEXT

Copyright © 2008 futuretext Limited
www.futuretext.com

Copyright ©2008 futuretext Limited
issue date 08.08.2008
Published by
futuretext
36 St George Street
Mayfair
London
W1S 2FW, UK
e-mail: info@futuretext.com
www.futuretext.com

ISBN   978-0-9556069-5-3□□□□

Contents

Foreword

Mobiles are an integral part of our lives – so much that many of us cannot remember a time without them. To have a mobile has become second nature and we are generally never separated from them – we eat, breathe and, yes, even sleep with our mobile phones – making them the most private and personal accessory we own today.

And yet, there is still a lack of understanding about how mobile can be a powerful, complimentary mass media. It can be boiled down to two key differentiators: 1) mobile is interactive; and 2) mobile has unique features including SMS and MMS. These differentiators create something that no other media can – the ability to respond to, initiate and maintain a dialogue between those wanting to communicate, whether they are family and friends, colleagues, or brands and advertisers. In Tomi Ahonen's book, Mobile as 7th of the Mass Media, he describes the differentiators associated with mobile in a thought-provoking way.

He brings to light some interesting insights about mobile as the 7th and most compelling mass media. While the book rightly concedes that mobile will not replace other media, he makes a strong case for why it will be the dominant media – namely because it will be more disruptive than the Internet was ten years ago. For example, SMS text messaging – the primary source of mobile communication – enables immediate response. Tomi points out that on average people respond within 5 minutes to SMS messages. Moreover, immediate response, interactivity and mass mobile adoption have been spearheaded by the youth generation. This insight sets the foundation for successful mobile media models – Blyk is an example of this – and illustrates how young people can be incentivised (e.g. free voice and texts) to engage in a dialogue with brands via SMS.

So with this, marketers would do well to heed Tomi's call to action and understand the scale of the opportunity presented by mobile as a mass media. Consumer behavior has made it clear that mobile phones are vastly important to our everyday lives and are the major vehicle by which we communicate with one another. Bearing this in mind, marketers must also recognize the importance of providing relevant mobile messages that add value to the life of people. I recall a post from Tomi's Communities Dominate Brands blog: "Brands in today's world need to be three things: 1) life enabling; 2) life simplifying; and 3) navigational (help me navigate my life better)." Mobile as a media can allow brands to be these three things.

Mobile as 7th of the Mass Media sharply describes how mobiles will change the media landscape and presents new thinking about how brands and advertisers will communicate with consumers in the future. Tomi articulates his vision for mobile as a media with a rare marketing prescience that is sure to benefit all that are listening.

Pekka Ala-Pietilä
CEO and Co-Founder, Blyk
Past President, Nokia

*"If I have been able to see farther than others, it was
because I stood on the shoulders of giants."*
Sir Isaac Newton

Acknowledgements

This is my sixth book. In some ways this is the "sequel" to my second book, *m-Profits*. It is also a culmination of all that is mobile-related from each of my first five books, and the blogsite. I have put more effort into this book than ever before, recognising that many of the readers of this book will have read some of my previous works, and I wanted regular readers to be able to find new insights. But this is even more an industry depending on collaboration, and my own insights have grown through the help of so many others.

I have to start with my three gurus. There is Voytek Siewierski, formerly with NTT DoCoMo in Tokyo and later in London, but now works in finance with Mitsui in California, simply the best brain in telecoms. Then Jouko Ahvenainen, the most pessimistic and sarcastic man I've ever met in an industry of pessimist technologists. We started our professional journeys sitting at neighboring cubicles at Nokia. Jouko went onto head Cap Gemini Ernst & Young's 3G consulting competence and now is Chairman of Xtract in London. My third guru is Alan Moore, co-author of my fourth book *Communities Dominate Brands* and CEO of SMLXL. He coined the term *Engagement Marketing*. Alan is my blogging partner at the Communities Dominate Blog. I also want to thank my other co-authors Timo Kasper, Sara Melkko, Jim O'Reilly and Joe Barrett.

Next I mention a couple of people who have supported my career for longer periods: Alex Tan Nokia-Siemens, Neil Montefiore M1, Steve Jones 3G Portal, Krzysztof Procska Polkomtel, Ajit Jaokar Futuretext, Russell Anderson Nokia, Lars Cosh-Ishii Wireless Watch Japan, Mikki Jang MEF Asia, Peter Holland Oxford, Sharon Haran Partner/Orange, Paul Golding Motorola, Luciana Pavan MTV, Mike Short O2 and MDA, Peter Miles SubTV, Dan Applequist Vodafone, Rory Sutherland Ogilvy, Mike Beeston and Olof Schybergson Fjord, David Cushman Emap, Esther Villancher Frost & Sullivan, Mike Wright Striata, Helen "Technokitten" Keegan Tanla, Faith McGary Infoxx, Rich Sepcic Dun & Bradstreet, Ed Candy Three, Jari Tammisto MoMo, Alvin Yap Nexgen, Jackie Danicki Qik, and last but by no means least, Taina Kalliokoski of Fujitsu.

Then there are the authors. And it is delightful to get to connect with many of these, so my thanks to Russell Buckley, Tony Fish, Chetan Sharma, Howard Rheingold, Christian Lindholm, Mark Curtis, Kim Dushinski, Rod Ghani Agha, Harri Holma, Antti Toskala, Paul May, Chavez Miguel Leon, Unhelkar Bhuvan, Tom Hayes and Ben Rigby.

Some journalists have been instrumental in helping me with my visibility. This is incomplete but I want to mention Vic Keegan and Michael Fitzpatrick at *Guardian*, Maija Palmer *Financial Times*, Derek Chen Channel News Asia, Kristie Lu-Stout CNN, Matthew Weigand *Korea IT Times*, Dennis Bournique *Wap Review*, Arik Hesseldahl and Stephen Baker *Business Week*, Stephen McClelland *Newsweek*, Jennifer Schenker *Red Herring*, Alan Mitchell *Marketing Week*, Mark Newman and Jessica Sandin Informa, Ewan McLeod *SMS Text News*, Seong-Ju Lee *Telecoms Korea*, Holly Owen *Mega*, Barry Welford *Web Pro News*, Joyce Schwarz *i Media Connection*, Diane Hessan and Julie Wittes Schlack *Brandweek*, Dan Nysted *Macworld*, Shashank Tripathi *CNet*.

And so many many more colleagues, so let me just mention Steven Chan AMI,

Daniel Scuka Wireless Watch Japan, Olav Henrik Kjorstad Telenor, Dr Hyun-Oh Yoo SK Communications, Kenneth Chang MiTV, Werner Braeg Stephan Eberhagen Rick Pryor Stefan Ciesielski Dieter Klein Dr Margit Brandl Siemens; Benjamin Joffe Plus8Star, Thomas Hansen and Jakob Holst TDC, Peta Spinks and Glenn Price Motorola, Gerhard Louw T-Mobile, Claude Florin HP, Patrick Scodeller M1, Klaus Muller Drei, Blums Pineda Globe, Teresa Richards Naked, Ted Matsumoto Softbank, Antti Öhrling Pekka Ala-Pietilä and Jonathan MacDonald Blyk, Ryan Wickware Amdocs, Karri Mikkonen TeliaSonera, Kazutomo Hori Cyworld, Garrett Johnston MTS, BJ Yang Aircross, Paul Lee KTF, Eleonora Villanova Buongiorno, William Volk MyNuMo, Peter McKinnon LG-Nortel, Hock Yun Khoong and Philip Heah IDA, Walter Adamson Digital Investor, Tracy Klinger Comverse, Ryan Wuerch Motricity, Marina Levina Ericsson, Trip Hawkins and Mika Tammenkoski Digital Chocolate, Heikki Karimo IBM, James Parton O2, Roberto Saracco TIM, Judi Romanchuk in Calgary, Kari Onniselkä Talent Partners, Steve "Keitai Steve" Flaherty, Dr Hannes Ametsreiter and Dr Alexander Kucher Mobilkom Austria, Claus Nehmzov Shazam, Gregory Gorman Open Group, Josh Dhaliwal Mobile Youth, Graham Brown Wireless World Forum, Alan Hadden GSA, Anna Peron CWTA, Christopher Billich Infinita, Agustin Calvo Movidream, Stephanie Frasco Basement Inc.

Then there are all the other bloggers that I read starting with Oliver Starr of Mobile Crunch, Xen Mendelsohn Xellular, Peggy Ann Salz M Search Groove, Colin Crawford Colin's Corner, Tommi Vilkamo S60, Emily Turrettini and all at Textually, Tom Hume Future Platforms, Richard MacManus ReadWriteWeb, Leo Blanco and all at Mobile Weblog, Greg Rollet and Jonathan Marks Critical Distance, Om Malik Gigaom, Rod McLaren Mobbu, Mark van t Hooft Uniquitous Thoughts, Richard MacManus Read Write Web, John Bell Digital Influence, Dennis Haarsager Technology 360, Alessandro Pace Biskero, Tim Lynch Molecular Voices, Robert Scoble Scobleizer, Michael Mace Mobile Opportunity, Michael Bauens Integral Visioning, Zahid Ghadiali 3G 4G Wireless, Gil Galanti Cult Case, Paul Sergeant Calico Jack, Clo Willaerts Bnox, Heike Scholz Mobile Zeitgeist, Dean Bubley Disruptive Wireless, Ronald Rovers Emerce Mobile, Tom Chandler Engagement Principles, Daphne Dijkerman Explore Media, Jon Anderson Spark of Accident. Bloggers by name: Enrique "CEO" Ortiz, Russell Beattie, Darla Mack, Cameron Moll, Jonathan MacDonald, Anja Merrett, Debi "Mobile" Jones; and blogs where I don't know the bloggers: Experientia, Futurize Korea, X Series, Slashphone.

There is a really long list of Nokia colleagues, I'll now just mention those who have been particularly supportive since I left Nokia after 2001. Thank you Ilkka Pukkila, Janne Laiho, Jochen Metzner, Nicole Cham, Arja Suominen, Lauri Kivinen, Keith Pardy, Samuli Hänninen, Kimmo Lehtosalo, Pekka Somerto, Harri Heikkinen, Bill Chang, Lauri Hirvonen, Ebba Dåhli, Tuula "Tupu" Putkinen, Mark Selby, Scott McMahon.

Finally my personal "laboratory". I love to see my nephews and nieces navigate the digital world Thank you Jon and Ere Luokkanen, Olli and Salla Kasper, and Ema and Joseph Moore. The next generation is coming, so soon I will stop reading bedtme stories to these and start to learn from them instead: Iiris and Aamos Lundgren; Luca, Leo and Timotei Lundgren; Maria and Katariina Karimo, and Nea Sukola. I also want to thank my family, Tiina Brans; Tepa ja Kari Lunkreeni; Jukka (Hifki) and Hanna Lundgren; Jari and Inkeri Lundgren; Pirjo, Roni, Kris and Petteri Jorgensen; Timppa and Tinna Sukola; Alan and Tricia Rowland; Robert, Maria and Salvatore Abiuso; and in memoriam Jarmo Luokkanen. PS in Formula One, Go Kimi! Go Heikki!. PSPS new 007 movie in 2008...

Book blog is **7thMassMedia.com** and please do write to me at tomi@tomiahonen.com

"The internet in every pocket."
Jorma Ollila, CEO of Nokia

I
Introduction
Cellphone: the only universal gadget

Because the need to communicate is more powerful than the need to compute, to be entertained, or to be informed.

At the end of 2007 there were almost three times as many cellphone subscriptions as there were total users on the internet. There were four times as many cellphones as there are personal computers of all kinds laptops, desktops and servers combined. There were more than five times as many cellphone subscriptions in the world as there were cars. Twice as many people had cellphones as had credit cards. The population of cellphones was twice as big as the population of TV sets in use. There were 2.5 times as many cellphones as there were fixed landline phones.

In fact, by late November 2007 there was a cellphone subscription for a staggering 50% of the world's total population. Since Taiwan first did it in 2001, today over 60 countries have achieved cellphone penetration rates of over 100% per capita. For comparison, the USA cellphone penetration rate was about 85% at the end of 2007, placing it second-to-last among industrialized countries. Canada was in last place with about 65% penetration. In the most advanced mobile markets such as Hong Kong, Taiwan, Italy and Finland, the typical first-time cellphone customer is well under the age of eight.

How can you reach over 100% per capita penetration rates? Hong Kong, Taiwan, Italy, Israel, the UK are all at 130% or above - means that an increasing part of the employed population has two or more subscriptions. Informa measured that by 2007 already 28% of all cellphone owners in the world already have two or more subscriptions. Moreover, in most cases this means also carrying two phones. Half of Western Europeans with a cellphone actually have two or more subscriptions - and most of them carry two phones.

There is no other gadget that is even remotely as widely adopted and spread across the planet as the cellphone. Anyone with a job and disposable income has a cellphone, so if you want to sell anything, anyone who is "economically viable" on the planet, carries a cellphone. Even in China (40% penetration rate per capita), India (20%) and Africa (15%) cellphones are everywhere. I will discuss the overall economics, the big picture numbers and contrasts to other major technologies in the next chapter about the numbers involved in this industry soon to hit a Trillion dollars in value.

60% take it to bed every night

Then I will examine the owners of cellphones and how they use the devices. I will explore the society and how our behavior is changing with this technology. Earlier, the only gadget the "whole population" used to carry was the wristwatch. However, even here the cellphone is trumping the watch: young people have stopped using wristwatches and rely only upon the cellphone to tell time. A global Nokia survey of cellphone users in 2006 found that 73% of cellphone owners use the clock on the phone. Not all of these have abandoned wearing a wristwatch, but an increasing portion of the world uses the phone as the only

---

There were 6.6 billion people on the planet in October 2007

Source United Nations

---

time-keeping device. The cellphone is the only universal device.

As the cellphone has become a universal gadget, it is also inducing remarkably addictive signs of behavior. Almost every cellphone user, 91% in fact, keeps the cellphone literally within arm's reach 24 hours, seven days a week, 365 days of the year according to Morgan Stanley in 2007. A 2005 study of global cellphone use by BBDO revealed that 60% of us actually take the cellphone *physically* to bed with us! When I was telling this to audiences around the world in 2005, I got a lot of smiles and laughter in the conferences. But then when I asked the audience members to raise their hands if they did so, invariably about half of the hands went up. In advanced wireless telecoms countries like Finland, Singapore and South Korea it was nearly the whole audience who admitted to sleeping with the phone.

Why to bed? Some use the cellphone now as the alarm clock - Nokia's 2006 survey found that 72% of the total phone owner population does this. Others use it to send or receive messages still late into the night, or to make (or expect) a nighttime call. A study by the Catholic University of Leuwen in Belgium found that the majority of teenagers send text messages from bed. I will have a whole chapter looking at young people and their cellphone behavior. The cellphone is the last thing we look at before we fall asleep and again the first

---

thing we see when we wake up. If you are into media, this is a powerful device.

A study by Unisys revealed that if we lose our wallet we report it in 26 hours. If we lose our cellphone, we report it in 68 *minutes*. As to those who are new to these phenomena, no, we do not only use the cellphone outdoors. A study by NTT DoCoMo the largest wireless carrier (mobile operator) of Japan discovered that 60% of all wireless data access by cellphone is done indoors, often in parallel with watching TV or surfing the internet on a PC. To help readers develop successful services, I discuss how to build magic for wireless services in one chapter, and use my theory of the 6 M's, the very widely referenced mobile service development system, in examining service concepts.

Center of convergence

The cellphone is becoming the evolution target for much of the digitally converging industries. I will show how the battle for the pocket saw the rapid victories by smartphones over stand-alone PDAs, soon outselling them by more than 10 to 1; cameraphones over stand-alone digital cameras by more than 4 to 1;

There were 3.3 billion cellphone subscribers in October 2007
Source Informa 2007

---

and more musicphones than iPods and other stand-alone MP3 players by a ratio of 7 to 1. Towards the back of the book I take brief looks at convergence also from the industries that are involved, in how the internet, TV and cellphones are converging today; and how the banking/credit card industry and advertising are joining into that convergence soon. I touch upon the features creeping onto the cellphone and show how the phone has added new functionalities from one, communication, to eight functionalities today in the chapter on the Eight C's. In the Disruption chapter, I also examine the role of the Apple iPhone as a disruptive technology, as well as the concept of the MVNO as a disruptive business model for the industry.

Powerful media platform

In the book, I devote several chapters to examine the early popular media categories for cellphones. I start with the music business. As 31% of all consumer dollars spent on music worldwide is already spent on cellphone music, I devote a chapter to this phenomenon. Yes, it starts with ringing tones, of course, but there is a bewildering array of more advanced music services in the 9.3 billion dollars that people spend on cellphone music services worldwide

---

today, such as true-tones (mastertones), ringback tones (waiting tones), music videos, music streaming, karaoke, welcoming tones, background tones, etc.

In videogaming we see the same pattern. Growing rapidly, in 2007 already 20% of videogaming software revenues came from cellphone games. Advertising is another industry headed to your cellphone, and by the end of 2007, the worldwide advertising spend on cellphones had reached 2.2 billion dollar in value. Spreading fast, more than half of all cellphone owners in countries as diverse as Japan, UK and Spain received ads on their phones.

The latest industry to discover the cellphone as a delivery platform is TV. The first cellphones with digital TV tuners (i.e. built-in "set-top boxes") went already on sale in South Korea in the Summer of 2005 an by the end of 2007 there were seven million of such advanced TV-phones in Korea, or 17% of the total cellphone subscriber base watching full broadcast TV on cellphones. I will discuss music, gaming, TV and advertising for cellphones each in detail in their respective chapters later in the book.

The texting divide

The impact of cellphones to communication is enormous, and that communication is shifting away from voice calls to cellphone messaging. Not wireless email like on a Blackberry, no: the big cellphone messaging system is SMS text messaging. Over 2.5 billion people were active users of SMS text messaging in 2007. For contrast, while there were only 1.3 billion users of the internet, only 1.2 billion active users of email who maintained 2 billion email accounts. So out of the planet's population of 6.6 billion, only 18% can be reached via email. Compare that with the 3.2 billion of all cellphone subscribers

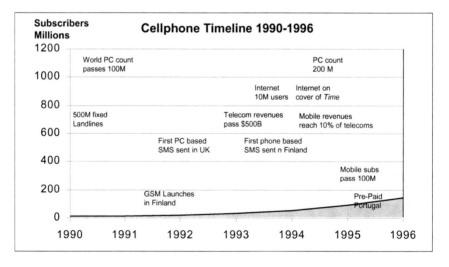

or 48% of the planet who are capable of receiving SMS text messages, and 2.5 billion or 38% of the whole population worldwide who are active users, and thus able to respond via SMS. No wonder all industries from automobile service garages to airlines to libraries to dentists are now rolling out SMS text messaging based customer communication systems.

SMS is perhaps the least understood of the new services on cellphones. It is definitely the most counter-intuitive service of them all and were it not for irrefutable facts and incredible usage patterns, no amount of logic could possibly explain the business or the use cases for SMS text messaging. That is why I have a whole chapter on this phenomenon. In addition, no matter how much you may love your Blackberry, trust me, the "Crackberry" is a *mild drug*, compared with SMS text messaging. With annual revenues of 100 billion dollars and still growing at double digits annually, this is a monster of a service and must be understood to grasp how compelling the cellphone can be as a media channel.

Multipurpose device clever at payments

Each cellphone can handle payments. There are some early examples of these appearing in the USA and Canada, so some may find the concept plausible, if not obviously practical. Nevertheless, keeping in mind that we carry our cellphone everywhere, if payment abilities are added to the device, it soon becomes the *preferred* means of payment. Why worry about having the correct change for the bus, the parking meter or to buy a can of Pepsi? You do not need to handle the small change: do the payment on the cellphone instead. Just click the button, and the payment appears on your next phone bill.

What may have seemed like novelties, are now real industries.

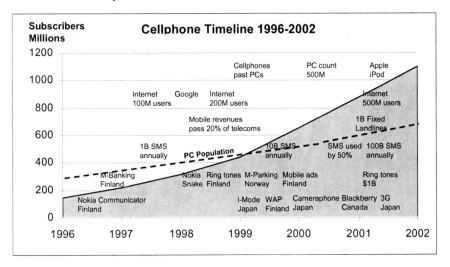

Payments by cellphone are very widely deployed already, ranging from paying for public transportation - trams, the subway and busses - as 53% already do via their cellphones in Helsinki Finland. In Estonia, *all parking* is now paid by cellphone. In Slovenia, all taxis accept payment by cellphone. In the Netherlands you can pay for your train tickets by cellphone. The governments are getting in on the action as well. In Finland, you can buy a fishing license by cellphone while in Abu Dhabi the police will allow you to pay for speeding tickets with your cellphone.

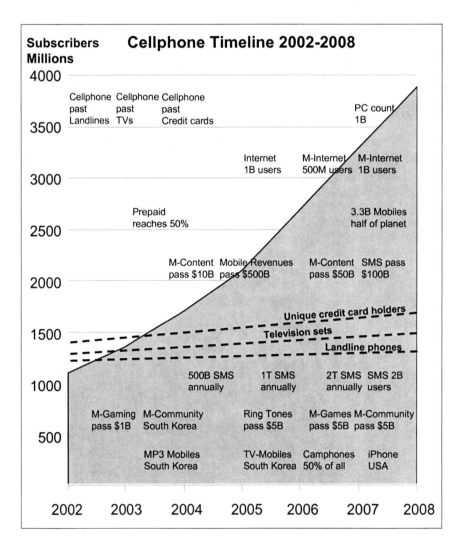

In countries from the Philippines to South Africa, many employers pay full salaries direct to cellphone accounts and in Kenya already a fifth of all bank accounts have migrated to cellphones. The Singapore government announced in 2006 that all egovernment initiatives would be made compatible with cellphones and SMS text messaging. Will it be the future? Today over half of Koreans use their cellphone for paying anything from public transportation to the grocery bill to paying for their petrol at the gasoline station. I will discuss the mobile payments and mobile banking later in this book, as well as the topic of how society is changing with wireless services on cellphones.

Cellphones in 2008
Estimate based on 2007 trends

Millions

4000

3.8 B Cellphone subscribers

3500

3000

2.7 B Active users of SMS

2500

2.2 B Cameraphones

2000

1.7 B Credit card holders

1500

1.5 B Televisions
1.4 B internet users
1.3 B Users of   1.3 B email users
mobile internet 1.2 B Fixed landlines
1000   **1 B Musicphones**

950 M All PCs

750 M 3G+ phones
550 M Desktop PCs
500

350 M Smartphones   400 M Laptops

200 M iPods

2008

Birth of Gen-C

I've already written a lot about Generation-C in my fourth book, *Communities Dominate Brands* with Alan Moore. One might assume it means Generation "C for Cellphones", or maybe it is "C for Content"; but actually the C in Gen-C stands for "Communities". It is the *Community Generation*, the first generation that experiences life, its anxieties, decisions, emotions, successes and failures, with the best buddies always at hand. Almost telepathically connected, living collectively, with a "hive mentality".

No longer reacting to a school bully alone, now Gen-C will fetch friends to rally to help - with the cellphone. While the gadget of choice for Gen-C is the cellphone, that generation is actually the first multidevice (or multiplatform) generation, using cellphones, text messaging, chat, instant messaging, blogging, multiplayer gaming, virtual reality worlds, social networks, search etc interchangeably and concurrently. Gen-C is the super-consumer of tomorrow. The preferred gadget of Gen-C is of course the cellphone. I will discuss Gen-C in its own chapter later in this book.

A related concept is that of social networking, known also as user-generated content, digital communities and Web 2.0. Since our book in 2005, recently most social networking experts have joined in our conclusion that the inevitable direction for all social networking services will be to cellphones. What may surprise readers is that while *mobile* social networking is only five years old, less than half as old as that of internet based online social networking, the cellphone variant already earns more money worldwide. Mobile social networking was worth 5 billion dollars in 2007 and as the business was launched in 2003, it makes mobile social networking the fastest-growing billion-dollar industry in the economic history of mankind. I will devote a chapter to it.

Over 50% of email users expect a response within 24 hours.
Source 160 Characters 2007

Before iPhone, After iPhone

There is one more element that has been changing perceptions of cellphones particularly in America, and that was the launch of the Apple iPhone in June of 2007. I have been saying, writing and blogging that the wireless telecoms industry will come to look back at June 2007 as a threshold moment. We can actually count cellphone development time, like two eras. The era Before the iPhone (BI), and the era After the iPhone (AI). Therefore, I discuss the iPhone and its impact in the disruption chapter near the end.

The cellphone started as a communication device, what I call the "first C". In a very short period of time that expanded to include consumption (the browser), then charging (payments), commercials (advertising) then creation (the camera). Now we are adding communities (social networking such as uploading pictures to Flickr), cool (fashion) and even control (remote control of our lives such as our locks, home heating, security systems etc). I will discuss this evolution pattern as the "8 C's" in its own chapter later in the book.

American creativity will wake up

The other benefit of the introduction of the iPhone is perhaps more subtle, but

---

more far-reaching. The June 2007 launch of the iPhone was certainly the most visible technology marketing campaign ever.

In the past American audiences have been poorly served by the handset makers and the wireless carriers. Americans have never had first releases of new top-line phones in the world - many of the top models by the giant handset makers have not even been launched in America at all. In addition, the American wireless carriers are also seen by the industry pundits as nearer Third World carriers than their more advanced rivals in Europe, Asia and Australia. Cellphone features, carrier services, pricing and interconnectivity are all much more advanced in other major industrialized countries than in America.

So American consumers and business executives have an outdated view of cellphones and wireless services. Imagine if you lived in an African country where the local airport only served propeller driven airplanes. You would have a hard time believing how comfortable travel could be in modern jetliners. Nevertheless, once that airport was expanded and modernized and modern jets started to serve your city, you would rapidly understand how relevant jet

---

84% of SMS users expect a response within 5 minutes.
Source 160 Characters 2007

---

travel is to world commerce today.

When Apple rolled out its iPhone launch marketing, suddenly every American executive noticed a large screen, color screen cameraphone with web browser and media player. Moreover, the prevalent thought was: *"Wow. I want one of those."* And the next thought was *"Why can't my business be on it?"*

So after the launch of the iPhone, suddenly every IT industry executive, every TV industry boss, every Hollywood mogul, every print baron, every gaming developer etc, woke up to the potential of cellphones. To illustrate how the North American cellular telecoms industry compares to the rest of the world, and to help discover regions where the cutting edge and bleeding edge of the industry currently exists, I end the book with an analysis of what factors have caused North America to fall behind in this rapidly growing industry.

Seventh of the Mass Media

This book looks at the cellphone emerging as the Seventh of the Mass Media. Print was the first, five hundred years ago. At the turn of the century around 1900, we had three "new" mass media in short succession, with recordings the second, cinema the third and radio the fourth mass media channel. Then around 1950 we had TV emerge as the fifth. Then after 1990, the internet appeared as the sixth. Now around 2000 mobile (the cellphone) appears as the latest, the seventh mass media channel.

It is not the dumb little brother of the internet, nor the dumb tiny screen version of TV. Yes, the cellphone is small, but it has attributes that make it a *superior medium* in many ways and a *dominating media channel* in the three most important factors - reach, audience accuracy and money.

I like to say that mobile as the 7th mass media channel, is as different from the internet, as TV is from radio. TV overtook radio almost totally as the predominant media channel, replicating all previously existing radio content, and then adding countless new content types and formats not possible on radio. Now we face a similar situation with mobile taking over from the internet - and very shortly will become the predominant interactive media, replicating most that exists on the internet, and creating already today numerous media formats that cannot be replicated on the internet. Early in the book, I go to considerable detail to explain exactly why the cellphone is as powerful as a media channel, can it truly be more potent than the internet? I devote one chapter just to understand the unique benefits of the cellphone as the seventh of the mass media. I then show how we can build magical new services for it.

To sum up

The cellphone is certainly the most widely spread technology. There are 20 times more cellphones than Playstations; 30 times more cellphones than iPods. It is the only universal gadget, and it has now become the newest media channel. The first media content to discover cellphones was music ten years ago and today over 31% of all music sold worldwide is consumed on cellphones. Videogames were the second category and over 20% of that industry has migrated to cellphones. TV, news, social networking, even internet services are all now headed to the cellphone, as the newest and most prevalent mass media channel. Advertising is also headed to a cellphone screen near you.

It is not easy to build successful services for cellphones. You cannot just copy the internet or other media and be guaranteed a success on the 7th of the Mass Media. However, by understanding what makes the cellphone unique, and more powerful as a medium than any of the six legacy media; that is how future media empires will be built. That is why we all need to understand the cellphone. This is a book to help you on that journey. I will start by putting the big picture into context, with the next chapter focusing on the numbers of this emerging giant industry. At the end of each chapter I will also showcase some example from leading innovators in this industry such as Blyk, Flirtomatic, Cyworld and SeeMeTV. For those wondering is the cellphone viable as a media channel, consider these words from the former Director General of the BBC, Greg Dyke, *"The time is coming where all the traditional broadcast shows will be available on your mobile phone."*

"When my information changes, I change my opinion.
What do you do, sir?"
John Maynard Keynes

II
Number Shock
It can't happen here

The time around the year 2000 could be seen as the tipping point. Close to that year 2000, there were roughly as many PCs, internet users and cellphones in the world, or about 500 million of each. Since then the world changed totally. The amount of PCs has grown very impressively and had reached about 900 million personal computers in use at the end of 2007. That corresponds with an annual growth rate of about 9% from year to year. The number of internet users has grown faster yet, reaching 1.3 billion. A faster growth rate, it is equivalent to a sustained annual growth rate of 15% for the seven years. All of us have marveled at the statistics as reported in the news media over the years.

However, those growth rates pale in comparison to the rocket-like growth of cellphones. By the end of 2007, there were 3.3 billion active cellphone subscriptions in the world. That averages to a sustained annual growth rate of 31% year on year for this decade. Selling one billion (actually 1,100 million in 2007) handset units annually, by the time you read this, there will be four times as many cellphones as all PCs: laptops, desktops and servers, combined.

In addition, what of other pervasive technologies and innovations. The modern automobile is over 100 years old - there are 800 million cars in use around the world. However, over five times as many cellphone subscriptions - and every car owner on the planet has a cellphone in the car when driving. Fixed landline phones? Also over 100 years old, there are about 1.3 billion landline phones. Nevertheless, there are 2.5 times as many cellphones as all fixed landline phones in the world. In America where cellphone adoption lags the industrialized world, about 10% of all homes are now without a landline phone altogether, using only cellphones. The most advanced country where this phenomenon was first witnessed is Finland, which in 2007 had more than half of all homes already abandoned their fixed landlines and use only cellphones.

TV became a mass-market proposition in the 1950s and today there are about 1.4 billion TV sets are in use. However, more than twice as many cellphones are in use. Should the television industry be concerned? New cellphones now are being introduced offering video and TV content; the most advanced TV-cellphones in Japan, South Korea, Italy, Finland etc have built-in digital TV tuners like your cable TV set-top box or your TiVo recorder, built-into the phone unit. Top executives ranging from the national broadcaster of South Korea to the BBC have said that future TV will be on cellphones.

Credit cards? Spread rapidly around the world around the 1980s today there are about 1.5 billion people with one or more credit cards in their wallet. Modern phones can do credit payments, twice as many people have cellphones as have credit cards. In advanced cellphone payment markets such as Japan, South Korea, the Philippines, South Africa etc, as much as half of the population use cellphone based credit cards and payment systems.

And what of the wristwatch? The only ubiquitous gadget - and I have not found total wristwatch penetration level numbers - but revealingly, the 2006 Nokia survey found that 73% of cellphone owners use their phone as their clock. Some also wear a wristwatch, but increasingly the wristwatch is an optional extra, a decoration, a "bling" piece of jewelry, whereas the phone has the alarm - used by 72% of phone owners according to the same Nokia survey. Let me take you onto a comparative trip to the world of new technology and user numbers.

A   EXECUTIVE TOY

During much of the 1990s, cellphones were expensive toys for the very rich. Not unlike laptop computers and PDAs, the cellphone was seen as an expensive gadget, one that many egotistical businessmen seemed to want just to show off how important they were. Today they are omnipresent. Pre-teen girls in Rome and Stockholm and Tokyo walk around with cellphones. What happened?

Is not yet another new technology

As you read technology stories in the issues of *Business Week, Wall Street Journal*, the *Economist* etc. they are littered with new technologies with impressive usage numbers. How can you decipher the iPod from Blackberry etc. When millions blur into billions, how can we get the big picture.

Let me place the technologies into perspective. Blackberry is an exciting wireless e-mail solution. Its users in North America liken it to addiction, often calling it the "Crackberry". At the summer of 2007, six years from the launch of their first wireless email cellphone/smartphone, Blackberry had about eight million users worldwide (and six million of those in North America). In spite of significant marketing efforts throughout Europe and Asia, Blackberries have attracted less a couple of million new users per year. For contrast, the

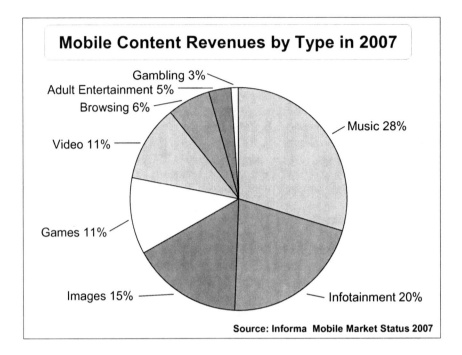

Mobile Content Revenues by Type in 2007

Gambling 3%
Adult Entertainment 5%
Browsing 6%
Video 11%
Games 11%
Images 15%
Music 28%
Infotainment 20%

Source: Informa Mobile Market Status 2007

cellphone industry sells 3 million new cellphones *every day* of the year, Saturdays and Sundays included.

Next, the business executive's favorite tool, the PDA. Personal Digital Assistants were at one point at the start of the decade forecasted to reach several hundred million in use by about now, but their annual sales stalled when facing off against the newer feature-rich cellphones, called smarphones (the Blackberry is counted as a smartphone, as is the Apple iPhone). The total non-cellphone "standalone" PDA population is about 75 million devices worldwide and annual sales of non-cellphone enabled PDAs are at less than 11 million per year. For contrast, in 2007 alone there were 120 million new smartphones sold.

An iPod generation?

The iPod seems to be the most popular new technology on the planet, as it is so visible with the distinctive white earphones. What seems to be the standard item of clothing for the young all around the world, iPods were launched in 2001 and by end of April 2007, Apple reached the cumulative shipment level of 100 million sold since launch. iPod sales currently run at a level of about 45 million per year. A huge success no doubt. What many iPod analysts fail to observe, is that MP3 playing musicphones were introduced three years *after* the iPod, yet by

2006 were outselling iPods and just during the year of 2007, more than 300 million musicphones were sold worldwide. White earphones yes. However, if you follow to the end of the connection of those white earplugs, you see on a young user, it is now more likely to be connected to a musicphone, than to an Apple iPod.

Moving up the scale, laptop computers get into serious user numbers, with about 400 million in use. Desktop PCs still outnumber laptops at about 550 million in use, although the year 2007 was likely the first year when more laptops were sold than desktops. I did not have final numbers when this book went to print, but if this did not happen in 2007, it will happen in 2008 that laptops sell more than desktops. Still, combining laptops and desktops in use, the total PC population of is about 950 million globally today.

How about the internet?

At the end of 2005 internet user numbers reached the billion-user level. By end of 2007 that had grown to about 1.3 billion. In addition, how does that contrast with only 900 million PCs in use in 2007? The second largest access method to

---

990 million PCs (laptops and desktops) in use in 2007
Source Computer Industry Almanac 2007

---

the internet, after access from PCs, is perhaps surprisingly... the cellphone. Today for about 350 million people their *primary* internet access is by cellphone. A total of 798 million people access the internet on a cellphone at least part of the time, or 24% of all cellphone subscribers according to Informa in 2007. Some of the biggest countries where the majority of internet access is from a cellphone include Japan, South Korea, India and South Africa.

I should be very clear about this that in the industrialized world most who may access internet services via a cellphone will usually also have access also on a PC, at either work/school or home (or both). Where they have access by both methods, usually the heavy usage in data traffic and time spent tends to be on PCs, and the more urgent uses - such as checking weather or reading emails of the inbox - tends to be on cellphones.

The pattern of cellphone based internet access (including WAP service access) is in the 30%-40% in many European countries such as Italy, Spain, Portugal, etc. Even in America, which lags the industrialized world in cellphones and related industries, already 34% of American adults access the internet wirelessly according to the Pew American Life Project survey of February 2007. A related study by IDC of American cellphone users found that 27.5% had

---

consumed wireless content bought on their cellphones.

Other major technologies, there are about 1.4 billion TV sets in use around the world. These tend to be shared within families, and in the Developing World, family sizes tend to be large, so the real audience of TV content is considerably larger than the 1.4 billion; but remember also that many of the TV sets are in the Western World where it is not uncommon for a single adult to have two TV sets, i.e. one in the living room and another in the bedroom.

Then there are credit cards. The total number of people who have at least one credit card is about 1.5 billion, and most of those will then tend to have more than one credit card account.

The 3.3 billion colossus

Now contrast them with the dominant digital device. Worldwide at the end of 2007, there were over 3.3 billion cellphones and 1.1 billion new cellphones are sold annually. In 2007, there was a cellphone subscription very literally for half of the planet. In the Western world this might be not such a stunning number, until we remember that five out of six human beings lives in the Developing

---

3,350 million cellphone subscribers in 2007.
Source Informa 2007

---

world. Yet there is a cellphone subscription for half of all humans. To put it in more practical terms, every *economically viable* person in the world can be contacted via cellphone. In the developing world the internet, broadband and PC penetration levels are so low that for any interactive services, the only *viable* means of delivery is through cellphone-based services such as SMS text messaging and WAP cellphone based internet.

So even with the enormous success of the internet, the cellphone user numbers completely dwarf those; nearly three times as many people use cellphones than have any kind of access to the internet - and nearly one in three internet users has the cellphone as the only internet access method.

Many digital delivery solutions are significant, PDAs, iPods, Blackberries, notebook PCs etc., but only one statistic is seismic, and that is the cellphone. At 3.3 billion users, this is your digital platform.

B   CELLPHONE OR LANDLINE

What of fixed or landline phones? Surely, there are more of those? In 2005 in the

---

USA the number of cellphones climbed past landlines, but in Canada, still the total number of fixed wireline/landline phones is still more than cellphones. The rest of the world has gone much beyond that. Landline phone penetrations are usually counted against households and businesses. Thus, the USA and Canada have had "full penetration" of fixed landline phones since the 1970s. However, so have advanced Western European countries like Sweden, Finland, Denmark, the UK etc. When counted against the whole population, rather than households, the fixed landline phone penetration is about 65%-80% depending on household sizes and for example how many second lines are installed for internet use, etc.

Since 1998 when it first happened in Finland, cellphone penetration numbers in every advanced Western country have shot past fixed wireline phone penetration rates. What may seem on first view as counter-intuitive (*"surely not everybody with a landline phone would replace it with a cellphone, my grandmother would not replace her rarely-used landline with a cellphone"*) by 2004 had happened in every other industrialized country except USA and Canada. Yes, already three years ago every other industrialized country had seen the cellphone population exceed the fixed landline population.

Second phones

A significant point is the cellphone penetration level of about 60% per capita.

Multiple Subcriptions by Region 2006

Region	Multiple subscriptions
Eastern Europe	73%
Western Europe	53%
Middle East	45%
Latin America	38%
Asia-Pacific	30%
Africa	24%
North America	15%
World Average	28%

Source: Informa February 2007

After that, two interesting phenomena are observed. First, many younger users start to abandon fixed landlines altogether. In Finland, this had reached 50% of all households by 2007 and Portugal it is also over 40%. The early signs of this trend were already reported in the USA as well with about 10% of households abandoning landlines according to the CTIA.

The other phenomenon is the second cellphone. Cellphone penetrations are measured against the whole population, i.e. "per capita". The 100% per capita penetration rates are not measured against "adult populations", but against the whole population. A 1-year-old baby cannot talk, doesn't know numbers and has no use for a phone. Arguably many 101-year-olds cannot hear, have forgotten numbers and in many cases also have no need for a phone. How do we then get to 100% penetrations? If the very young children and some elderly do not have phones, then it means some people have to have two subscriptions.

This has been examined since the phenomenon was first observed in 1998 in Finland, and I reported it in my second book, *m-Profits* in 2002. Now we know much more. Roughly speaking, after the 60% penetration level is reached, every other added cellphone subscription is going to a second phone. Yes, totally normal people start to get two cellphones. An Informa report on total worldwide cellphone subscriptions at the start of 2007 found that 28% of all cellphone owners worldwide had two or more subscriptions.

How high can it go?

The world's most advanced cellphone penetration countries (excluding some countries with tiny populations that can skew analysis, such as Luxembourg and Monaco etc) are Hong Kong and Taiwan, at over 135% penetration rates for cellphones at the end of 2007; Hong Kong reported 139% in December 2007. Italy is at over 130% as is Israel. By end of 2006, the average penetration rate of cellphones per capita in Europe was already at 105% and will be near 115% by end of 2007 when final numbers come out for the year.

This may again seem odd. Nevertheless, keep in mind that when countries like Spain, Singapore, Russia and the Czech Republic joined the 100% penetration group, it meant that cellphone were not luxury items, but common communication tools. The Singapore government decreed in 2006 that all of its e-government initiatives would be made accessible by cellphone. Yes, all the government forms for taxes, driver's licenses, health insurance, passports etc, would be made accessible - and interactive - via cellphones - and using SMS text messaging as the default method for interactivity.

The Finnish government was the first to slap on taxes for employer-provided cellphone benefits, so some employees choose *not* to accept an employer-paid cellphone, as they do not want to be taxed for that benefit. As employers use cellphones as normal tools at work, they often also issue rules about personal calls, and using data services for personal benefit.

Why a second phone?

An obvious "early" reason especially in countries that lag in the quality of cellular networks, is cellular network coverage. If one network does not cover the home, and for example, the other network has bad drops on the driving route to work, it makes sense to carry two phones on rival networks, one for the calls at home, the other for calls in the car, etc.

Another common use is to have employer phones and private personal phones. One might have the work cellphone number printed on the business card and then want a private cellphone that is not known as broadly, or for example to prevent calls on weekends and evenings. Furthermore, if you get a "free" phone from work, it may have restrictions on how it may be used, such as international calls, web access or payments. For example, as it is possible to pay for parking by cellphone, or pay for Coca Cola's from vending machines by cellphone, an employee could secretly have the employer pay for parking, soft drinks, etc. If you think that is petty, note that in many countries you can pay for tickets to rock concerts, lift passes at ski resorts, train and airplane tickets etc by cellphone.

Replacement cycle for PCs was 42 months in 2007.
Source: Semiconductor Industry Association 2007

Every day brings new uses of mobile payments around the world. The potential for abuse is considerable. Thus, employers have issued rules about what may and what may not be consumed on the phone. When these kinds of rules come into place, some employees prefer to get their own cellphone in addition to that from the employer.

A growing reason is competitive pricing plans. Often networks offer lower price calls to phones that are on the same network - i.e. a Verizon caller who calls another person with a Verizon phone. Then it becomes appealing to get a couple of phone subscriptions on the networks where the main friends, family and colleagues are.

SIM card switch

In Europe, which is practically all on the GSM standard, the little memory card that identifies the phone subscription and phone number, called the "SIM card" (for Subscriber Identity Module) is removable and on most networks in most countries, unlocked and interchangeable. It is a small memory chip about the size of a fingernail and is inserted to the phone typically underneath the removable battery. The SIM card can be removed and replaced by the consumer. So

---

customers on the GSM phones can usually get a SIM card on a rival network, and only exchange SIM cards to allow hopping between networks while keeping the same phone. This is also common in some advanced Asian markets where GSM is the dominant standard on all or most networks, like Singapore, Malaysia, Thailand, Indonesia, etc. This does not work if the other networks use incompatible technologies or if the phones are locked to one network/carrier.

When SIM cards can be exchanged, the user does not necessarily need to carry physically two phones, but can switch the SIM cards around. Some young people carry the rival SIM card or cards inside the phone, under the battery. Then they become very efficient at the "SIM card switch" replacing SIM cards rapidly to optimize calls on the different networks often for price reasons.

I should point out that not all GSM phones on all networks in all countries work this way. Some carriers have decided to employ a "SIM lock" by, which a phone is locked to operate only with that carrier's SIM card. The Apple iPhone is typically locked in this way, for example. Then of course, there usually are some clever programmers who set up shop unlocking such locked phones for a small fee.

Replacement cycle for cellphones was 18 months in 2007.

Source: Semiconductor Industry Association 2007

Some people get a second subscription for use in clandestine situations. This could be black market work, or actual criminal behavior, or for example to hide an extramarital affair. Already in Italy, the information on cellphones is the biggest source of evidence of infidelity in divorce cases. In Japan so-called pre-paid (or pay-as-you-go) accounts are associated with criminal behavior such as being a member of the Japanese mafia or working as a prostitute, etc. However, in most countries where second subscriptions and phones are commonplace, this kind of stigma is no longer attached to the second phone.

There are many other reasons for multiple subscriptions. Some networks offer better "roaming" deals for when you travel and want to use the phone abroad. In addition, sometimes a second subscription is taken to gain access to a given type of special phone handset, one not offered by the current provider (such as the iPhone). Sometimes the second subscription is gained as part of a network promotion, such as a cable TV/internet/telecoms provider offering a triple play or quadruple play offer, giving SIM cards to users on rival networks, to try to capture their cellular telecoms business in addition to the existing bundle of cable TV, internet etc. There are many reasons, but most of all the statistics are most clear: the facts cannot be argued with. One could ask also why do some young single people feel the need to buy two TV sets as they

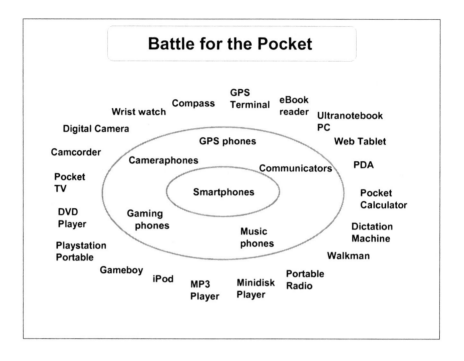

they often do in industrialized countries, etc.

C   BATTLE OF THE POCKET

I discussed the "Battle of the Pocket" in my third book *3G Marketing* with Timo Kasper and Sara Melkko in 2004. There are numerous pocketable electronic gadgets that we can carry from transistor radios and cassette players (the Walkman) of the 1970s to the pocket calculator and pocket TV of the 1980s to the pagers/beepers and PDAs of the 1990s to the digital cameras, iPods and GPS receivers of today. Nevertheless, in the contest to become king of the pocket, the cellphone is the undefeated heavyweight champion. The short history of its ascendancy to prominence has been a series of early round knockout victories.

The surrender of the PDA

PDAs (Personal Digital Assistants), the little handheld computers that business executives seem to love, had developed into a significant niche of the IT industry during the 1990s. By 2000, the total volume of PDA sales had exceeded 10 million units per year and many analysts were forecasting PDA sales to continue to grow and reach sales levels of 60 million units sold annually by the year 2005. To put it into context that was close to the total global sales of laptop computers annually in 2000 when the forecasts were made.

The forecasters were right in forecasting the growing market for PDA *functionality*, but did not count on the appeal of integrating PDA features to cellphones. The first of what we now call a smartphone was Nokia's iconic (and truly "brick-sized") clamshell PDA-palmtop computer-smartphone, the Communicator 9000 in 1996. By 2000, there were other collaborations of fitting various levels of PDA functionality to cellphones. This new category of phones was called "smartphones." Clearly, a compromise as the cellphone technology posed size, weight, processor power, battery life and price penalties in contrast with stand-alone PDAs, it took the cellphone industry about two years to get the form factors and value propositions right.

The PDA makers were pooh-poohing the smartphones as mere toys and gadgets, not serious threats to PDAs and not viable alternatives. The PDA makers pointed out that on a PDA there was a much larger screen; better user interface - usually including a stylus; better data storage capacity; a vast multitude of custom applications, etc. In almost every way the PDA was "inherently better" for personal data management, than the cumbersome tiny and very limited smartphone. But those busy businessmen who were using PDAs did not want to carry all the extra electronic gear - and to worry about

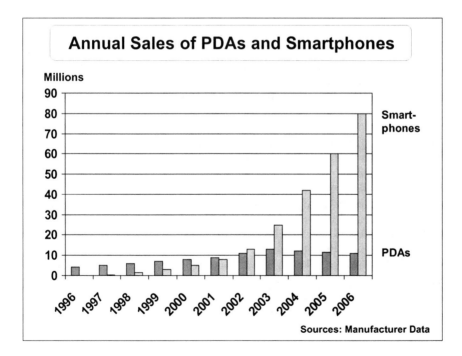

Annual Sales of PDAs and Smartphones

Sources: Manufacturer Data

synchronizing with them all - and to worry about all the rechargers, docking bays, backup systems etc. If one converged device could be delivered, and it had the must-have feature - connectivity i.e. the cellphone - then it actually would be "good enough." Not perfect. Not technologically supreme. Just good enough.

In 2003, the smartphone sales exceeded all expectations, and while stand-alone PDA sales lingered in the 11 million per year levels, smartphones sold 13 million units. By 2004, smartphones were outselling stand-alone PDAs by more than four to one. By 2005, more smartphones were sold that year than all stand-alone PDAs ever made. The battle was decisively over. Still today in 2007 stand-alone PDAs do sell, in the sub 10 million annual sales levels, while smartphones sell more than 120 million units annually.

The capitulation of the digital camera

Maybe the PDA was an isolated example? Or was it. In 2001, the first cameraphones appeared in Japan, as a mass-market offering first on the J-Phone network (since Vodafone KK and now Softbank). These had very poor quality cameras, small screens of poor resolution and the memory and storage ability of the camera features on the phones were dismal.

On the surface of it, trying to patch together a voice telephone and an optical film-based camera seems like trying to combine an airplane with a submarine or combining an oven with a refrigerator. There seemed to be no logical synergy between these very distinct and diverse technologies.

However, as cellphones converted from analog to digital systems in the early 1990s and as cameras entered the digital age about the same time, it became technically possible to create digitally converged devices combining both. Even so, there were little practical areas of synergy during the 1990s as both technologies were relatively bulky and there was no excess capacity in processors, storage units, battery capacity, etc.

Then at the turn of the decade, smartphones introduced color screens for internet surfing, and digital cameras started to abandon the optical viewfinder for the digital color displays to be used as the viewfinder. Now suddenly it was no longer a prohibitively bulky converged product to add the camera functionality to the cellphone. There were other areas where components could be shared, such as the battery and memory. By 2004 the industry calculated that the cost of adding a basic camera functionality to a cellphone added only about 5 dollars to the manufacturing cost of the cellphone.

Japanese wireless carrier J-phone was the first to take the strategic step into cameraphones in 2001 and less than two years later by end of 2002 a massive 60% of its 12 million subscribers had migrated to cameraphones. Clearly, consumers loved this innovation.

By 2003, the integrated camera started to appear on many top-end cellphones outside of Japan. The large Japanese camera makers like Nikon,

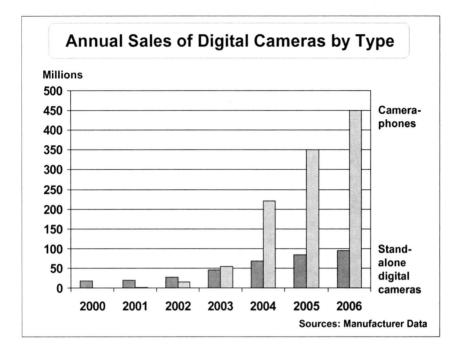

Minolta, Konica and Canon were soon singing the same song as the PDA makers had a few years earlier that the cameraphones were toys that there was no contest in comparing the two; that "real" i.e. stand-alone digital cameras were far superior to any cameraphone, *from a technology point of view.* Yes, stand-alone cameras are better, *by technology*, with multi megapixel resolutions, high quality optics, storage ability, compatibility, flash, self-timer, etc features.

The cellphone makers were not deterred. They learned fast and focused on the basics of the simple point-and-shoot camera for the phone. The camera makers were caught off-guard when the final numbers came in for 2003 and cameraphones had outsold stand-alone digital cameras. By 2004, the world's most sold digital camera brand had become Nokia and in 2005, more cameraphones were sold than all stand-alone digital cameras ever made. Today Konica and Minolta have quit the camera business altogether and Canon and Nikon focus more on the high-end professional and semi-pro camera markets.

Wedding photos on cameraphones?

Again, I am not trying to argue that the cameraphone would be better technically than a stand-alone digital camera. A wedding photographer will not show up with a Motorola Razr cameraphone to take the wedding portrait. A professional sports photographer will not trade in his 300mm lens and Canon SLR professional camera for a SonyEricsson Cybershot no matter how good the cameraphones's resolution or digital zoom might be. There will be a market for high-end digital cameras, yes, and the professionals and serious amateurs will appreciate the difference in quality.

Meanwhile the gap in performance between stand-alone digital cameras and cameraphones keeps shrinking. By the Spring of 2007 Nokia was offering on its top-end N93 smartphone a camera of 3 megapixel resolution, with a Carl Zeiss branded high quality (i.e. "professional camera" quality) lens, and 3x *optical* zoom (the high quality kind, versus the digital zoom, which is low quality) and a built-in flash. In video mode, the phone recorded DVD quality video and stereo sound. Meanwhile Samsung of South Korea had released a phone with 10 megapixel resolution. Of course, there were again more powerful stand-alone digital cameras but the gap between a high-end cameraphone and a mid-range stand-alone digital camera was diminishing to the point of vanishing.

What makes the case for the cameraphone almost too good, is that in most countries the cellphone sales are subsidized. If you are a heavy spender on your phone bill, you get the top-end smartphone for free at your next upgrade. For stand-alone digital cameras there never is a subsidy, you have to pay full retail price for the camera, which alone can easily cost 500 dollars or more.

Moreover, on usage the world is also tilted totally in favor of the cameraphone. The best digital camera is the one you have with you when you want to take the picture. Most of the time, most of us do not walk around 24/7 with our digital cameras strapped around our necks. However, clearly we do walk around 24/7 with our cellphone in our pocket. Even if the quality of that camera is only mediocre, if it is the only camera upon us, that is the one we use.

The massacre of the iPod

Some readers may be passionate about their iPods. I will discuss that in the music chapter, but let me summarize the battle. For the first four years since its launch in 2001, Apple has had most of the MP3 player market to itself. The cellphone makers like Nokia, Motorola, Samsung and SonyEricsson do not get interested in market sizes that count globally "only" in a million or two per year. They want markets that measure literally in the dozens of millions per year or more. For context, Nokia sells a million handsets every day, 365 days a year.

Furthermore, cellphones are replaced at the incredible rate of every 18 months, globally, according to the Semiconductor Industry Association, more than twice as fast as PCs and laptops are replaced. The iPod was totally a techie geek device back in 2004, and served only a niche market. Once it started to sell in the tens of millions in 2005, the cellphone makers became interested.

In a matter of months the cellphone industry steamrollered into the portable MP3 player market. In 2006, Samsung brought its MP3 player musicphones from South Korea to the rest of the world. Nokia released its N-

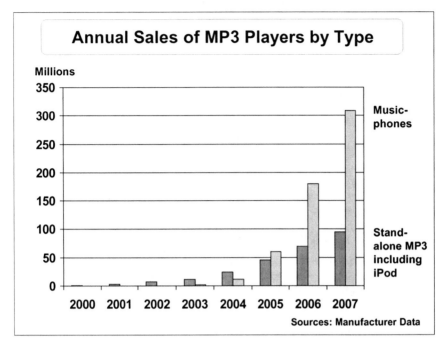

Annual Sales of MP3 Players by Type

Millions

Music-phones

Stand-alone MP3 including iPod

Sources: Manufacturer Data

Series. Motorola added MP3 player functionality to its hot selling Razr series. LG released its Chocolate musicphone and SonyEricsson went one better, adapting its Walkman brand and releasing a vast range of Walkman phones. As Alan Moore and I predicted in my fourth book, *Communities Dominate Brands*, the iPod had no chance whatsoever in the "Battle of the Pocket".

At the end of 2004, Apple's iPod had held an 80% market share of the global MP3 player market. During 2005, all cellphone makers got into the musicphone game. During the year 2006 Apple sold a record 46 million iPods. The newer musicphones however, sold a massive 309 million units in 2006. The musicphone lines of Nokia, Motorola and SonyEricsson *each outsold the total output* of the iPod in 2006. Musicphones outsold iPods at a ratio of 7 to 1.

Exactly as it did earlier for PDAs and digital cameras, the cellphone easily took the title in the battle for the pocket. By clear knockout. By July 2006, Apple CFO Peter Oppenhemer admitted that Apple was rushing its phone project and by January 2007 Apple CEO Steve Jobs announced the iPhone. The era of the stand-alone MP3 player like the iPod had lasted less than five years.

The converging device

We are seeing ever more functionality converging to the cellphone. Mobile telecoms experts and authors Ajit Jaokar and Tony Fish give examples of converged devices - and predicted the iPhone - in their book ***Open Gardens***:

> *Will users use one device for many functions or will they use different*
> *devices each specialized for a specific function? The Nokia n-Gage was*
> *a seminal device since it was the first large-scale attempt to combine a*
> *gaming device plus a phone. Other variants are possible - an iPod with*
> *a phone and so on.*
> - Ajit Jaokar & Tony Fish, ***Open Gardens***, 2004

Obviously such converged devices are now appearing in all kinds of forms and again, the Apple iPhone is perhaps the best example for those not familiar with this industry. I will discuss the evolution of the cellphone in detail in the chapter on the Eight C's and then also discuss the digital convergence of industries in the Disruption chapter at the end. Nevertheless, on this battle for the Pocket, we are witnessing the undefeated world champion of the pocket. The cellphone takes on all comers and ends up still standing after the battle. As I write this book, Nokia is projecting that for 2008 they will sell more GPS (Global Positioning Service) enabled phones than all stand-alone GPS devices sold. What the cellphone wants, the cellphone gets.

Tri-centric convergence

Please do not misunderstand me. While the cellphone is winning the convergence battle for the pocket, we actually have three focal points of convergence. At the office, the focal point has become the office PC (or laptop PC). It does our word processing, spreadsheet calculations, Powerpoint presentations, internet access, email, Google searches and all of our proprietary computer services such as CRM (Customer Relationship Management) systems and so forth. We are even abandoning the desk phones in favor of having Skype or Vonage calls through our PC and the internet. The battle for the office is over, and the personal computer is left standing, on the desk.

The battle for the pocket is also over, with the cellphone the clear winner. Nevertheless, the battle for the home is still raging strong, with our cable TV provider competing with our broadband provider, the TiVo box, the Sony Playstation 3, with Microsoft and Apple all wanting a piece of our home entertainment system and services. That competition is still wide open.

30 minute tasks and 30 second tasks.

While the cellphone rules the pocket, our office work is ruled by the PC and we do not even know who will emerge victorious on the third front in that contest, the home. I wrote about the 30 minute tasks and 30 second tasks in my third book, ***3G Marketing*** with Timo Kasper and Sara Melkko in 2004. That concept helps illustrate how most users in the Developed World - who tend to have access to a personal computer - will approach services and content on the cellphone, and contrast those with larger devices, such as a laptop or TV set.

Many of the tasks we want to do in our lives, whether at work or at leisure, are planned tasks. I call these "30 minute tasks". Therefore, this could be doing our emails at work, or preparing a presentation, or writing a proposal. At home, this could be the search for the new car or booking a trip for our next holiday or watch the football game or *Desperate Housewives*, etc. When we have 30 minute tasks, we plan them in advance. We do them seated. We use a tool for this (typically a PC or laptop computer connected to the internet, or our plasma screen TV). We want a large screen, a good keyboard and mouse. This is how we compose documents, do Google searches and surf the internet.

Then there are "30 second tasks". These appear suddenly, without warning or plan. They often need immediate response. They often arrive on our cellphone, increasingly via SMS. We address 30 second tasks while standing or walking. We use the best we have, so the tiny keypad on the phone, the small screen and what tools we might otherwise be able to use, say the built-in camera. We may need to do mobile access to some WAP site or search engine etc, and in these urgent times, we may be willing (or be allowed by our employer) to use more expensive mobile internet services, but we intend our usage to be of short duration and limited scope. This is not how we tend to create documents (with

30 Minute Tasks and 30 Second Tasks

30 Minute Tasks	30 Second Tasks
Planned	Unplanned
Sitting	Standing/Walking
Create	Consume
Big display	Small display
Keyboard and mouse	Keypad and camera
Concentrate	Multi-task
Email	SMS
PC/Laptop	Cellphone

my apologies to all Japanese girls writing mobile books on their cellphones). This is how we *react* and *respond*.

I think the 30 second task and 30 minute task metaphor is a good illustration why the PC based internet and laptops will continue to be major tools in our lives, and a growing mass media for the foreseeable future. So please do not misunderstand my point in this book that mobile would somehow "kill" the internet; certainly not. However, mobile will supercede the legacy internet for most users worldwide, and that will happen fast. In fact, the Japanese internet provider Softbank, known better in the West as Yahoo Japan, bought Vodafone KK, the underperforming Japanese subsidiary of the world's largest wireless carrier group, because they understood the central role that cellphones play in the multi-platform media environment. Executive Vice President Ted Matsumoto of Softbank said in his keynote to the South Korean iMobicon conference in 2007 that Softbank bought the cellular telecoms asset from Vodafone, because of all their media platforms, the cellphone is the only *indispensable technology.*

Ubiquitous

By the end of 2007, the world had 3.3 billion cellphone subscriptions and there is a cellphone subscription for literally half the planet. No other device has ever been so widely spread, no other communication technology has ever had such wide reach. Africa and India are moving from 10% to 20% penetration levels. China is rapidly approaching 50% penetration levels. Parts of Latin America are catching up with Canada. Russia and parts of Eastern Europe have already moved past USA in cellphone penetrations. Moreover, in the most advanced parts of the wireless telecoms world, from Taiwan and Hong Kong to Finland and Sweden, to Italy and Israel, there are nearly on average two cellphones for every employed person in the economy.

The cellphone is the ubiquitous device, in fact the only ubiquitous device on the planet. Wherever you find electricity, you will also tend to find cellphones. Moreover, in many parts of the developing world from Afghanistan to Mozambique there are villages without electricity but, which still have cellular coverage. The villagers use hand-cranked cellphone rechargers and the telecoms carriers/operators have self-powered base stations with their own electrical supply to provide the telecoms service.

During this decade the media industries, advertising, banking and credit cards, and the internet players have all discovered the cellphone. Google's CEO, Eric Schmidt tells anyone willing to listen that Google's future depends on the *next internet*, on *cellphones.*

Case Study 1 from Japan:
i-Channel on NTT DoCoMo

Japanese cellphone carrier/operator giant NTT DoCoMo launched its i-Channel news service in 2005. This service was a "news ticker" like the CNN news ticker on the bottom of the TV screen, which scrolls breaking news headlines onto the idle screen of the cellphone. This is a service that the phone owner could customize. Someone wants sports news, another wants financial/business news, another wants international news, and another wants the celebrity gossip, while yet another wants pop music news etc. The breaking news delivered to the cellphone is displayed always when the phone is in idle mode, for example on a table or desk as we work etc.

Note it is always at least as fast as the CNN style news ticker - often faster, as we may not be near our TV set but will always have our phone within arm's reach. It is also far more relevant than the main headlines on the CNN news ticker. The analogue cable and satellite TV broadcasters cannot personalize all news feeds to personal tastes of millions of their viewers, but on the cellphone, it is very easy to focus the interests to those of the individual consumer.

Still better than typical newspaper or TV content, when you find a headline that is interesting, you can click on the headline and get more news about the story, including pages of text, pictures, sound and video (depending on story obviously). A far superior news experience to getting news on radio, TV or the newspaper because the user can select how much more information - and in what format.

How is it doing? It is not free. Japanese consumers are charged 200 Yen (1.70 dollars) per month to view i-Channel news. And any clicks to further news stories are then charged per page viewed or clip downloaded on normal mobile news rates. So how is it doing in Japan? 18 months from launch, by January 2007, *Wireless Watch Japan* reported that i-Channel was already subscribed by 8 million paying subscribers on NTT DoCoMo's network. An adoption rate of 16% of all subscribers on that Japanese wireless carrier/mobile operator. Since then rival KDDI has launched a similar service in Japan the idea is spreading around the world, with Vodafone Portugal the first European carrier to launch a similar service.

Should this be of interest to the news media business? i-Channel is not a free service. As a paid service 16% of Japanese phone users already signed up for it. At 163 million dollars of annual revenues just from i-Channel alone for the NTT DoCoMo's breaking news unit, this is the kind of new media service and revenues that any news media boss would love. To put it into an American media context, if 16% of American cellphone subscribers adopted this kind of service, and paid $1.70 per month for it, the idle screen news ticker for cellphones would produce revenues of 734 million dollars annually, in the USA alone. That always gets the attention of print media audiences. Yes, we have seen the future of news media. It is rapidly headed to a 7th Mass Media channel near you.

"Progress is impossible without change,
and those who cannot change their minds cannot change anything."
George Bernard Shaw

III
Society and the Cell
Why prefer the cellphone

The cellphone is changing society. In Finland today, dentists will coordinate cancelled appointments by cellphone and libraries will send reminders of when your book is due, via cellphone. Did you want to renew the library book? Simply send a reply via SMS text messaging and keep the book for another 2 weeks, it is that simple. As the nine and ten-year-old kids come home from school, they report in to their parents, using their personal cellphones.

Dating no longer starts with the clever pick-up line at a bar; it now starts with a clever original SMS text message from the digital Romeo to his electronic Juliet. Grandparents connect with their grandkids, using picture messaging and text messaging. TV producers are building new formats to capture audience interaction and bonus revenues out of SMS text voting such as on *American Idol/Pop Idol* and other such reality TV formats. Japanese homes are now introducing locks that are operated by cellphone and in South Korea they are experimenting with systems where the cellphone can locate the nearest available parking place for you as you drive. How far can it go?

A   OUR MAIN TOOL FOR CONTACT

In Finland if you turn to any of the commercial TV stations at night, you will not find the test pattern or an info-mercial selling some fantastic slendering gadgets or miracle cleaning detergents. Finnish commercial TV runs all night SMS-to-TV chat boards, on all commercial channels. As there is limited space to run the chat comments, and an ever-increasing demand for people to send messages their personal messages to the TV screen, the price has been climbing quarter after quarter. Today the premium rate starts at over 13 times more than the price of regular person-to-person SMS text messages in Finland or well in excess of a dollar per chat message. Yet all three commercial TV channels are full of chatting messages - or their cousins, the SMS based TV games - all night. Yes, it is like chat boards on the internet, but also understand that Finland has one of the highest penetration rates of personal computers, internet access and broadband internet. Why chat on TV when it would be free on the internet? Because you see your name on the TV screen. We all want to be famous.

Then there is the idea of sending text messages to strangers in their cars based on their license plate number. Fancy the blonde in the BMW? This requires car owners to register their license plate with a cellphone to participate and then pay premium text messaging rates to communicate in this way. The idea seems doomed as a business. Yet in the UK, alone, this idea generates one million text messages per month and some £3 Million (US $6 Million) in annual revenues. Similarly, nightclubs, pubs and discos in the UK, have installed public texting boards that patrons can send messages for all to read. Yes, premium SMS of course. These deliver over 100,000 messages per month.

B   CONNECTED AGE

I have discussed the shift from the Networked Age to the Connected Age in my previous books and to great length in *Communities Dominate Brands*. It is worth discussing here as well, as that shift from the Networked Age - and all of the currently so familiar digital "information age" thinking, technologies and phenomena, from "googling" i.e. search to eBay auctions, Amazon bookselling etc. to blogging, wikis, MMOGs and so forth - are all symptoms and developed under thinking of the Networked Age. There is a newer age emerging.

The Networked Age was a vital half-step in mankind's evolution to the information society, but it was only that: a half-step. Everything you know about the digital world is only a prelude to a much more profound evolution currently taking place. That is the rapid ushering in of the Connected Age. The advent of the always-connected society, enabled by cellphones, is this new era. If you think changes in the past ten years, brought about by the "pervasive" internet have been enormous, be prepared for much greater changes in the next decade.

Needed access

The Networked Age was a good term for the last decade in the 1990s, as it did describe how we as humans approached "the network" i.e. the internet - we logged on, we accessed our e-mail and we surfed seeking information. The Networked Age was the dawn of how humans could build virtual communities, and is a necessary step on our evolution to the Connected Age.

Networked Age vs Connected Age

Networked Age	Connected Age
PC focused	Cellphone focused
One internet	Multiple networks
Place-centric	Omnipresent
Scheduled/planned use	Spontaneous use
email, fax	SMS, IM, blogs
Hippie-like, free	Business-like, commerce
Semi-private	Personal and unique
Search and consume	Share and co-create
USA-led	Asia and Scandinavia-led

Half step into the Community

The Networked Age is like the early Industrial Revolution... before electricity. The first steam-powered machines were huge, noisy, central engines, like a big heart in a factory, and all devices were then connected by gears and pulleys and belts and other mechanical means to such engines. The first factories such as for clothing worked like this. There was one central steam engine of for example 200 horsepower in its rated output, and it physically powered all sewing machines of the factory all connected by a complex system of belts and pulleys. In addition, there could be 50 separate sewing machine stations in the factory. Each was connected by pulleys and belts to the one central engine that made it all work. The noise in the factory was enormous. Needless to say, if the steam engine broke down, all sewing machines stopped. If you remember Charlie Chaplin's silent movie *Modern Times* - with Charlie caught up inside a machine - that was the industrial age of steam.

When constructing a factory, which was steam-powered, the whole design from the steam engine power plant to the power transmission, to individual sewing stations had to be carefully planned and built. The factory and its working stations were very precisely tied to explicit locations. There was not much room for variation or expansion in this design.

Just like we today may be seeking a WiFi hotspot or inquire about broadband availability in our hotel room, in the same way the early industrial age was tied to specific locations. Yes, you could have machine power (internet access) but only in this location with these limitations. Not everywhere.

It was much better than no engine at all, obviously. Moreover, it was truly the start of an upheaval in mankind's history: the industrial age. Yet today we do not buy one steam engine into our home, and then connect our vacuum cleaner and our washing machine and our blender to that central engine. All of the advances in our lives are based on a second stage of the industrial revolution.

Electricity

It was not until the advent of electricity that it became possible to have an omnipresent power source - the electrical grid - and machines and workers to perform differing deeds in differing locations. Much more importantly for any growing business, it allowed a smooth expansion of capacity by just plugging in more devices to the electrical outlets and paying a bit more in the electricity bill. Only electricity could bring the "business/enterprise" benefits to the masses.

The analogy to the fixed Internet is that while readers may think the Internet has created immense changes to their business, it is like the first mechanical machines for the industrial age. Yes, these were an enormous change

---

Mobile Data Devices and Users 2007

Excluding basic SMS text messaging and MMS picture messaging users

Mobile Subscribers globally	100%	3,3 Billion
2.5G+ data service capable phones	88%	2,9 Billion
Data service enabled phones + subscriptions	76%	2,5 Billion
Download-capable phones (Java/BREW enabled)	42%	1,4 Billion
Active mobile data users	32%	1,0 Billion

Sources: Online Publishers Association, TNS Survey, Morgan Stanley, TomiAhonen Consulting   2007-2008

---

at the time. However, considering the history of mankind, steam was only a *transitional* technology. The full extent of the industrial revolution came with electricity. This analogy is relevant to the internet. Any changes you have witnessed due to the current "fixed" and "landline based" Internet - either narrowband or broadband - will become dramatically *more pronounced* and far-reaching via the cellphone-boosted wireless Internet during the next ten years.

From clumsy to clever

Much like our ability to connect to "the network" whether by accessing our e-mail, accessing our voicemail, or accessing the internet, there was a two-step process. Something might have happened in the virtual world - like us receiving an e-mail - and we had to check in periodically to see what, if anything, was going on. This is a clumsy two-step process.

The connectedness was by necessity limited to telephone outlets. Our internet and voicemail were accessed through the telephone network, which in the middle of the last decade was a fixed wireline network. Nevertheless, like the advent of electricity, now telecommunications is omnipresent, wirelessly, through the cellular (or in European telecoms terminology, *mobile*) telecoms network. Now digital networks can grow and move as the need emerges. Just like electricity.

Most importantly, the newest technologies are all built on an "always-on" principle. The power and speed of SMS text messaging is not with the sender. Yes, of course we like it that we have the "sending machine" of SMS texting capacity on our phone in our pocket all the time. The true factor of speed is that every *recipient* also carries the same device on their person, and is able to *receive* text messages even when voice calls are not practical. (I will discuss this in detail in the SMS text messaging chapter; but if you find the concept difficult to accept, think of the Blackberry, and how neurotically some Blackberry users are dependent on them. It is not that they need to *send* emails all the time; they want to see if any messages *have arrived*.) SMS text messaging has shrunk the receiving side of human communications. That is why a new telecommunications term, "reachability" has been coined.

Addictiveness of connectedness

In my fourth book **Communities Dominate Brands** my co-author Alan Moore and I introduce Generation C for the Community Generation. When we consider Generation-C and other connected people living with electronic communities, it is possible to connect with traditional electronic media, particularly the fixed Internet, e-mail and chat, but the real power of communities arrives only through connectedness. We achieve connectedness through the cellphone. Rather than our internet access, which is mostly locked to a place such as our desk at our office, one room in our home, the computer lab in the school, or our WiFi hotspot at Starbucks; the cellphone is on our person, with us at all times.

Rather than an actually or potentially shared device, such as the personal computer often is at home, and may be at work where a secretary or colleague or boss might suddenly borrow your computer, or walk in and see what is on your screen, the cellphone is always personal and private. So private in fact that a *Wired* survey in 2006 found that 63% of all cellphone users will not share a phone with anyone, not even their spouse. It is that personal.

Most of all the other networked systems require logging on, we have to set aside time to access our network, our internet, our e-mail, our chat, our session in *Facebook, Second Life* or *Warcraft*. However, the cellphone is always connected. Moreover, we do carry our phone with us literally 24 hours a day, 7 days a week as I showed in the previous chapter. The Nokia global survey of mobile phone users in 2006 found that 72% of phone use the phone as their alarm. The study on cellphone addiction by the Catholic University of Leuwen in Belgium found that over half of teenagers wake up to incoming text messages at night. I will look at young people in a later chapter in this book.

The phone is with us at all times. It is our most personal communication device. Moreover, differing from the internet, our cellphone is always connected. Thus while yes, the PC, laptops, PDAs, the internet, WiFi and broadband were going in the right direction for digital community mindset, they were only a half-step. That was all Networked Age. The full step is the Connected Age.

Howard Rheingold, the pioneer of virtual communities never loses sight of the primary purpose of the cellphone. Other uses are coming such as shopping and consuming content, but the power of the cellphone is *communication*. In enabling cooperation, as he says of the cellphones in his book *Smart Mobs*:

> *They amplify human talents for cooperation. They also change the way people shop, how they gather information on products they want to buy and where they decide to make that purchase.*
> Howard Rheingold, *Smart Mobs*, 2002

The insight is remarkable. Cellphones "amplify human talents for cooperation". A brilliant observation, and very powerful. Yes, all of us have some ability to cooperate, but in every cooperative situation, if you equip all members cooperating with cellphones, their productivity increases. This in turn emphasizes the need to have speed of contact. Moreover, SMS texting rules the day. Friends summons others with text messages to join into IM and chat discussions. To join in an exciting moment inside *World of Warcraft* or *Second Life* or *Habbo Hotel*. To participate in a reality TV event, etc.

With the emphasis shifting from withholding information to sharing, the most rewarded contributors are those who are fastest at sharing. They get a reputation for information communicators, those who "always know". They will

Tomi T Ahonen

invariably be rewarded by their contact network and peer group, where others will send information to them, in return. This enriches those who know how to share. Equally, anyone who is found to be hoarding information, withholding it, not sharing, is punished. In a very real sense, it means that in the Connected Age, sharing information is power.

C   MOBILE PAYMENTS

As the society and industry discover the power and pervasiveness of the cellphone, a vast new range of services and applications are invented. With only a few years of experiences and concrete data, the early numbers are nonetheless breathtaking. The airline industry reports that 2% of all airline travelers now use cellphone based tickets or boarding passes. A rock concert in Vienna Austria found 20% of the fans paying for the concert via cellphone. In London 20% of the city's congestion charges are paid by the car drivers directly from their cellphones. 20% of Kenyan bank accounts are now mobile banking accounts. 22% of Norwegians already use their cellphones to pay for purchases. 25% of Visa cards in South Korea are enabled on cellphones.

In Helsinki Finland 40% of all single tickets to the subway trains and 55% of trams tickets are paid by cellular phone. In Japan 54% of cellphone

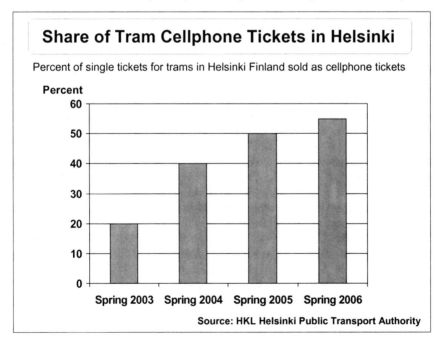

Share of Tram Cellphone Tickets in Helsinki

Percent of single tickets for trams in Helsinki Finland sold as cellphone tickets

Source: HKL Helsinki Public Transport Authority

owners receive advertisements on the phone, in Spain 72% do so. A barbershop in Soweto Africa takes more than half of the payments of its customers for haircuts, via cellphone. Over half of internet surfers in India do so by cellphone rather than PC. Over half of South Koreans make regular payments on their cellphones. In Slovenia every McDonalds accepts cellphone payments. In Japan 84% of cellphone users already pay to receive news on the cellphone. Moreover, we have even reached the ultimate Connected Age occasion where you could not even join without cellphone access. In the UK, a nightclub/disco called *Detonate* in Nottingham held their anniversary and only those patrons who bought tickets via cellphones - and displayed on the cellphone screen rather than paper ticket, were admitted. 100% of the patrons that night entered via cellphone ticketing.

In Estonia, the government found that there were enterprising criminals who put on an official-looking uniform, and placed "out of order" signs on parking meters, and collected cash parking fees from unsuspecting motorists. As Estonia's cellphone penetration was already over 100% and various mobile commerce applications were commonplace - such as the world's first lottery which could only be paid for by cellphone - the Estonian government decided to

---

17.2% of American cellphone owners had received ads.
Source: M:Metrics October 2007

---

put the parking meter scam artists out of business. They instituted a law that only cellphone payments could be used for parking. The crime vanished, and the government achieved not only more fees, but a more efficient means to collect the money directly, digitally, than sending people to empty the cash from the parking meters daily. Today if you go to Estonia and want to park your rental car, the only way to pay for your parking is with the cellphone.

What of the future? The Finnish government decided in 2005 that the national emergency communication system would be based around cellphones, no longer broadcast like radio and TV, simply because every Finn had a cellphone. Japan is building apartment buildings with locks perated by cellphone.

The Singapore government studied different forms of its citizens to access e-government services and decided that all e-government must be enabled via cellphone. Taxes, health, drivers licenses, parking fees, etc. All via cellphone. This because the Singapore government noticed that the only interactive technology that all Singaporeans have, was the cellphone. Moreover, bear in mind, Singapore PC penetration and broadband penetration is one of the highest in the world, and Singapore also is rolling out a nationwide free WiFi network. Still, cellphones are the access method of choice for the advanced Asian nation.

Is the cellphone changing society? You bet it is. Will this happen in the

USA? If these changes happen in the countries mentioned above, of course they will also happen in the USA (and Canada too).

D   SMART MOBS

The person who discovered the notion and concept of "smart mobs" or "swarming" was Howard Rheingold. He wrote about it in his book called *Smart Mobs*. Rheingold identified change in behavior that was due to the cellphone. Before, if you wanted to meet someone, you had to agree beforehand that the meeting would be held at a specific location. Swarming is the exact opposite. You know you will meet at an approximate time, but the final destination is set by the community at the last moment. For example one of your work colleagues might go out first, find the right bar or pub, and then tell the others where to come. Earlier young people would sit at home on a Saturday waiting for the calls to discuss what to do. Now they go out, and catch up with friends later on, via their cellphones.

75.4% of Spanish cellphone owners had received ads.
Source: M:Metrics October 2007

The key to the power of cellphones is that they liberate people from their desktop telephones and computers, moving the action out to that much larger portion of life that encompasses wherever and whenever humans roam. Social swarming, Rheingold argues, involves sharing your life with others in real time. It means pulsing to the rhythm of life with one's community of friends. It means a non-stop emotional connection to one's swarm.

Always spontaneous

The preferred method of coordinating is the SMS text message, as it is non-intrusive, immediate and private. Only being connected via the cellphone allows last-minute changes to our daily schedules. It starts with the occasional "I am running 15 minutes late" type of SMS text messages and voice calls from cellphones. There is almost no point in attempting a "15 minutes late" message via e-mail, as more often than not, our recipient will not even be at his/her e-mail within the next 15 minutes. Soon that kind of last-minute behavior transforms into the pattern of *"let's not decide yet"* kind of behavior. We agree to meet for beers after work, but lets not pick a place and time until later today. Since every one of us has a cellphone, it will be easy to decide later. The first one to leave the office picks the place and the others will appear there. It is what makes life exciting, the sudden decision to do something unplanned; a mini adventure in our daily lives.

Flash mobbing

A new type of behavior capturing this mentality has been coined as "flash mobbing" and it is happening with greater frequency. Perhaps the first such event happened in Finland when local pop band Nylon Beat released its newest hit song not as a CD or MP3 file or for radio airplay, but as a ringing tone in 2000. The band then had its fans all converge on a hill in Helsinki where fans were to play the song together. To the cacophonic sound of plink-plonk of the early ringing tones on mostly Nokia phones, the event collected thousands to celebrate their favorite band.

This incident could be dismissed as an isolated example. In fact, it was just the very tip of the iceberg for group behavior. Now cellphones are becoming the tool of choice for any group behavior needing urgency, and being adopted in all countries with high cellphone penetrations. In the UK, what was called the "Pillow Fight" took place outside St. Paul's Cathedral on 6th October 2004 when 500 Londoners suddenly appeared with pillows outside the famous huge historical landmark cathedral. The result was one of the biggest pillow fights ever. It started and ended suddenly and then all participants scattered and took their pillows and went back home.

Another vivid example of the power of swarming comes from birdwatching in Finland. As all Finns have cellphones, an amazing 5,000 birdwatchers recently gathered in the area of Viikki, within 60 minutes of a sighting of a rare bird for the Finnish climate, a male gray-headed woodpecker.

Varying feedback loops

The last decade has seen the progressive introduction of ever-faster feedback methods. From the letter to the editor in the 1970s to the fax in the 1980s, to the e-mail in the 1990s, today many TV programs request feedback via SMS text messaging. As these messages are short, do not include a header that would need to be stripped, don't have attachments, and in 160 characters cannot have much beyond the main point, SMS text messaging is exceptionally well suited for broadcasting the feedback.

Many TV shows have introduced viewer comments in the form of a "news headline ticker" scrolling on the bottom of the screen. Viewers can send in comments, and a human editor selects, which to pass onto the system for sharing. Feedback has become ever faster and now is in real-time. This creates user-generated content for legacy media like television, radio and print. They even ask for pictures and videos by viewers such as CNN with its i-Report.

Tomi T Ahonen

Cameraphone Sales 2001-2008

Year	Sold	Cumulative	In Use	As Pct of all
2001	3 M	3 M	3 M	0%
2002	10 M	13 M	13 M	1%
2003	58 M	71 M	68 M	5%
2004	250 M	321 M	299 M	18%
2005	345 M	666 M	575 M	27%
2006	450 M	1,116 M	851 M	32%
2007	852 M	1,968 M	1,385 M	42%
2008	1,040 M	3,008 M	1,942 M	50%

Source: TomiAhonen Consulting 2008

Media are learning to capitalize on the speed and reach of cellphones, moving from the Networked Age to the Connected Age.

Disposable memories

The rapid spread of cameraphones has created a different way to use its in-built camera. Not to have precious images to cherish and share for years to come, but rather to create temporary, disposable memories. One of the things I do now regularly with my cameraphone in any city that I visit, is to take a picture of the subway map. I keep it for the trip, and delete after the trip. Nevertheless, during the trip I never have to search for the paper version of the map that I forgot into the other suit or that is in my bag at the hotel, etc. My cameraphone is always with me.

Some take pictures of where the car is parked. Others take pictures of the license plates of the cars parked next to you, in case of any damage. Still others take pictures of rental car scratches before starting off with the car, rather than walking 10 minutes back to the rental office to complain that there are two little scratches on the car that were not marked on the form. I travel a lot through Heathrow airport in London, which seems to be in perpetual evolution, as different airlines are shuffled to varying terminals. I snap a picture of the current terminal-and-airline chart every month as I pass through Heathrow, and delete the older one. This way I always have a current listing of, which airline is in, which terminal, to help me plan my flight connections from Hong Kong to Europe and back.

These kinds of images are all disposable. We never send them via picture messaging, so-called MMS (Multi-Channel Messaging Service). We keep these only for a short while until we delete them. We don't show these to our friends etc. Just a convenience tool, a memory aid. Soon we will find hundreds of such uses, as we start to remember that we have a camera upon us always.

Eight rules of cellphone conduct from South Korea

So where do we go from here? We see "rude" people in restaurants chatting loudly on their cellphones. We hear phones ring loudly at the cinema or at a Broadway play etc. How should we behave with this new gadget.

The Korean wireless carrier KTF has published what it calls "Eight simple rules" for cellphone etiquette. They were featured in the English language web periodical *Telecoms Korea* in an article on April 20, 2005. The 8 rules are:

1. Switch to silent mode in public places.
2. Make your conversation quiet and simple.
3. Switch to silent mode in a class or meeting room
4. Ask the person you call if he or she can answer the phone at the moment before you start conversation
5. Don't start conversation with someone who is driving. Call back later.
6. Refrain from using mobile devices around medical equipment or during a flight
7. Identify yourself when you send a text message
8. Care about others' rights and privacy before you use camera phone. Never take pictures of others without their consent.

These are very good simple rules that I can warmly endorse

E   ANTI-SOCIAL BEHAVIOR

For all the good that can be ascribed to the cellphone, it is after all only a technology, and it will be used for bad things as well. There are dozens of examples of antisocial behavior that is now capitalizing on cellphones.

The first and foremost is cheating in class. As younger kids get cellphones, and these can handle secret, silent messaging, the kids will attempt to cheat in tests in class, using SMS text messaging. I have personally interviewed close to a hundred teenagers on this issue, on six continents. Sometimes it is in a formal context such as a youth clinic on cellphones, other times it is the children of a colleague, etc. Every one of them has admitted to trying to cheat in an exam, using SMS text messages. The typical answer is "of course." A recent study of students in Korea revealed that 40% admit to sending messages in class.

Teachers have of course caught onto this. The Philippines was the first where school boards had all parents register for SMS alerts on their kids, and today whenever a child misbehaves in school, the parents get immediate notification via SMS. No longer was there any chance of a child forging a parent's signature on a paper "note" sent from the teacher.

But the youth environment of school does find other sad instances of cellphones and antisocial behavior. One is the bizarre instance of bullying by SMS and cellphone. Kids are bullied, frightened by text messaging. These typically are done via anonymous servers, so the recipient of the bullying message does know who the bullies are in school, but there is no obvious easy proof of evidence of who sent the message. Tracking and solving these kinds of secret messages is a new nuisance for school guidance counselors.

Peeping Toms

Cameraphones have brought new opportunities for antisocial behavior. When first introduced in Japan in 2001 that society also witnessed the first abuses. Teenagers would go to newsstands, open up youth magazines, and snap cameraphone pictures of the magazines, without buying them. Then read the magazines and copy the pictures from the images stored on the cameraphones. This became so much a national epidemic in 2003-2004 that today all Japanese newsstands feature the notice "no cameraphones".

The other obvious abusive use of cameraphones is the "Peeping Tom" type of behavior. A Japanese businessman was found guilty of perverse behavior when he used his cameraphone to snap pictures under the skirts of women in 2001. Since then at most swimming pools today the use of cameraphones are forbidden in the dressing area. This was particularly threatening to pedophiles who found it easy to get pictures of naked kids as they undressed to go to swim.

Happy slapping and cellphone chicken

Video cameras on the phones introduce again a new twist. A sad development in the UK, is what is called "happy slapping." This craze has someone ready with a videophone, shooting video of his friend, as the friend attacks a passer-by by slapping the person on the head, preferably very hard to get a big reaction. The whole thing is caught on video camera on the advanced cameraphones, and usually then shared with friends.

Now an even more dangerous variant of that activity is the game of

UK Mobile Phone User Findings 2006

70%   replace cellphones every 18 months.

45%   of grandmothers use cellphones to connect
         with grandkids

42%   of parents ask kids for help with cellphone

36%   would snap a picture of a celebrity

25%   of young adults send texts to friends their
         partner or family would not like

14%   only turn cellphone completely off for sex

9%   of 18-24 year olds admit cellphone addiction

Source: Carphone Warehouse Mobile Life Study 2006

"cellphone chicken" by, which kids in Britain jump in front of an onrushing train, and wait until the last possible moment to jump off. The whole activity is recorded by friends on the video feature of their advanced cameraphones.

Even worse, if there is a sadistic bent on a deranged person, now cameraphones allow further abuse. In the UK, the ***Daily Mail*** reported an incident of a girl being shot in the leg just so that this incident could be recorded onto cameraphones, and the clip then shared with the very maladjusted older teenagers.

I don't want to dwell on the darker side and bad effects of the cellphone. It is a new technology. Some will find good in it, others will find a way to be antisocial with it. However, I do not want to hide from the bad side as well. We need to understand this new technology. That it is so pervasive, and as the phones are replaced every 18 months, the newest digital technologies will appear on the cellphones and achieve global penetrations that way. What for someone may be the benefit of barcode scanners or fingerprint scanners, to someone else might be a tool for forgery and trickery. We need to be vigilant about this.

Who is digital gatekeeper

The changes in society will see an emergence of a new player controlling the information flow related to our society, its members, and increasingly, the digital communities. That entity is the wireless carrier (mobile operator, cellular telco), which almost by accident has become the dominant player controlling the access to services on the most preferred personal digital device - our cellphone. Furthermore, in complete contrast to all the players involved in the internet, the cellular carriers/mobile operators control a digital environment with a rigid and powerful payment system and because of the design and technology of cellular networks; they continuously collect data into their billing systems. This makes the cellphone carrier the aggregator of the most complete, in-depth and intimate knowledge of all economically viable persons on the planet, amounting to the most in-depth user data on the viable part of the global population.

Up to this time, the best customer insights have come from marketing research, which used consumer surveys, focus group studies and so forth. The two main problems with marketing research are that they reflect the stated opinions of the interview subjects rather than their actual behavior (many users of adult entertainment services will typically not admit to it in surveys for example) and also that they rely on relatively small interview sample sizes, which introduce considerable error in the statistical reliability of the findings.

The internet promised to get full and accurate customer insights by accurately measuring its users and the digital services they consumed. Today the internet customer information accuracy is known to be quite unreliable. A given customer may have multiple accounts, using multiple computers and multiple identities. Many computers are behind firewalls such as most at work. Many computers are shared such as those at university computer labs and internet cafes. The users themselves often hide and disguise their identities, deliberately. The use of cookies to collect data from users has led to many malware programs to remove cookies.

On cellular networks, there is an absolute need to get perfect customer information, because every call or connection is measured and usually billed (or at least counted against the minute or message allowance of a given customer). Every phone has an absolute unique identity. Even those who have prepaid (pay-as-you-go) accounts and who may have given "Mickey Mouse" style false identities to the network are still uniquely tracked and fully accounted. We may not know accurately what is your real name and where you live, but we do know how many times you visited the *Playboy* site last month on your cellphone, etc.

What is even more valuable to marketing professionals than what you consume personally is the "social context" of that consumption. Who did you consume it with. Whom did you forward it to. Who recommended that to you. The social context of the consumption. Bringing that "social networking" element that is so powerful on *Facebook* and *MySpace* and *YouTube* and *Wikipedia*, bringing that to customer insights. The author and CEO of British engagement marketing specialist SMLXL, Alan Moore says: *"Raw data has no value. Social network intelligence is the black gold of the 21st century."*

Companies such as Xtract are now deploying deep social networking analytics solutions to dig for these insights.

The wireless carrier will yield enormous power in deciding who gains what information and at what cost. Even more significantly, for understanding the behavior and power of digitally connected communities, the telco can track and analyze social network communications. For those who are interested more in the economic functioning of the mobile telecoms business including the business case for the carriers, and the various content and application partnerships that form modern mobile business, I refer to the business book that is the "bible" for the business of the telecoms industry, my book *m-Profits*. Suffice it to say here that the mobile operator/carrier will grow greatly in importance to the market understanding of end-users and their communities.

E Pluribus Cellum

The steam engine did launch the industrial age, but the steam engine did not invade every home and every life. Electricity did change the planet. Now we see a similar pattern with the PC based internet, and cellular phones. Yes, the internet was a vital half step for society to start to understand the digital "information society" but the internet is as limited as steam engines were, tied to a place and having no flexibility. Cellular phones reach a far wider population, provide permanent access in virtually the whole planet and add many powerful elements including perfect customer data and the ability to track payments. This is the dawn of the Connected Age for society and the key to that change is the cellphone, in every pocket, and on the other hand, of the employed young adults of the world, there already is the second phone. There will be many who will try to argue against the changes that are now happening. That is nothing new. Change is difficult to accept. As Lyman Beecher said, *"No great advance has ever been made in science, politics or religion, without great controversy."*

Tomi T Ahonen

Case Study 2 from the UK
Flirtomatic

Flirtomatic is a UK based flirting and dating service available on cellphones and the internet, which was developed by Fjord. It launched in May 2006. Much of Flirtomatic is predictable in concepts similar from dating/flirting online services. It has user profiles, with pictures, and the chance to send messages across to other Flirtomatic users. Where Flirtomatic goes far beyond the traditional online services is in its new business and service concepts built around the 7th Mass Media channel.

One of the features of Flirtomatic is the virtual gift, which includes anything from virtual roses to virtual champagne to the virtual kiss (yes, virtual kisses...). These are paid for by "Flirt Points", a virtual money system, which can be topped up by cellphone users with premium SMS payments as well as other payment methods.

There is a strong emotional and communication element to the virtual gifts, so for example there is the animated graphic of a girl smiling and twirling a bra. This is a clear suggestion of the fun to follow, from the woman sending that animation to the man (or woman) of her choice. These kinds of gifts are all charged either to the user, or offered via sponsorship deals, such as L'Oreal sponsoring the virtual Big Wet Kiss.

Another money-making feature is built around the personalization. Users get to rate their flirting partners and obviously some pairings will yield bad reviews. Flirtomatic allows its members to remove a bad rating, but at a premium cost.

The service has taken the auction-based advertising idea from Google Adwords and developed a Flirtomatic version of that idea. Members can bid for the top slots of the opening page, to be the "First Face" featured Flirtomatic member of the hour. These are auctioned. The current rate will cost about 8 UK Pounds (16 US dollars) to gain six hours on the Flirtomatic opening page as their First Face to generate flirting contacts. Flirtomatic has brought not only user-generated ads to cellphone based dating and flirting, but also *auctioned* personal ads just like Google Adwords.

How is Flirtomatic doing? By the autumn of 2007 Flirtomatic had 80,000 members, 20,000 on cellphones using its WAP service and the other 60,000 as web users. The cellphone users generated more than twice as much traffic as the web users, and cellphone users were far more active, logging into the site on average 8.5 times per day.

The best success story is the virtual Red Rose. During 2007 Flirtomatic sold 3.5 million virtual red roses to its 80,000 members, and generated £805,000 (US$1,710,000) in revenues. 3.5 million roses in the year? That is almost 10,000 roses per day out of a total user base of only 80,000. Flirtomatic is already one of the largest florists in Britain today. With all the innovative revenue models Flirtomatic CEO Mark Curtis announced in April 2007 that Flirtomatic was terminating its subscription fee altogether - as unnecessary!

"The mobile will be the main device to enjoy radio and TV
programs anytime anywhere. "
Yun-Joo Jung, CEO Korea Broadcasting Service

IV
7th Mass Media
And the fourth screen

We made a thorough case study of digital convergence from the experiences of the most advanced information society with Jim O'Reilly in my fifth book, **Digital Korea**. In the book, we explored various media heading to digital platforms and concluded that there will not be only one network or medium. Much as I believe in the addictiveness, pervasiveness and sheer dominance of the cellphone, still in our lifetimes we will tend to have multiple overlapping networks and all seven of the mass media. Just like TV did not kill off cinema, and radio did not kill recordings, and the internet did not extinguish the business of newspapers and magazines, so too the cellphone will be more of an *additional* new media, than the final end-state of all media.

Still, the cellphone will become the ever more *predominant* media channel. It will be cannibalizing elements from all previous of the mass media. Mobile as the newest mass media channel is by far the least well understood. Nevertheless, make no mistake about it, mobile is not the dumb little brother of the internet. In a way similar to how TV took over from its predecessor, radio, as the dominant media of the late 20th century, mobile will soon take over from the internet and emerge as the dominant media of the early 21st century.

We have much to learn from the previous transitions when a newer media channel emerged. Television came in the 1950s and it rapidly repurposed all of the formats of content from radio. However, newer content formats created for TV the newer media, were not all able to migrate back to radio (most game shows and reality TV would not work on radio, and obviously music video without video is only "plain old music" etc).

Similarly, everything we can do on the internet today, we can also do on an advanced cellphone today - not always as well obviously, but all can be done. Yet there are many types of services that already exist on the newer media, mobile that cannot be replicated on the PC based internet (such as ringing tones for example). To understand mobile as the 7th mass media channel fully, we need to start by examining the previous six mass media channels.

A   FIRST FIVE MEDIA ARE UNI-DIRECTIONAL

The first five of the mass media are mature, over 50 years old each. Even the sixth media - the internet - is well into its teens. So let's examine them all briefly, with a focus on each of the transitions from the older media to the newer one.

First mass media channel: Print

The first mass media is print, which arrived with the printing press. At about 500 years old, it gave us first books, then pamphlets, then newspapers, and later magazines etc. Early on, it was even the only mass media for selling of music? Yes, before recordings (records, tapes, digital MP3 files etc) and radio, the only way to sell music was through the sheets of notes - "sheet music" - that the musically inclined could then play on their pianos at home. Now, five hundred years and six newer media channels later, print is still going strong. No matter that with almost every newer mass media there were predictions that newspapers,

---

The Seven Mass Media

First Mass Media Channel - *Print* from the 1500s

Second Mass Media Channel - *Recordings* from 1900s

Third Mass Media Channel - *Cinema* from 1910s

Fourth Mass Media Channel - *Radio* from 1920s

Fifth Mass Media Channel - *TV* from 1950s

Sixth Mass Media Channel - *Internet* from 1990s

Seventh Mass Media Channel - *Mobile* from 2000s

---

magazines and books would disappear.

Print introduced the concept of advertising for the mass media. Moreover, its format was a buy-to-own model. Printed items are totally portable and even though much of the printing process has been digitized, still almost all print material (on print mass media, see recording and internet as separate media below) is "analogue" or paper-based. Print also introduced the subscription model, in particular for many magazine titles.

Second mass media channel: Recordings

The second of the mass media appeared about 1890, as recordings. The first recordings were music, starting with "clay" records at 78 RPM (Revolutions Per Minute) and later with LP (Long Playing) record albums at 33 RPM and singles at 45 RPM. Early records also were used to sell speeches, spoken books and comedy routines of comedians. Other analogue recording materials appeared such as open reel tape, c-cassette and cartridge/8-track. Videocassettes appeared to allow recording television content and the sale and rental of movies. Then digital formats appeared for content on computer disks, CDs and DVDs. Music shifted from vinyl to CD and movies from videocassettes to DVD.

Like print, recordings are also a "buy-to-own" media, although there are many rental services as well, in particular for movies. Recordings are not as inherently portable as print, as you also need to have a player for its given format, i.e. a CD player or iPod to listen to music today, or DVD player to watch the movie, and Playstation or other gaming console for videogames. Recordings soon cannibalized much of the music from print, but not that much of the content from books and magazines, and nothing from news.

Recordings introduced a new type of media talent, the ability to have a "pop music star" who was not necessarily the writer of a song, but rather the performer. Edith Piaff, Frank Sinatra, Elvis, the Beatles etc built their worldwide following through the sales of their recordings.

Looking at all recording formats (music, movies, computer software and videogaming) - the total recording business is growing at very healthy rates, even though individual elements, in particular music recordings, especially on CD formats are shrinking. During 2007, the DVD sales seemed to hit a plateau for movies but still growing for TV series content. Videogames and PC software recordings continued to grow strongly.

While some advertising existed on early recorded media, and today some ads appear inside videogames and on DVDs, this media is not very strongly conducive to advertising support.

Was first "new media"

Note that about a hundred years ago, recordings were the first "new media". As such, recordings were also able to totally cannibalize a previous media format. The sheet music sales that were the only way to sell popular music through the late 1800s rapidly disappeared in the early 1900s as recordings (and later also radio) demolished this part of the music industry. Today, when thinking about how the internet is cannibalizing newspaper content or mobile is cannibalizing music, this is actually nothing new. Often a newer media will discover its particular strengths, and previous ways to deliver given content may well migrate to a newer media channel. We just need to understand that it is part of being in the media business. More importantly, recordings did not *destroy* print, and after the advent of recordings, print has continued to grow as an industry.

Another fascinating side note was the emergence of one media discussing another media. Songs on records became a topic of magazines (and even books). Youth pop magazines appeared in most countries in the 1960s and 1970s as pop music artists became staples in all markets. Therefore, the advent of a new media channel can spawn more content formats for a legacy medium.

---

439 million people bought newspapers globally in 2007.
Source: Deloitte Media Predictive Rport 2007

Third mass media channel: Cinema

The third of the mass media was cinema, from about 1910. This was the first "pay-per-view" format so every time you viewed the movie (at the cinema) you had to pay again. This was also the first "multi-media" format incorporating moving pictures and sound. It should be noted that with the early technical limitations, movies themselves were silent, and a pianist would typically play the music score of the movie as it played in the cinema. Eventually cinema developed sound movies ("talkies") to allow a richer sound experiences.

Cinema started to migrate the long-form stories of books onto the silver screen, eventually having authors write directly to screenplays that never were released as books, or that are only released as books after the movie has become a success. Cinema also provided the first threat of a newer media challenging an older one in the area of news. In the late 1800s and early 1900s, the only way to consume news media was via the newspaper. In the 1920s and 1930s, the cinema became the weekly viewing place for "newsreels" - a kind of grandfather for what is television nightly news today. While popular before the main feature of a night at the movies, newsreels did not seriously cannibalize news content from newspapers, which continued to grow in influence during this period.

The cinema introduced continuing storyline films i.e. the cliffhangers that were often released on a weekly basis (precursor to today's soap operas).

Cinema also produced the world's first global celebrities starting with Charlie Chaplin. Cinema content was consumed in large groups (i.e. not privately). The advertising in cinema was shown before the main feature started.

Many suggested cinema would be the end of printed books. Of course, nothing could be further from the truth, the print industry has grown steadily for most of the glory days of cinema and much like recordings, cinema also spawned its own magazines and its own sections in the newspapers. Many successful books and comic books were turned into movies, and where some movies were original screenplays and became surprise hits, they in turn were turned into books, magazines and comic books, such as recent *James Bond* movies, which appear on cinema first, and are released as books later.

Fourth mass media channel: Radio

The fourth mass media channel appeared also very close to that time, essentially

---

798 million, 24% of cellphone owners on mobile web in 2007
Source: Informa 2007

---

around 1920: radio. This was the first broadcast media, where the consumption was a "streaming" concept. The listener did not own the content and the listener could not replay it. It took 50 years until about 1970 that technology emerged for mass-market use to capture broadcasts onto tape recordings, when Philips introduced the c-cassette. Radio was mostly personal or consumed in a small group, but almost from the start, the format was portable, or mobile. Radios started to appear in cars - this was the start of Motorola for example. After the Second World War personally portable pocket radios became possible and popular with the use of transistors in the manufacturing of ever smaller radios.

Radio became a very serious outlet for news. Radio ran regular drama and comedy shows including stories with continuing storylines. We know the style as soap operas on TV today. Families would gather around the favorite broadcasts and listen together. Weather became a serious separate content category, as did live sports that up to radio could not be delivered on any mass media. In some countries, the radio broadcasts were paid for by radio licenses, in other countries paid for by advertising, or a mixture of both.

Radio started to dominate other media - a pop music artist who was favored by a radio DJ would then become a hit on selling records. Thus for the music industry very specifically there became a close symbiotic relationship between radio airplay and record sales.

And again like recordings and cinema, radio spawned print titles that focused on it. The BBC's *Radio Times* was one of the famous publications that discussed what was to be broadcast in the coming week and similar magazines appeared in all countries. Newspapers would add pages with daily radio schedules.

While weather reports had been part of the newspaper industry, they now also appeared on radio. It did not kill off weather reports in newspapers.

B   TV AND THE INTERNET

The fifth mass media channel is the biggest and most dominant to our culture today: TV. Invented in the 1930s but introduced to the mass-market in about 1950, TV did not really introduce anything new. As we consider mobile as the 7th mass media channel, this is a very important point to understand. Each of the first four mass media did introduce something new, but TV did not.

TV gave us nothing new

We had multimedia in the cinema, and broadcast in radio, so all TV did, was to combine those two. Nothing new as such. Even the business models of licenses, advertising (from radio) and subscription (from print) had been seen prior to television. Yet in spite of not providing anything new, as TV combined two very powerful media elements, the multimedia experience of cinema with the immediacy and reach of broadcast, TV soon came to dominate the media space.

TV is consumed in small groups at home with a few members of our family or alone. TV is mostly not portable (yes, pocket TV have existed for 25 years but few actually own them, and even fewer bother to carry them around).

Television was a monster at cannibalizing content formats and stealing media audiences from older media. TV soon took over totally the newsreels from cinema but radio and newspapers were able to hang on to their news reporting. TV took over much of the drama series from radio, now called soap operas, and more gradually many of the live sports broadcasts.

TV was at first only a "streaming" proposition - if you did not see the show or episode on TV, you missed it forever. It was not until the mid 1970s that home video recording appeared pioneered by Philips in Europe and then by Sony Betamax around the world.

TV discovered the power of the celebrity, and soon shows emerged that promoted celebrity (e.g. talk shows) and those that propelled normal people into temporary celebrity status (e.g. game shows, reality TV). TV reduced attention spans, cutting drama series durations from two hours to 90 minutes to one hour; and making the 30-minute sitcom a standard format. Music TV (MTV) and music videos cut the standard storyline length to about 3 minutes. Continuing storyline soap operas emerged killing the serial movie concept from cinema, and

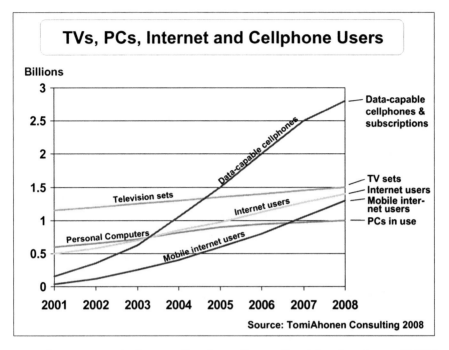

TVs, PCs, Internet and Cellphone Users

Billions

- Data-capable cellphones & subscriptions
- TV sets
- Internet users
- Mobile internet users
- PCs in use

Data-capable cellphones

Television sets

Internet users

Personal Computers

Mobile internet users

2001 2002 2003 2004 2005 2006 2007 2008

Source: TomiAhonen Consulting 2008

removing most continuing storyline drama from radio. After the advent of MTV music videos, suddenly the connection between radio and music recordings was severed, and MTV became the deciding factor to a music artist's success.

Today, roughly half of the industry revenues are derived from advertising and another half from subscription fees. TV displaced radio as the daily most relevant media, and pushed radio to a niche opportunity. Radio is listened to in the car, or as background noise. TV also started to generate content expansions into previous media - e.g. TV shows turned into movies (e.g. Mission Impossible, Star Trek); TV shows turned into recordings (DVD collections); and a lot of further print content relating to TV - in the UK, there are for example seven TV related weekly listings magazines, similar to the familiar *TV Guide* in the USA.

BBC TV and news anchors

A great lesson on the difficulty of transition from a legacy media to a newer one comes from the transition from radio to TV. The early "services" on TV (i.e. programming formats) actually avoided TV's particular strengths. For example, the BBC guidelines for TV news broadcasters in the late 1940s and early 1950s were based on BBC radio's considerable experience and reputation in radio. The radio experts had said that news would probably succeed also on the new TV

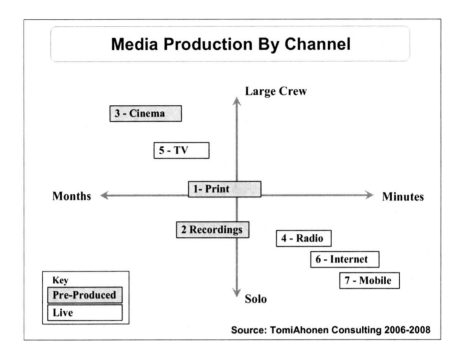

Media Production By Channel

Large Crew

3 - Cinema

5 - TV

Months ← 1- Print → Minutes

2 Recordings

4 - Radio

6 - Internet

7 - Mobile

Key
Pre-Produced
Live

Solo

Source: TomiAhonen Consulting 2006-2008

format. So they thought long and hard about how to make news a success on TV. They were thinking with a radio mindset. They knew that on radio, the listening audience was identifying with the familiar and reassuring *voice* of the news reader (or "news anchor" as we might know the job description today).

So the BBC guidelines said that TV news were allowed to show images of what the news item was about, such as maps from the country, pictures of the politicians involved, and any news film that was recorded by any on-site news crews. However, in the broadcast it was expressly forbidden to show the face of the person reading the news (i.e. news anchor)! The prevailing thinking (from a radio mindset) was that if TV viewers would see the news reader's face while reading the news, the TV viewer would be distracted by any emotions that the news reader might display on television.

Isn't that quaint? It took about a decade until TV news discovered that viewers preferred to see the news reader, and that the home viewers identified with, learned to trust, and connected to seeing the regular anchor every night on the news. Only after the advent of the modern TV news anchor could we have such TV news super celebrities as CBS icons Walter Cronkite and Dan Rather or say CNN's Larry King. It was only after TV learned to think beyond radio that the concept of the "tele-visual" TV celebrity could be discovered.

Today , TV is full of the kind of programming that they cannot do on

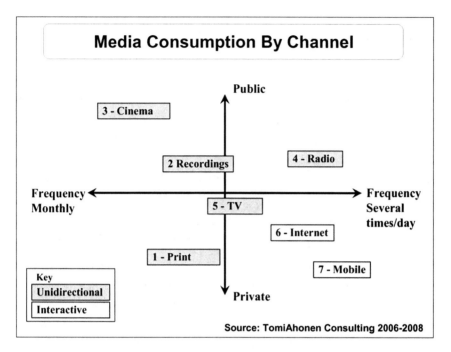

radio. This all falls under the broad category of "reality" shows. We want to see the expressions of our talk show hosts like Oprah and Letterman and Conan, and their various celebrity guests on chat shows. We want to see the faces of gamers and quiz masters on a game show, or the people participating in any reality TV "vote the player off the show" type of show like American Idol, the Apprentice, Big Brother, Survivor Island, etc.

Sixth media channel is the internet

So enter the sixth mass media channel, the internet, in the 1990s. This is very young as a media channel. Its most radical innovations were interactivity, search and community/social networking.

Recalling that TV offered nothing new, yet it grew to dominate the four older media, now consider the internet with its three innovations. First, the internet is inherently interactive. Not only can we offer content to audiences, we can have the audience rate our content, comment on it, link to it, blog about it. Then the internet has search. This is a very powerful ability, which makes the online archives of major newspapers and magazines so much more useful than a stack of back-issues in a bookshelf. Moreover, finally social networking, the community dimension. Everything from YouTube to citizen journalism and Wikipedia, we can now collaborate online and bring our audience to co-create our media experience. Massively multiplayer games like *World of Warcraft* and *Lineage II* have up to 20 million active users engaging with each other.

Inherently threatening

As a mass media, the internet was the first "new" mass media that was "inherently threatening" to all five previously-existing mass media channels. The web could offer equivalent content as all of the other five previous media - we can read books, magazines and newspapers online; we can view movies; we can listen to radio and podcasts; we can view TV content in clips, video streaming and IPTV; and yes, we can download the digital equivalents of recordings e.g. MP3 files, MPEG movies, computer software, videogames etc. In its short life the internet has already moved rapidly into content areas of each of the older established media, including several arguments, debates and even legal actions about the legality of distributing content via the web. These include music with Napster, television with YouTube and printed books with Google.

Not all media are inherently threatening. Upon quick observation, it is easy to think that any media can cannibalize previous media. We have seen

---

TV could not replicate all legacy media; had no new benefit
Source: SMLXL White Paper 2007

---

music go from print to recordings, radio and TV, news appear first in print, then in cinema, radio, and TV, and so forth. You might think that every newer media can "automatically" cannibalize all older media. Actually, none of the first five media could offer all that their preceding media could provide. For example you cannot deliver a dramatic news picture, think Abu Ghraib prison pictures, from a newspaper page, to listeners *over radio*. You cannot sell a top 10 rock song through the cinema screen. You cannot read a book you selected, through broadcast TV (someone could read a book for you on TV, but that would be the same book for the whole nation at the same time). No previous media could offer all of the previous media contents through its medium.

The internet is different. It is an *"inherent threat"* media channel as it can efficiently offer all of the main content types of all of the previous five mass media. This is why the internet is so greatly a concern to the existing media giants from newspapers to TV to radio to the movies and so forth.

The internet is based on philosophies of freedom and shareware and collaboration. There are subscription models and advertising revenues also but most content is "free" and the revenues are earned via advertising. In terms of content "ownership", it is a total hodgepodge, some stuff you can own, others

---

you should not and still others are very difficult to capture to own. Nevertheless, with interactivity and community/social networking innovations on the web, opportunities emerged ranging from citizen journalism to *Wikipedia* to multiplayer gaming and virtual worlds, like *Second Life*. Meanwhile search has allowed a replacement to reading encyclopedias and visiting the library. I will be returning to the internet more in the chapter about the mobile internet.

A final comment of relevance of the internet is its cost, which is almost nothing to the media content owner. You can become an internet service provider at trivial costs compared to any of the previous mass media; and to become a website or blogsite, you do not really need more than your connection. If you have free access say through the local library, you can become a web publisher for totally free.

As to cannibalization, it is too early to make absolute statements, remember the internet is less than two decades old as a mass media channel, but the early signs are very strong that print and recordings are strongly threatened by the web. Radio and TV are feeling the heat, TV in particular with the new IP TV concepts. Movies are also increasingly facing piracy and with faster broadband speeds, the cannibalizing threats will no doubt only rise.

Mobile can replicate all legacy media; has 7 new benefits
Source: SMLXL White Paper 2007

C   SEVENTH OF THE MASS MEDIA: MOBILE

So how of the 7th mass media channel? The cellphone was realistically only a voice device for the masses through the 1990s and only emerged as a mass media outlet from 1998. At ten years of age, the youngest of the seven mass media, mobile is by far the least understood. It might be tempting to think that with a tiny screen and a cumbersome limited keypad, the cellphone is somehow "lesser" than for example the internet or TV as a media channel. That would be a hasty generalization. In reality, mobile is a remarkably powerful mass media channel. Like TV is to radio, soon so too the mobile will be to the internet. That much more important as a media channel.

Mobile is also inherent threat

Similar to the introduction of the internet before it, mobile is also an "inherent threat" mass media channel. Yes, today the cellphone can replicate everything that all previous six mass media can do. So from an abilities point-of-view, cellphones can be at least as disruptive as the internet has been so far. You can consume newspapers, read magazine articles and books (don't laugh, I'll give you an amazing case study from Japan later in the book), listen to radio and podcasts, buy MP3 songs and video games, watch TV, even watch whole movies on the phone. (Nokia was shipping the full movie version of *Mission Impossible 3* with its top-of-the-line N93 phone 2007; the movie works well on the 2.5 inch screen)

Remember that for cannibalization the experience *need not be as good* on the new media, only that it is *possible*. Consider the quality of the experience. Take cinema content. Certainly, nobody can deny that the typical Hollywood movie is better suited for consumption at the cinema, rather than on a TV screen, but all movies ever released have managed the transition to the TV screen. The experience need not be as good, only that it is technically possible and commercially feasible for migration to the newer medium. Radio could not show movies, but TV could. Radio cannot technically cannibalize movies, but TV can.

Now let me return to the cellphone. So yes, any web content can be consumed on the phone, and the phone easily supercedes the interactivity of the web, because e-mail and IM Instant Messaging are already available on cellphones, but SMS text messaging and MMS picture messaging are unique to mobile. In 2007 with over 2.5 billion active users of SMS text messaging, there are over twice as many people using messaging on cellphones worldwide, than are using any kinds of messaging on the internet. Similarly, search already exists on cellphones and is used by over 10% of all cellphone users worldwide. In addition, as to social networking or digital communities as the third innovation of the internet, yes those already exist on cellphones as well, as I will illustrate in a whole chapter dedicated to mobile social networking later in this book.

D   MOBILE HAS SEVEN UNIQUE BENEFITS

The power of the cellphone as a mass media channel starts from its reach, which I discussed in the numbers chapter. That is only the beginning. The cellphone is also very versatile as a media channel - being digital, multimedia and interactive; with the ability to deliver broadcast content. Mobile is also only the second inherent threat media, capable of replicating all that the previous six media can do - even inherently threatening to the internet. It should be noted that the opposite is not true that the internet cannot replicate all that the phone can do. In fact, the cellphone as a mass media channel introduces seven new benefits that do not exist on any of the previous six mass media, including the internet.

Unique Benefit 1 - The phone is the first truly personal media.

Compared with the legacy mass media, all of which are shared or include consumption by groups, cellphone content is consumed in private. A book, magazine or newspaper is typically consumed in private but can very well be

Tomi T Ahonen

Cannibalization Threat by Media Channel

Threat to be cannibalized	Ability to cannibalize other media content						
	Print	Record'g	Cinema	Radio	TV	Internet	Mobile
Print		Some	No	No	No	Yes	Yes
Recording	No		No	Some	No	Yes	Yes
Cinema	No	Yes		No	Yes	Yes	Yes
Radio	No	Yes	No		Yes	Yes	Yes
TV	No	Yes	Some	No		Yes	Yes
Internet	No	No	No	No	No		Yes
Mobile	No	No	No	No	No	No	

shared after it has been read by the first reader - many couples will split a newspaper in the morning with the husband starting with the sports section, etc. Movies are consumed in public. Radio and TV often consumed with others in the room. Even the internet often has others around a screen or at least people can easily be within viewing range, such as parents keeping an eye of what teenager kids are doing on the family computer, so at best, the internet is semi-private.

Cellphone content is consumed almost totally in private. As I said earlier, 63% of the population does not share the phone even with one's spouse. Now we can deliver media content that is dramatically more personalized than on legacy media. I explain two in case studies in this book: Blyk the UK based advertising funded telco and i-Channel the breaking news "ticker" service on NTT DoCoMo's network in Japan using the idle screen of the cellphone.

Unique Benefit 2 - The phone is permanently carried.

The cellphone is within arm's reach of most users. A survey for the banking industry by Unisys, who supplies banking computer systems, found that the average time it takes to report a lost wallet is 26 hours. However, the average time to report a lost cellphone is 68 minutes. It takes us a day to notice we have misplaced our wallet, but just over an hour and we notice we're without our phone. We cannot imagine going through our day without our phone.

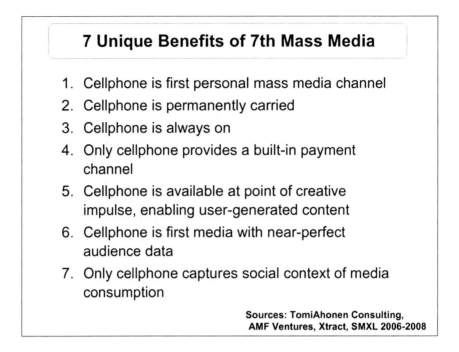

7 Unique Benefits of 7th Mass Media

1. Cellphone is first personal mass media channel
2. Cellphone is permanently carried
3. Cellphone is always on
4. Only cellphone provides a built-in payment channel
5. Cellphone is available at point of creative impulse, enabling user-generated content
6. Cellphone is first media with near-perfect audience data
7. Only cellphone captures social context of media consumption

Sources: TomiAhonen Consulting,
AMF Ventures, Xtract, SMXL 2006-2008

And it is not just in our daytime. As I have said, 91% of the population keeps the phone within arm's reach 24 hours a day, seven days a week. We sleep with the phone. As I often say, we do take the phone to the bathroom with us.

Unique Benefit 3 - first always-on mass media

Beyond the device being upon our person at all times, the cellular network and phone allow it to be the first mass media that is designed to be "always-on". Yes, we might leave our TV set on all the time and some even sleep with the TV still on, but television was not *intended* to be permanently on for the viewers. Yes, we have 24-hour news, but the concept is that we tune into CNN or Sky News or BBC to catch up the latest up-to-the-minute news when we want it. However, the channel was not designed to be consumed 24 hours a day by the home viewer. The cellphone is different. It is designed to be always-on. That is the only way it can receive the inbound calls and SMS text messages (and emails if it is a Blackberry) for us.

Why is this relevant? Now we have a mass media channel that can deliver news and entertainment services, which capitalize on breaking stories. The scandal by the baseball player. A live chase by the police. Alternatively, what is happening in a reality TV show, etc. There even are alert services, which let you know when your favorite rock stars are performing on radio etc. Only the cellphone can deliver such breaking news services directly to your pocket.

Note that this is not the same benefit as permanently carried. We can carry our iPod permanently, but it is not always connected. In addition, we can leave our home PC on, permanently 24 hours a day on our broadband connection ("always-on"), but that PC is not permanently carried. Only the cellphone is both permanently carried, and always-on. Thus, these are two distinct benefits.

Unique Benefit 4 - built-in payment mechanism.

Perhaps the most powerful unique attribute separating cellphones from the legacy media is money. On mobile as the 7th mass media channel, you can directly handle payments. No other media has a built-in payment mechanism. You cannot point to a page on a newspaper and have the money deducted from your bank account. On radio, you cannot somehow "grab" the transmission and make a payment. Even on the internet, you have to subscribe to PayPal or provide a credit card for payment.

On cellphones, however, the payment ability is built-in. Any click, any link, any content. If the carrier enables the payment, or if the payment is handled by premium SMS services, all you need to do is click, and the money is charged from your cellphone account. Click to buy. Just like buying a ringing tone. Teenagers who do not qualify for credit cards, no problem. Pay for a Sprite at a vending machine as in Poland, or a movie ticket as in England or parking as in Croatia or a ski lift ticket as in Norway or public transportation as in Finland or an airline ticket as in Japan. Not just content bought onto the phone. Already today, older media collect payments through the phone. Habbo Hotel the web online playground collects payments using premium SMS. TV shows from Big Brother to American Idol earn billions via SMS votes. Some gaming and chat cable TV channels earn 80% of their total revenues from mobile payments.

Unique Benefit 5 - available at creative impulse

The media world is moving away from a uni-directional media experience where professional producers (Hollywood, Madison Avenue, etc) create the content and then push it via media channels at the audience. Today user-generated and co-created content is spreading rapidly from original clips at YouTube and pictures at Flickr to the *i-Report* news clips and pictures sent to CNN. Amateurs and semi-professionals are joining in media creation from blogs to wikis to citizen journalism such as **Ohmy News** in South Korea.

For this new trend in media of user-generated content the cameraphone is a critical tool. The cameraphone is the only gadget that is always available at the point of creative inspiration, as we were told by the author Tony Fish, the CEO of AMF Ventures. Mostly when the photo opportunity emerges, our digital camera sits safely at home in its camera case. Nevertheless, the cameraphone (which is also our video recorder and podcast recorder) is in our pocket, always at the ready to snap images and clips when the mood hits us.

Unique Benefit 6 - most accurate customer information

The biggest impact specifically to media owners is that only on the cellphone we know every time the exact composition of our total audience, individually, explicitly, completely and exactly. Not even on the web do we have this level of precision and accuracy. Audience measurements, media (and advertising) targeting etc will be revolutionized! AMF Ventures measured in 2007 the relative audience information accuracy of three mass media. On TV, they found that only 1% of the total audience information is captured. On the internet, about 10% of audience information is captured, far better than TV obviously. However, on cellphones, 90% of audience information is captured. Dramatically better than anything else. Not perfect customer insights, as some of us have multiple phones and accounts, some phones are shared, etc, but by far the most accurate. In addition, if we can capture 90% of audience data, for any mass media that is as good as perfect audience activity data, if the next-best media can only capture 10%.

Unique Benefit 7 - only the cellphone captures social context

All interactive media have the potential to capture our digital footprint, what we do. Nevertheless, no other media so accurately identifies every user in the network that we can also capture the *social context* on cellphones. What is social context? It is measuring not what we do, but *with whom* we do it. Therefore, if a user sends lots of text messages during the broadcasts of *American Idol*, to a set series of other phone owners, and some of those others also vote on *American Idol*; we can rather safely deduct that our target person is watching *American Idol*, even though that person never voted on the show. We know it not because of his/her direct activity, but rather because of the social context.

The leading customer analytics company, Xtract, which specializes in social analytics, reports that nearly three out of four consumer decisions were most influenced by recommendations of friends. They have also measured that the 2% most influential members of a community will know personally 58% of the total group sharing that passion or interest. This kind of insight leads marketers to develop a whole new dimension of customer insight, which Xtract calls social context. Xtract President Jouko Ahvenainen explained in 2005:

> *Customer analytics is becoming a key competitive edge. Traditionally customer analytics has been focused too much on the past, looking at a rear-view mirror. It is not enough to analyze individual customer*

behavior, analysts must now learn to isolate the social networks among the customer base, and start to market to the most influential of the groups. We now have to learn to utlize the social context in marketing and personalization.
- Jouko Ahvenainen, President, Xtract

The kind of revolution that happened this decade, when the internet moved from "web 1.0" or single users consuming internet content mostly alone to "web 2.0" with user-generated content and shared experiences; we now will see in "data 1.0" about the single user consumption patterns to "data 2.0" where user information incorporates the patterns of fellow users, fans, colleagues, friends; the social context of media consumption. This is the pot of gold...

With these seven benefits, the cellphone as a media channel is not only an inherent threat mass media; it is an *inherently superior* mass media. Remember that mobile is the youngest mass media. Its older sibling, the internet, is now demolishing existing industries from the media (music, gaming, newspapers) to main street businesses (travel agencies, music stores) etc. Then consider that all you can do on the internet, can also be done on the cellphone but there are now seven unique aspects to the cellphone that cannot be replicated on the PC-based internet. Moreover from a media perspective, if we have all

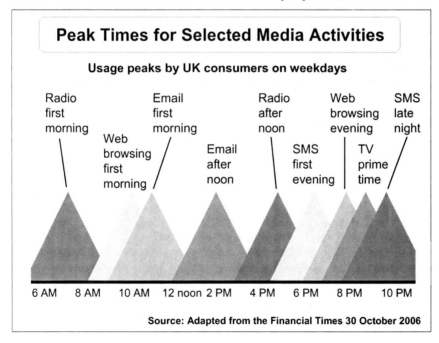

Peak Times for Selected Media Activities

Usage peaks by UK consumers on weekdays

| Radio first morning | Web browsing first morning | Email first morning | Email after noon | Radio after noon | SMS first evening | Web browsing evening | TV prime time | SMS late night |

6 AM   8 AM   10 AM   12 noon 2 PM   4 PM   6 PM   8 PM   10 PM

Source: Adapted from the Financial Times 30 October 2006

existing media content, a far wider reach, and add powers of near-perfect audience information and the ability to enable payments; this is the inherently superior media channel.

Some day soon - within about five years - most phones in use around the world will be equivalent in performance to the iPhone today (screen size, data connection speed, etc) - look how quickly all personal computers were more capable than the original Apple Macintosh computer. In addition, in our world, when a new cellphone is automatically replaced every 18 months, how quickly will many people stop replacing the old family PC that nobody uses anymore. Moreover, recognize that while today the iPhone or Nokia N95 may seem like an extremely valuable gadget, after two generations and thus three years, they are the hand-me-down phones given to 10-year-olds as their first or second phones, when we buy "superphones" that are far more powerful for our own needs.

What of the small screen and lousy keypad

Yes, I hear that all the time. Again, on first glance, it is easy to fall prey to the misconception that cellphones would have "fatal flaws" due to the tiny screen and poor keypad. These are not fatal limitations by any means; and in both cases, there are far more powerful benefits to outweigh the screen and keypad; abilities that make the cellphone far superior for media consumption. The screen is also in our pocket every day and we look at it more than once per hour, all waking hours, on average. The keypad has less keys than a PC keyboard that is true; but the phone has also the camera - a powerful scanner - which gives it far greater creative and input power. I will expose the myth of these "supposed deficits" of the screen and keypad in the chapter on Creating Magic for cellphone services.

As different from the internet as TV is from radio

With its seven unique benefits, mobile as a mass media channel is as different from the internet as TV is from radio. As TV was soon absorbing most of the content concepts from radio, so soon as well, cellphones will absorb most of the content from the internet. Weather services have already migrated to cellphones, with more internet access to USA based weather services coming from cellphones than personal computers as Telephia and Comscore reported in November 2006. Soon other web services will follow.

Before long, as the content owners and application developers learn to create new, unique content for mobile, a vast new media opportunity will emerge. As I will show in the music chapter soon in this book, music on mobile is almost five times larger than music on the internet. However, most music on mobile is ringing tones, ringback tones, and other such music services that would not even work on the internet or on an iPod.

Much like on TV we have reality TV shows and music videos and the

Tomi T Ahonen

Audience Data Accuracy by Media

AMF Ventures measured the relative accuracies of measuring audience data by the three major media channels, TV, internet and mobile in 2007 and found that:

On TV, the total audience data that
can be captured is   1%

On the internet, the total audience data
that can be captured is   10%

On mobile, the total audience data
that can be captured is   90%

Source: AMF Ventures 2007

CNN ticker, these are all broadcast TV innovations that would not work on radio (nor indeed, in the cinema). Yes, soon the time will come when media content and services on cellphones will be better than those on the internet will be. In addition, if you travel to Japan or South Korea or India - countries where the majority of internet access is from cellphones already - that is the case today. Content is formatted for the small screen as a default, as that is the predominant access device.

The Guardian newspaper reported on 24 May 2007 that the global value of paid content on mobile at 31 billion dollars was bigger than paid content revenues on the fixed wireline internet at 25 billion dollars worldwide. We have already passed the tipping point. The younger media has passed its older sibling in size. Moreover, earlier in this book, I told you that mobile content revenues for 2007 reached 45 billion dollars worldwide. More devices, more users, growing faster; now already more revenues. There is no going back.

Will not kill other media

I do need to make this point as well, please do not misunderstand me. Like we saw before with the emergence of newer media channels, the new medium will not kill the older media. Therefore, this book is not an argument that the phone would *kill off* older mass media like the internet; it will not. All seven mass media will continue. However, what I stress in my workshops, seminars and executive briefings all around the world, and at my short courses at Oxford University, is that mobile as the Seventh of the Mass Media is the youngest, newest, most far-reaching and most powerful. With seven unique benefits that cannot be replicated on legacy mass media, not even efficiently on the internet.

Here is where we have enormous opportunities. As recordings created global giants out of EMI, Warner Music and Universal; and how Cinema created a motion picture industry out of Hollywood, Bollywood etc; each dawn of a new mass media channel has created economic openings for new companies to establish global positions. We saw it again over the past ten years as the internet spawned billion dollar giants out of Ebay, Google and Amazon. Now we are facing the dawn of another new industry. It will have its own creative and technical competences, unique to this medium, as different as it is to edit a newspaper compared to directing a live TV news studio. New competences will be needed and here the young, SMS-addicted Generation C for Community youth will be in the driver's seat for inventing and mastering the new required professional competences. I will devote two chapters to these customers so we can start to "get into their heads" in trying to deliver services to satisfy them.

Mobile will bring about a new media ecosystem and be fertile grounds for new giant corporations of the next decade. Those companies will be built understanding mobile, its unique benefits, and services, applications and media formats that will capitalize on the new areas, will be built with the tools in this book. Most importantly, the eventual winners will not be those who only copy the legacy media; one has to "create magic" as I show using the 6 M's mobile service creation tool in the next chapter.

Only those who understand the power of mobile as the newest mass media channel will be able to share in its success. Just like those who understood interactivity and search on the web, or those who understood reality and celebrity on TV. I should mention that even though we have six newer rivals to it, the first mass media - print at 500 years - is still very healthy, and none of the seven is seriously at risk of ending as a commercial opportunity. So while the internet and the cellphone show very powerful strengths to cannibalize areas of the established five media, all seven mass media will co-exist for a long time to come.

With that, it is clear that mobile is the only mass media channel capable of replicating each of the previous six media, and mobile offers seven unique benefits. It will become an increasingly important media channel for all media content. Maurice Levy, the CEO of Publicis the world's second largest media company, put it very well in 2006 when he said, *"In a couple of years, most of the information you share, most of the advertising you read, most of the messages you send, most of the music you listen to will transit through your cell phone."*

Case Study 3 from South Korea
Cyworld

The converged virtual environment of *Cyworld* in South Korea is considered the most advanced service of its kind. Think of a turbo-charged version of *MySpace, Facebook* or *Second Life*; of *Habbo Hotel* meets *iTunes* meets eBay. The ultimate social networking experience fully available on cellphones. *Cyworld* is owned by SK Communications in South Korea and available on broadband internet and 3G cellphones. Cyworld has reached over 95% penetration rate among its initial target segment, the youth. Today overall *Cyworld* is used by over 51% of the total South Korean population. Housewives share cooking advice on *Cyworld*. Politicians post their policies on it. Pop music artists connect with their fan clubs via *Cyworld*. Its a completely new social phenomenon; like blogging on speed.

Cyworld users can access the service either through a broadband internet connection or using an advanced 3G cellphone, bearing in mind that South Korea leads the world in 3G phone adoption (as well as broadband adoption), with over 90% of all phone subscriptions upgraded to 3G by the end of 2007. Mobile blogging alone generates 3.40 dollars per user per month of data revenues to the carriers in Korea.

A major element of the *Cyworld* social networking experience is the Miniroom (similar to your hotel room inside *Habbo Hotel* or your island on *Second Life*) for each user where they can interact with friends. The *Cyworld* persona is an avatar, i.e. a virtual puppet representation of the user, called a "Mini-me". These minirooms and mini-me's then are customized at extra cost. There are massive amounts of furniture and decorations for the miniroom, many of, which are branded, to the degree that a Mona Lisa painting can be bought with a license fee going to the Louvre. The same is true of the avatars. Most fashion brands in Korea offer branded fashion accessories to the Mini-me.

Benjamin Joffe, the CEO of Plus Eight Star an Asian IT/telecoms expert consultancy, explained about the economics involved, using the 2005 financial data, and said:

> *SK Communications made US$67 million directly from Cyworld in 2005, and its mother company SK Telecom, Korea's largest mobile operator, derived an additional US$30 million from the mobile service. The total was thus close to US$100 million in 2005. South Korea's population is 1/6 of the US and average GDP per capita in Korea being about a third of that in the USA. When adjusted for a USA economy and population, the service annual revenues are on par with US$1.8 billion a year in the USA.*

While the Western World contemplates the relevance of virtual worlds, and pontificates on the emergence of real companies selling virtual goods and services in such online environments as *Second Life*, this point has long since passed in South Korea.

Inside *Cyworld* there are over 30,000 registered businesses operating in the virtual world. Of course, they are there, when over half of the nation's total population is active inside *Cyworld*. Every relevant brand in the Korean economy has a virtual presence inside *Cyworld*. Do they sell content? Half a million items of branded virtual content are already available inside *Cyworld*, in addition to millions upon millions of items of user-generated content.

"Services on mobile should do things not possible on older media.
Make mobile services seem like magic."
Tomi T Ahonen

V
Creating Magic
The Six M's of Mobile Services

I have now shown in the previous chapter that mobile has seven elements not possible on any mass media: it is the only personal mass media; it is permanently carried; it is always-on; it has a built-in payment mechanism; it is available at the point of inspiration; compared to any other mass media, mobile provides the most accurate audience data; and only mobile captures the social context of our media consumption.

We can of course try to copy TV programs or web pages or banner ads or other traditional media formats onto the cellphone and yes, some of them will probably succeed. Nevertheless, this is severely under-utilizing the true power of the 7th Mass Media channel. In this chapter, I hope to ignite the reader's mind to think beyond the obvious. Reach past the existing, into what now becomes possible. In addition, in so doing, create media services, content and formats for the cellphone that are truly magical.

A   MAKE SERVICES MAGICAL

I want to recreate magic. Depending on how old you the reader are, there was probably one of three separate moments that defined a moment of magic as it relates to the telephone. Moreover, to put us in the right spirit, let me show three examples of magic, depending on how old or young you, the reader, are.

Magic of the answering machine

The oldest service on cellphones is voice calls. In addition, for almost 100 years prior to the first commercial cellphones, there were fixed landline telephones. Moreover, for most of the existence of the landline phone system, up to the

1970s, if someone was not there when the phone rang, to pick it up, you missed your call. That is why older generations were so strongly taught at home to answer the ringing phone. It could be an emergency, a "very important call". Quite literally, it could be that someone had died. In addition, that is also why business people employed secretaries. Their most valuable job was to take the calls that boss was not physically present to answer. Real business was at stake. Obviously soon thereafter, secretaries - and even family members - were then also used to screen calls that one might not want to take.

It was not until the invention of the dictation machine using the C-Cassette by Philips in the late 1960s, which enabled the cassette-based early telephone answering machines (pre-cursor of today's voicemail).

If the reader is in his or her 40s or older, I ask you to go back in time to your first answering machine. Remember the time you had installed it, and tested that it worked. Then you left your home. One day soon thereafter, you came home to the blinking light on the device, which told you that you had a message. In addition, you listened to it, and it seemed like magic. Your best friend Billy had called and left you a message, and you immediately called him back, etc.

That is what I mean by magic. Suddenly discovering something that

---

$1B of MP3 music sold on internet including iTunes in 2006
Source: IFPI 2007

---

was not possible before. That until we heard of the invention, seemed truly magical. Prior to it, we could not even *imagine* that such technology might exist. An idea, which seemed "impossible" prior to this new gadget or invention.

Magic of cordless

For those readers who are in their 30s or perhaps some in their older 20s who lived a part of their adult or teenager life without cellphones (and various cordless phones), here is your magical moment. Remember the time you did not have any cordless or wireless or cellular phone in your household. Moreover, then you got the first such phone. Then remember that moment, that you had that call soon thereafter, when you were no longer seated, but you were able to walk to the other room to fetch what you were talking about, or step out of the home to the yard - or in the office to walk to the hallway or into an empty conference room for some privacy, etc. The freedom suddenly of being "cut from the cord".

That was magical. You could still talk and you were free. I had a colleague mention about his trip to Machu Pichu the historical breathtaking tourist site high in the mountains of Peru. Most of Machu Pichu is pristine, pure

---

nature and the ancient historical site. My friend had recently started a relationship with his new girlfriend and he also recently had gotten an internationally roaming cellphone. He tried to make a call on the top of the mountain, and sure enough, there was a cellular signal. He made a call crystal clear, to his new girlfriend on another continent to share that spectacular moment. That is magic. Something that had seemed impossible before.

Magic of ringing tone

For those of my readers who are young, in their 20s, who probably do not remember a time before cellphones, I think the best example of magic is the ringing tone. Remember about 5 to 10 years ago, when you had your own phone - perhaps your first cellphone - and then you found out for the first time that it was possible to buy a ringing tone of your favorite music artist and the latest hit, to be your ringing tone? It may be one of your close friends who had discovered this, or perhaps if you were one of the last ones to get a cellphone, it might be that your friends were already using this service and you wanted it too.

Then you finally downloaded your first ringing tone that you had

---

$6.2B of ringing tones sold onto cellphones in 2006
Source: Informa 2007

---

selected yourself. Your absolute favorite song of the time. Moreover, then when your phone rang, you were "soooo cool" to have just the right song as your ringing tone. You probably have grown past that and do not change your tune anymore every two weeks as the top of the chart changes, but go back in time and recall that moment. When for the first time you could set your phone to sound different from the "Nokia tune" and rather to play something that truly identified you as the fan of 50 Cent or Coldplay or Britney Spears or whatever it was you liked back then.

This is the kind of magic I want our industry to strive for. To go beyond copying TV and internet and print content onto the phone. Let me use the full power of the phone and use our best creativity and make services that are truly magical. We do have a tool to get us onto that path, and it is called the Six M's.

B   THE SIX M'S

In my book *M-Profits* in 2002, I wrote about the service creation theory I then called the Five M's, which I had developed with Joe Barrett of Nokia. Later my

---

The 6 M's Mobile Service Creation Tool

Movement - Escaping the fixed place

Moment - Expanding the concept of time

Me - Expressing myself

Multi-user - Extending my experiences to my friends

Money - Expending financial resources

Machines - Enabling automation and machines

The 6 M's mobile service creation system and management tool was developed by Tomi T Ahonen with Joe Barrett of Nokia and Paul Golding of Motorola

good friend Paul Golding, the Chief Applications Architect at Motorola and author of *Next Generation Wireless Applications*, argued that one of my five "M's" - *Me* - needed to be split into two, so based on Paul's analysis, I now call that theory the Six M's. It has been adopted at almost all major industry players as the primary service creation tool for our industry used by such global giants as Ericsson, Orange, Motorola, Nokia, NTT DoCoMo, T-Mobile and Vodafone. About a dozen books already mention the theory (either as the Five M's or the Six M's) as well as *Wikipedia* etc.

The Six M's is primarily a service creation tool helping find ways to build applications and services for cellphones and wireless. The Six M's can also be used as a management evaluation tool, to compare and contrast rival wireless service concepts to determine, which might be more successful in the market place. Let me go through the Six M's and illustrate.

The first of the Six M's is *Movement*. This is the attribute that defines cellular networks as those allow untethered mobility and access to wireless services and applications. Movement is not just "Location-Based Services" (LBS). Movement can be a welcoming greeting when you first turn on a phone in a new country. It can allow access to services that are in other locations - your hometown TV listings or the stock market in the country where you trade, etc. I have often made the point that this attribute often leads to over-emphasis of LBS.

Moment is the second of the Six M's. Moment means expanding the concept of time. Moment includes catching up on past time (yesterday's sports scores) or postponing time (putting a person on hold) as well as managing time (calendaring). Cellphone also allow multi-tasking, such as driving a car while talking on a hands-free phone system in the car. Multitasking can also be on telecoms services, such as talking with one person on one phone while simultaneously sending an SMS text message to another person - in fact 48 percent of British teenagers admit to sending SMS texts to friends while talking to someone as we will see in more detail in the next chapter you youth.

Me is the third of the Six M's and refers to the personalization and customization of the phone: expressing oneself. Ringing tones are a typical example of a service with a strong Me attribute. Me also includes the kinds of services and applications that relate to matters we might be embarrassed about, such as adult entertainment, gambling, health-related matters and so forth.

Multi-User is fourth among the Six M's, for extending into the community. Multi-user brings the community and social networking benefits to cellphones. Chat and user-generated content are typical Multi-User services. Games and virtual applications are also increasingly going to multiplayer and even massively multiplayer environments. The fixed online game *World of Warcraft* had 8 million gamers in early 2007 while *Second Life* had two million registered users who had created avatars of themselves. Now new mobile rivals are emerging for these, such as the *Pirates of the Caribbean* multiplayer mobile pirate game, *Elven Legends* the multiplayer combat dwarf game, and *Cyworld Mobile* with its avatars now also available on mobile.

Fifth among the Six M's is the *Money* attribute, expending financial resources. It need not be only "micropayments" or monetary exchanges in the value of a can of Pepsi or the price of a public transportation ticket or parking. In Kenya the limit of how much money can be moved in one transaction from one cellphone account to another is one million US dollars. However, the Money attribute includes more than strict cash and equivalents. It includes bonus points and loyalty points like frequent flier miles and retail shopping benefits. Money also allows sponsorship and third party payments such as the employer pays or perhaps the service charges of a child are paid from the phone bill of the parent.

Last of the Six M's is *Machines*, empowering automation and gadgets. The cellphone is the ultimate remote control device, already today to control air conditioning in the home remotely, to turn on the sauna bath as one approaches the home, to turn the home lights on and off. There are numerous gadgets that can be remotely controlled by cellphone from personal video recorders in Italy to the teakettle in Britain to the home robot in South Korea. As most technical gadgets and machines become digitally controlled, there is almost no limit to what could be eventually controlled by cellphone.

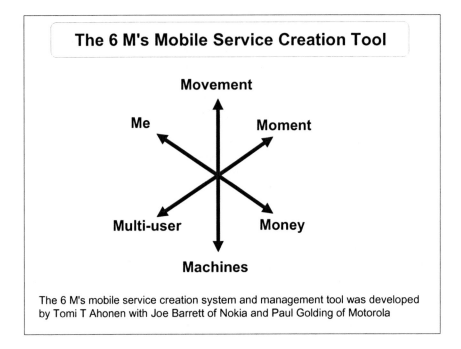

The 6 M's Mobile Service Creation Tool

Movement

Me   **Moment**

Multi-user   **Money**

Machines

The 6 M's mobile service creation system and management tool was developed by Tomi T Ahonen with Joe Barrett of Nokia and Paul Golding of Motorola

Not categorization, are dimensions

Each of the Six M's is an attribute of a good mobile service for cellphones. They should not be considered as a service categorization system (not a group of *Movement* services, then a group of *Moment* services etc). Rather, a good service has several of the attributes, such as a strong *Me, Moment, Money* and *Multi-User* attribute.

The Six M's are also dimensions, with the ability to improve the service. Consider them as arrows, away from the center. So if my service updates every 30 minutes and my rival's service is launched, which updates every 10 minutes, his service has become better on the *Moment* attribute. Then perhaps I release a version that is updated every 5 minutes again moving further along on that *Moment* axis.

The Six M's can be used as a management tool to measure and evaluate prospective services. It can also be used as a service evolution tool. If today the service is strictly for the individual customer (and thus strong on the Me attribute) we can explore the Six M's to find where to expand the service, perhaps adding a social networking or community element, thus expanding the service to the *Multi-User* dimension.

C   LIMITATIONS OF THE SCREEN AND KEYPAD

But Tomi, the screen is so small! One of the comments I hear most frequently in my workshops and seminars is that the cellphone screen is "too small". The phone has a screen smaller than that of TV or a PC or laptop screen, that is true. Nevertheless, this is actually nothing new. Remember the other of the 7 mass media. There once was the "first screen" - cinema. In addition, it faced a rival "small screen", TV. Some movie experts said that a movie that had been filmed for the giant silver screen could not be enjoyed on the small TV screens at home.

Content will succeed on smallest screen

Consider the math involved. An average cinema screen is 12 meters (36 feet) wide. At 6 meters tall, the total area of a typical mid-size cinema screen is 72 square meters in area. Then let us take a large home TV set of the 1990s: a 25-inch classic picture tube TV set (50 cm wide and 38 cm tall, i.e. 4:3 aspect ratio) has an area of 0.19 square meters. Therefore, the average movie screen is 379 times larger than a (large) home TV set from the last decade. To put it in another way, the TV is only one quarter of one percent the total size of a cinema screen.

Yet every single motion picture ever created by Hollywood, Bollywood, and other movie production houses has been released for TV. Not one has failed "because the TV screen was too small."

Now let us compare the laptop screen and the smartphone screen. A 14-inch laptop screen has a size of 27 cm across and 20 cm high. This means it is 540 square cm in size. Then lets take a typical Nokia smartphone today - I do not want to compare it to the biggest pocket screen that of the iPhone - most of the N-Series Nokia standard size in 2007 was a 2.5 inch screen. That is 4.2 cm wide and 3.6 cm tall (or opposite depending on how you orient the phone). That means it has a screen area of 15 square cm. How much is the difference? The laptop screen is "only" 36 times larger than the smartphone. Or to put it another way, the smartphone screen size is about 3 percent the size of the laptop screen.

If all cinema content survived the transition to a screen 379 times smaller on TV, then is it not likely that at least *most* of the current internet content on the laptop will survive the shift to the smaller screen on the smartphone that is only 36 times smaller?

Screen size is not a fatal flaw. Screen size is easy to notice, to make that hasty generalization that content cannot survive that transition, because you are wealthy enough to buy this book, to own both a laptop and a cellphone. Moreover, since you have the luxury of the choice, you do not want to squint with the small screen. However, what of the 1.5 billion people on the planet who are not as lucky as you to be that wealthy to own both? The people who do own a cellphone *but who do not own a PC.* For them a cellphone is the ***only way*** to get to internet content. They do not have the luxury of choice.

Then think of your kids. They are happily using a similar size screen on the Playstation Portable - and indeed smaller screens on the Video iPod, Nintendo etc. They are quite happy to consume videogames, music videos, even movies on the tiny screens. Screen size is totally a red herring. Yes, we *prefer* larger screens but size alone will not kill the cellphone's chances as a medium.

On the other hand (you have your other phone)

As content migrates to the cellphone, the content owners will start to design for cellphones. At that time, ever better experiences will be had on web services custom-designed for the small screen. This has already happened in Japan and South Korea, countries leading the world in broadband internet and digital TV, but where the majority of all internet access is from 3G cellphones.

The small screen size is balanced against it being always with us and being viewed at a closer distance than a TV or laptop screen. The cellphone is often used in parallel when watching TV - 30% of Japanese TV viewers already do this; 20% of the British vote via cellphones in reality TV shows. Most of all, the cellphone has the idle screen, which we can build upon. A TV or PC screen has to be turned on and connected. It is not with us all the time and even if we carry our laptop, it is not permanently connected and "open" (we carry laptops closed). The 7th mass media screen is always visible, in our pocket, on the desk

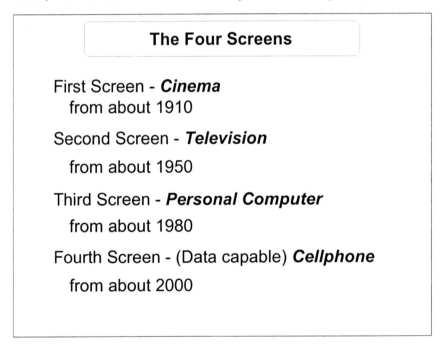

The Four Screens

First Screen - *Cinema*
   from about 1910

Second Screen - *Television*
   from about 1950

Third Screen - *Personal Computer*
   from about 1980

Fourth Screen - (Data capable) *Cellphone*
   from about 2000

or table with us. Its idle screen is a powerful communication platform, as I showed in the i-Channel Case Study from Japan earlier in this book.

Keypad

The same holds for the keypad. Yes, a laptop has a better keyboard, and writing a book for example is much easier on a PC than triple-tapping on a phone keypad. However, number of keys is not the Holy Grail. Consider the personal computer and the Playstation. The PC has many more keys on its keyboard than the controls on a Playstation, but kids prefer playing games with the Playstation controls rather than on a PC keyboard. The keys on the Playstation control are better suited for gaming use. The *number* of keys is not the absolute benefit.

As I will show in the youth chapter, it is not unusual for teenagers to send as many as 100 SMS text messages per day. Consider that at the maximum length of 160 characters per message that would be 16,000 characters. For comparison, the average chapter in this book has about 32,000 characters. Some kids type out daily text output rivaling half a chapter from this book. No, keypad size is no obstacle in any way, to the "digital natives" who have learned to send texts since they knew how to write. Only for those who are "digital immigrants" - such as many adults reading this book who may still be using predictive text and other crutches to try to keep up with this phenomenon - only for those would the keypad size perhaps seem like an obstacle.

If a user thumbs out 100 short messages using the "clumsy" keypad of the cellphone, the user truly can send messages blind, knowing the phone keypad instinctively. For anyone who sends more than 20 text messages per day, the phone keypad is actually better for them in composing text than a classic 101 key QWERTY keyboard on a personal computer. Again, there are opportunistic businesses capitalizing on this: in 2007, we saw the first examples of custom keypads for computers that used the phone keypad as the format and connect via the USB port to the PC. Yes, a teenager can type faster triple-tapping on the 12-key phone keypad than using the full 101-key QWERTY keyboard of a PC.

Phone input is superior

The cellphone actually trumps the PC keyboard with more input methods. The phone has the camera (a picture worth a thousand words), the microphone (voice IVR systems to recording podcasts), and now the latest innovation: 2D barcodes.

Read my mind: 2D barcodes

Something that seems almost like the cellphone is reading my mind, is what are called QR Codes (Quick Response Code) or more commonly called 2D Barcodes (Two Dimensional Barcodes). The first thing you need to do is to forget the concept of "barcode" in this service. We are not at a supermarket scanning milk.

The point of 2D Barcodes is to get past the limitations of the small keypad of the cellphone. Yes, on a PC we can type with all ten fingers (if you have learned to touch-type) and yes, we have a mouse and separate numeric keypad. Nevertheless, if you have to type a typical website address such as that to my blog, which is:

www.communities-dominate.blogs.com

...that is a lot of typing. On my Nokia, it takes 74 keystrokes to get the 34 letters typed. In addition, it is painfully slow to key in such long web addresses on the keypad triple-tapping on a cellphone. The matters become even worse with the added hassles of predictive text attempting to outguess a typical web address.

What if the cellphone could know where we want to go, without any typing? As if the cellphone was reading our minds? Now consider the 2D barcode (like the one on this page). A 2D barcode is a little square scribble of computer printout, looks almost like a square fingerprint. However, into that fingerprint we can embed a lot of information. Moreover, then the kicker: we use the camera on our cellphone for this.

Now, rather than any typing, all we need to do is point our cameraphone at any 2D barcode, and the phone display will show us the intended text, such as the text relating to the website. All we need to do is to click on the site and there we go! Far superior to any keyboard, a 2D barcode will allow us to do no typing at all. This is magic. As if the cellphone can read our minds.

Where to use them?

Any billboard where you would print your company web address, now you include the 2D barcode. Any place where you would like to offer additional information online, such as a magazine ad, newspaper ad, etc. Any printed packaging, such as wine bottles, supermarket groceries, restaurant menus etc. Business cards. Today most Japanese and Korean business cards already include the 2D barcode as a courtesy for the business colleague, where they can go for more information. I added the 2D barcode to my business cards back in 2006 to not seem too out-of-touch when visiting my customers in those countries.

2D barcodes were introduced in Japan by the largest cellphone carrier, NTT DoCoMo in 2005 and three years from launch, 76% of Japanese were using the feature. The Japanese customers utterly fell in love with this utility on their cellphones. Now in China the largest Chinese cellphone carrier, China Mobile, has teamed up with Nokia the largest handset maker in the world and Google the biggest internet company, to introduce 2D Barcodes to China. Globally, Nokia started to roll out 2D Barcode readers to the top end of its cameraphones in 2006.

We are now seeing the introduction of 2D Barcodes by various online and offline services in Europe such as newspapers in Britain.

This is going to be an enormous innovation for the IT/telecoms and media industries, as well as banking, advertising etc. 2D barcodes also are an excellent example of where the cellphone totally trumps a laptop PC on its keyboard and mouse interface. Yes, the cellphone has a limited keypad, but today almost every cellphone is a *camera*phone, and very shortly, every cameraphone will also have the 2D Barcode reader. Most of all, however, 2D Barcodes illustrate the magic. Like reading my mind...

D   MAGIC TODAY

Now that we know how to build mobile services, let us return to magic. Lets go back a bit in media history to illustrate this from how media has made magic. Lets look at cinema and how it learned to make films magical for audiences.

Cinema and the theater

First movies about 100 years ago were film recordings of stage plays. Remember that these films were without recorded speech so the acting had to be pronounced, with big movements and vivid visual acting. The very first full-length movies were typically stage productions of plays, which were filmed. The camera - usually only one camera - was set at the back of the theater and filmed the actual play as if it was one member of the audience seated in the back of the theater. They did not shoot scenes of the play; they shot as long as they had film, and interrupted the play only when the film ran out of the camera.

The view was static, the actors small on the stage, and the experience similar to sitting in the back of the theater of the play but not hearing anything said by the actors. Gradually film makers discovered the power of bringing the camera closer for some scenes to capture facial expressions of the stars as the theater drama developed, etc. Nevertheless, the whole cinema experience was still in its infancy. Cameras were static and the filming was continuous.

From a practical point of view, the art of cinematography was not invented yet. So early pioneers of the silver screen, such as Charlie Chaplin and Buster Keaton, innovated to create this format. They started to experiment by moving the camera - such as Keaton putting the camera on the train as he did his daredevil moves. They started to move the camera on its axis - panning, moving from side to side. They used different camera angles, different camera focal lengths and soon discovered that they wanted to "zoom" into and out of shots.

Therefore, they went "beyond" the stage and set pieces shown in the theater. Yes, you could have the same drama and set pieces, like a discussion between Charlie Chaplin in a room with the girl he loves and her father who

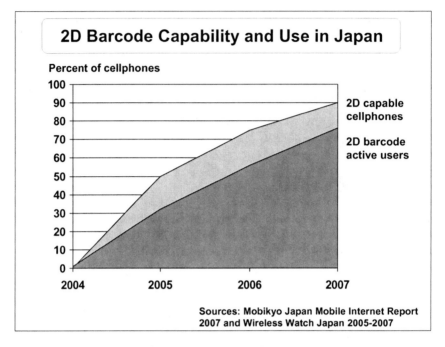

2D Barcode Capability and Use in Japan

Percent of cellphones

2D capable cellphones

2D barcode active users

Sources: Mobikyo Japan Mobile Internet Report 2007 and Wireless Watch Japan 2005-2007

hates Charlie. Classic set piece. The movies allowed us to "cut" to scenes that were happening simultaneously, like the policemen climbing the stairs and soon to bust into the room to capture Chaplin. In the theater some of that could be done with sound, etc, but mostly in the classic theater setting, multiple *simultaneous* storylines were not practical. In addition, mixing between them, back and forth, was near impossible on stage but easy to do on film.

All kinds of tricks were invented by early Hollywood from the action scenes - as hundreds of horses in a typical battle scene from a Western movie with the "Attack of the Indians" scene, etc. Now the movie was expanding beyond theater, into grand spectacle. The era of the grand action movies, like say the epic Oscar winner *Ben Hur*. Cinema also added the tricks of editing, allowing the pausing of the shooting of the movie, doing changes to the set or makeup etc, and make it appear that someone is shot, bleeding, etc. These are the kinds of tricks again that you cannot do in a live play, as the live play cannot be paused.

My point is that cinema started by placing a movie camera at the back of the theater, filming the actual stage play. Then creative talent started to experiment and discover the power of cinema. It made movies so "magical".

Where is the magic?

What producers of content for cellphones need to learn from the above is that the rules that govern the previous six media and first three screens are not necessarily relevant to the seventh mass media and fourth screen. Only by experimenting and discovering new formats and services can we deliver true success in cellphone-TV and video services. When my dear friend Alan Moore, the CEO of British engagement marketing specialist firm SMLXL, did his treatise on my initial concept of the 7th Mass Media Channel, he wrote in the SMLXL White Paper in 2007 calling for the magical:

> *Reach past the existing, into what now becomes possible with this, the newest mass media. And in so doing, create media services, content and formats for mobile that are truly magical. Like the first time at the start of the last century, when our great-great-grandparents went to their first movie and saw the story of* Lawrence of Arabia *in moving pictures in front of their eyes. Or how magical it was when live baseball games were broadcast for the first time from another city on radio. Or when Neil Armstrong stepped onto the moon, shown on live TV. Or the first time in a fax and letters age, when you sent one of your first e-mails, and the other person sent an immediate response? That seemed like magic. Or the first use of a search engine, which gave your hundreds of pages of content you never knew they even existed. Today they seem ordinary, commonplace. But the first time those were truly magical experiences. That is what mobile as the 7th mass media can bring to us. That is what we should strive to invent.*
>
> Alan Moore in SMLXL White Paper
> *Mobile As the 7th Mass Media*

Alan was totally right! Mobile is the Seventh of the Mass Media. Let us not treat it like the earlier less advanced, and indeed *limited* mass media. The cellphone is not the dumb little brother of the internet. It is not the stupid little screen sibling of TV. It is not the limited, crippled cousin of print. Actually as a media channel, the cellphone is *far superior* to any of the six legacy media that came before it, including the internet. We only have not seen the true potential of the cellphone yet.

Little bits of cellphone magic

There are thousands of little cellphone services that do little things for us. Turn on the air conditioning at home, track the vehicle of our shipping company, get an alert that our library books are due, etc. Literally thousands of such services. My first three books cataloged over 300 of them, I have been quoted in the press talking about over 500. Moreover, in my public conferences by the end of 2007, I had shown over 1,200 of these, that I call my "pearls" to conference audiences and I have over 4,000 in my private collection that I use in my various customer

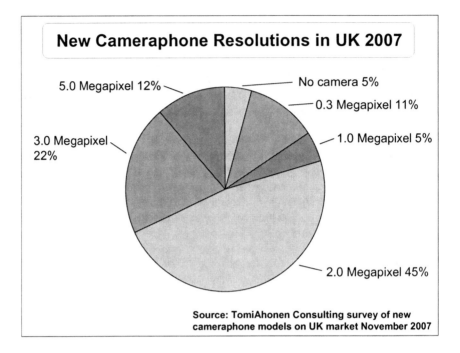

New Cameraphone Resolutions in UK 2007

5.0 Megapixel 12%

No camera 5%

0.3 Megapixel 11%

3.0 Megapixel 22%

1.0 Megapixel 5%

2.0 Megapixel 45%

Source: TomiAhonen Consulting survey of new cameraphone models on UK market November 2007

workshops around the world. Let me give a couple of examples here.

Vending machine

Imagine you are thirsty. You come to a Coca Cola vending machine. To your disappointment, you notice you do not have any spare change. The cool drink is waiting for you, but you just happen not to have the money to get to it. Then you notice that there is a sign saying you can also pay by cellphone. Dial this number; send this message to this number; the price is the same.

You pull out your phone. You send the message, and a moment later, the vending machine is activated, and you hear the clunk-clunk sounds of your can of cold beverage falling out of the machine. That is what I mean. It seems like magic. Wow. I received a can of Sprite and I achieved it with my cellphone. Coke vending machines are old hat in many parts of the world - the first was installed in Finland in 1997. But to the thisty person without change, magic!

Airline check-in

There are a multitude of such services already, usually very much on the side of the mundane, but still seem like magic the first time you use them. Finland's airline Finnair was the first airline to introduce cellphone based mobile check-in for its frequent fliers in 2001. You show up late at the airport. You rush to the check-in counter and observe a terribly long line (apparently it is a busy weekend or perhaps the airline is short-staffed this morning or whatever). You can tell the line is more than 30 minutes long to your check-in counter, and you are afraid you will miss your flight. Nevertheless, in your panic you then notice the sign that says you can do your check-in also via cellphone.

Wow, magic. Dial this number, enter your reservation code, select your seat, click enter, and you are done. Did not have to stand in line for half an hour and risk missing your plane. This is what I mean, services that seem like magic. However, services can be far more exotic than these, when we use more of the true potential of the always-connected device and the full power of the network.

Incidentally cellphone based check-in is spreading and used by airlines from Lufthansa in Germany to Air Asia in Singapore to Norwegian in Norway to JAL in Japan. The IATA airline industry association reports that in 2007 already 2% of all airline check-in is already handled via cellphones. On Finnair's busiest routes as much as 20% of the travelers use the service.

Shazam as in magic?

The first modern cellphone service that truly deserves to be called magical is the Shazam music service launched in the UK, in 2002 and now available in several dozen countries. Let me set you up with its situation. You hear some music. It could be radio, could be TV, could be at a bar or restaurant. You hear a song you recognize yet you cannot remember who is the artist. It could be the new song on the radio you want to go buy the CD, or perhaps it is the favorite artist of your wife and you would like to buy the full album for her for your anniversary, or maybe you are with friends in a bar and get into an argument about, which band is currently playing, etc (*"That is Roxy Music. No, it is clearly T.Rex..."*).

When you hear a song you want to identify, you dial Shazam's number, then point your cellphone at the source of the music. The phone listens to the music for about 10 seconds and then hangs up the phone call. A minute later, you receive an SMS text message with the name of the song, the artist, the album it is on, etc. You are charged 35 UK pence or 70 US cents for the query and message, which Shazam calls a "tag" of a song.

Technically this is a modest service with some incredible requirements. There is a recorded digital sample of essentially every recorded song ever relevant in that country. There is an algorithm that compares the "listened to" sample of the song to the recorded database and establishes a match (or no match). After a match, Shazam pulls up the related data about the artist and song title, album name, etc and sends that as a text message to the person who made the query.

The big constraint here is the database and the algorithm. The database of "every song" ever recorded is enormous. Moreover, the power and memory of the computer banks that allow this real-time song signature conversion within a minute against the millions of songs in the library, is something that currently requires a very high-end computer in processing power and storage. Something far beyond current generation laptop computers or PDAs or cellphones.

This kind of service cannot be deployed on any other platform currently, not on an iPod, not on a DVD, not on a stand-alone PC, not on a (stand-alone) PDA, etc. Nevertheless, it works perfectly on cellphones because the cellphone can connect to the big computers that Shazam has dedicated to this service. In the UK, three years later they had reached their 10 millionth "tag" and made 7 million dollars in the process. This in a country of 60 million people.

Still another remarkably magical service was recently launched in Japan and called the *Kamera-Jiten*. It is the "Camera Dictionary". I like to think of it as the "magical magnifying glass, which translates". I will discuss Kamera Jiten in its own Case Study, but that is a brilliant example of magical new services for the 7th Mass Media Channel.

Abracadabra

These are merely the first steps into a new age. Just like drama, transferring from the stage to cinema, when it learned that actors did not have to be shown from beginning to end, and that the story could be edited, and things that were not possible on stage, could be shown on film. Similarly TV did that when moving live concerts and music records from radio to TV. Toss in some creativity and crazy advertising executives, and before you know it, someone launches MTV and we have a new format only-for-TV, called music video. Its still music - also sold on records and played on the radio - but *better* when you add the unique benefits of TV.

These are the kinds of innovations we need to do with mobile today, to not only replicate the web and TV etc experiences, but also to go beyond them. Invent to mobile what were reality TV and talk shows and game shows on TV, or what are social networking and wikis and blogs on the web. Be bold, be daring, be inventive. Try to create that magical moment of delight within your customer base. We are dealing with a powerful new media. With that, I'd refer to one of my favorite Sci Fi authors, Arthur C Clarke, who said, *"Any sufficiently advanced technology is indistinguishable from magic."*

Case Study 4 from Finland
Just-in-Time Dentist

A surprising innovation happened in Finland a few years ago. As libraries were sending renewal offers via SMS text messaging, and Helsinki public transport was selling SMS based tram and subway tickets, and Finnair the domestic airline offered SMS based cellphone check-in, a private dentist office in the small city of Lahti, about 100 km (60 miles) North of Helsinki, decided to trial a customer service innovation for its dental patients.

Dentists have a particularly pervasive problem with last-minute cancellations. Many fear the dentist, and will take any excuse to cancel at the last moment, or simply not show up to an appointment. So dentists all around the world react the same way: they over-book dental appointments, expecting some of the patients to cancel, thus keeping their dentists fully employed.

This fails of course on a regular basis. Sometimes there are few cancellations, and congestion at the dentist office. The dentists are hurried to the end of the day, not getting any overtime pay. At other days there are many more cancellations and the dentists have nothing to do for much of the day, while still being paid a full day's salary.

So the dentist office in Lahti asked its patients to sign up for last-minute alert service, to fill in cancelled appointments via SMS text message. The cancelled time slots would be filled on a first-come, first-served basis. All who would sign up would receive the message at the same time, and the first to respond would get the cancelled appointment. In this way, for someone with an urgent need to get dental care, they could snap up the first available cancellation. I call this service the *Just-in-time Dentist.*

The service was an instant hit. The customers loved it for getting the chance to service their aching teeth more rapidly. The dentists loved it for filling in the gaps in their schedules. The dental office loved the efficency and savings over the previous system of over and under-bookings.

The Just-in-time Dentist turned out to be so popular that soon the city of Lahti took over the running of the service and expanded it to cover all dentists in the Lahti area. The service won the award for the best new mobile service in Finland for 2004.

Will this work in other cities and countries? Of course it will. Will it work in other areas of medicine, why not? And other service industries? Perfect for hair dressers and barber shops, for example.

"Every child is an artist. The problem is how to
remain an artist once he grows up."
Pablo Picasso

VI
Kids and Phones
My phone is my best friend

Anyone doubting the pervasiveness and addictiveness of cellphones should simply look at teenagers today. From the 13-15-year-olds in America to the 11-13-year-olds in Germany and the UK to the 8-10-year-olds in Finland and Japan, the cellphone is the most critical toy and tool for children today. Yes, they may love their Playstation Portables, and spend countless hours on the web in chat rooms, playing multiplayer games wearing their iPods and using IM, but if forced to select only one, increasingly the gadget of choice is the cellphone.

Even late at night, when parents tell their kids no more TV, no more internet, no more Playstation and turn off the music, the lights are turned off in the children's bedrooms but the communication continues. The kids take their cellphones to bed and continue, silently into the night. Their favorite late night "fix" is that of text messages on the cellphone.

A   TEXT MESSAGES ARE THE LIFELINE

The cellphone has become the must-have device. It is seen as a major element in the definition of a young person's emerging persona. My phone. What it tells others of me. The need to have not only a cellphone, but also the right type of phone of the right brand. This follows a time-honored pattern seen with earlier generations of having the right brands of jeans or the correct make of sneakers/trainers.

Some sociologists in the UK, have shown that what earlier generations associated as factors of being cool in smoking cigarettes is now seen through the cellphone. The Mobile Youth study of 2005 revealed that young people today spend less on cigarettes, alcohol and chocolates because their money goes into their phone bill.

SMS: Adults just don't get it

The heart of a young person's phone is SMS text messaging. It is the mischievous and frivolous use of messaging used in this way. There is a counterculture for the young to have cryptic messages that adults are not even supposed to understand. Texting supports the need to be creative, to have entertainment - jokes - during the day. SMS is ultimate youth communication, fast, no grammar, limited characters and secretive.

What may seem to many of us as the particularly strange behavior of our own children, is in fact a universal trend all around the world. The young generations show a clear preference of SMS as their communication channel of choice. Several studies around the world show consistently that the young users prefer SMS to voice calls and prefer SMS to e-mail. Professor Timo Kopomaa chronicled his early findings of youth use of mobile phones and text messaging in Finland in his study *"Tietoyhteiskunnan Synty"* (literally translated means "The Birth of the Information Society"), which he later released also as a book in English entitled *The City in the Pocket.*

The first systematic global findings were in the landmark Nokia Messaging Study in 2001 covering 10,567 young mobile phone users in six countries on four continents. Since then similar findings were discovered by Orange's survey of British and French youth in 2002, Siemens's study of Asia-Pacific phone usage in 2003 and several other such research.

The Catholic University of Leuwen in Belgium went much further than just a survey of youth opinions, in their extended study of youth and mobile phones, and proved that youth are *addicted* to SMS text messaging. Young people will display standard withdrawal symptoms if forced to be without their phones. They get cranky if they do not receive contacts. More than half awake to arriving messages at night and 20% of teenagers *regularly* wake up to incoming SMS text messages. A follow-up study at the Queensland University in Australia revealed that SMS texting is as addictive as cigarette smoking.

SMS text messaging is the private and secret communication tool for the youth. It is a private communication channel to their mates and friends, by, which they can connect always, immediately, secretly, almost telepathically. Rather than voice calls where parents and siblings might be listening in, through SMS texting teenagers can privately connect and communicate.

100 text messages per day

How instinctive is this use? Heavy users easily average up to 100 SMS sent per day. For the waking hours, that is one every ten minutes all day every day. In addition, even more revealingly, teenagers are totally comfortable sending messages to someone while they are talking with someone else. The survey by YouGov for Carphone Warehouse in 2006 found that 48% of teenagers in the

Youth Cellphone Experiences 2006

Carphone Warehouse/YouGov Survey of 1,258 UK tees aged 11-17

Will not let parents snoop inside phone	68%
Can stay out later because of cellphone	53%
Have sent SMS text messages in class	50%
Send text messages while simultaneously talking to someone else	48%
Avoid contact by parents to their phone	37%
Communicate with someone their parents would not approve of with cellphone	35%
Have had their phone stolen	11%

**Source: Carphone Warehouse/YouGov
Mobile Life Youth Report September 2006**

UK, send text messages to someone *simultaneously* while they are talking to someone else. That might be on a phone, or talking to a real person in their presence. Yes, half of the youth admit to sending texts while carrying on spoken conversations. This could easily be someone they are not happy with, such as being scolded by their parents or teachers etc. As the tears roll down the cheeks, the hand is in the pocket and text messages are silently sent to the best friend.

Even America is following the trend. At the end of 2007 already half of Americans send text messages according to the CTIA and more specifically to the youth, ComScore Media Metrix found in June 2006 the first sign where American youth e-mail use was dropping as SMS use was growing. Even with American youth, SMS is the preferred method, duplicating the identical preference already shown in earlier studies covering Scandinavia, UK, France, Asia etc. *"E-mail is, like, so yesterday"* say American youth according to the California-based *Mercury News, which* reported on the ComScore finding on 9 June 2006.

A Disney survey from July 2007 among American teens found that for one in four teenagers (26%) the first thing they do is send a text message, before they brush their teeth or head to the kitchen for breakfast. The same survey found more than half of US teens send messages from the movie theater (this is how "dog" movies now die sudden death; the youth start bad-mouthing bad movies

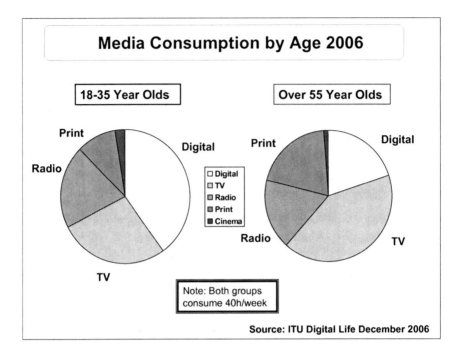

before the end credits start to roll, straight from the cinema) and 28% admit to sending text messages from the dinner table.

Texting is becoming so central to communication that schools in New Zealand now allow students to submit essays and exam replies using the grammar and abbreviations of SMS text messaging. In Japan five of the ten best-selling printed books of 2007 were based on "mobile books" that have been written by the youth, on cellphones for cellphone consumption, using the short text structure, grammar and abbreviations of text messaging. I will discuss the mobile books as their own Case Study near the end of the book with the mobile internet chapter.

B   SMS SPAWNS GEN-C

An interesting phenomenon appears with heavy SMS text messaging use. Young people - and even many older people - start to exhibit what I call "Generation C" behavior. By Generation C or I mean the *Community Generation*. I will discuss Gen-C in the next chapter in greater detail. Moreover, I should point out not all youth are part of Gen-C and not all Gen-C members are under age 20. Furthermore, Gen-C will typically use multiple methods to communicate on multiple platforms from online gaming to instant messaging to the speakerphone feature on the phone. However, the distinguishing factor with Gen-C is the use of SMS text messaging. That is what enables the "hive mentality" and the power of the gang mobilized by the cellphone. However, Gen-C is not limited to youth use; there are plenty of over 30-year-olds in Scandinavia who are fully-fledged members of Gen-C today. I will discuss the peculiar behavior of Gen-C in its own chapter next. Let us keep this chapter focused just on the youth, those under the age of 20.

Response time to SMS

With traditional email, there is now a tendency to attempt to reply to emails within 24 hours, and most think that if the response does not come in 48 hours, it will not arrive at all. Contrast that with SMS. A survey by 160 Characters in May of 2007 found that 84% of users of SMS text messaging expect a reply within 5 minutes. 5 minutes or 48 hours? This is not a contest with SMS winning, it is a bloodbath.

Japanese studies by Dr Fujimoto and Dr Ito of Keio University, of youth cellphones and text messaging reveal that text messaging is now used for courtesy and with a particular youth-behavior etiquette. I need to point out that Japan does not have the exact same SMS text messaging service as in most other countries, the Japanese equivalent is a "short email" mobile message, but that is close enough, and is certainly cellphone messaging and is not email on a phone (which also exists in Japan). Returning to the Keio University study, one part of their findings is that short text messages are used to schedule voice calls. The youth think it is appropriate first to agree on a call, via text messaging?

Another is the respect of a text message: Japanese youth culture has now evolved so that the correct thing is to respond to a text message within 30 minutes or else your friendship is in trouble. Being in school in class, taking an exam, or for example being in a job interview, is no excuse. If a friend contacts you via text message, and needs your help, you have to reply within half an hour or your friendship is in trouble.

Imagine the efficiency gains of human communication as this trend creeps up the "chain of command" within the business world? Where it is so common today to avoid opening email messages to give some time before tackling some pressing work issues. What if all employees also expected a reply to a (text) message in five minutes? This is exactly why executives in almost all advanced markets *prefer* SMS text messages to any other communication methods, because they get near-immediate replies.

Out of money

Where is the money coming from in SMS texting? Obviously the heaviest spenders are teenagers. In addition, while some adults might think it is economically moronic to waste 10 cents per message on a text message when an internet e-mail is free, teenagers are known for "being financially irresponsible" and preferring their own clannish communication methods, and instant gratification, all of which feeds the traffic and spending on their own cellphones.

A study by the Mobile Data Association in the UK, on disposable income of 16-24-year-olds in UK from August 2003 found that youth spend £400 (about $700) per year on the cellphone and services, more than they spend on any other typical teen entertainment i.e. their music and stereos, TVs, video games and PCs, movies etc. The Mobile Youth study of 2005 revealed kids spend eight times more on cellphones than on music. No wonder Apple rushed from the iPod to the iPhone in 2007.

As increasingly kids all around the world have phones as their toys, they are now used in playing. Then as kids grow up, the phones become a part of the flirting and dating experience. A related finding by UK based flirting/dating service Flirtomatic, which can be accessed via PC or cellphone, has found that cellphone users not only access Flirtomatic more times in any given week than

---

71% of UK parents willing to track kids by cellphone
Source: Carphone Warehouse Mobile Youth Life 2006

PC-based users, the cellphone users also use the service more on average than PC-based users. It all comes down to privacy, always-carried availability and the preference of the channel. Young people prefer to do everything on the cellphone if they can.

For context, if you are wondering if your precious 12-year-old should have a phone, in the UK - an average European country, not the cellphone leader by any means - according to the Mobile Data Association in 2005, the age of the first-time phone buyer was down to eight. Yes, eight years of age in 2005. In Japan KDDI already offers new *camera*phones aimed at the under-10-year-old segment. Yes, these are not old, hand-me-down discarded phones from the parents. These are brand new youth phones - and cameraphones at that - so tailored to the under 10-year-old market that their older brothers and sisters will not like these phones anymore. I will examine these peculiar phones and why they are all the rave in Japan, later in the Case Study to this chapter.

How rational and reasonable are young kids? Not so. Under ten-year-olds forget their phones at McDonald's. They attempt to flush them down the toilet or feed the phones to the family dog. They overspend on their account. Nevertheless, that is why most kids get hand-me-down phones as their first phones. Moreover, they learn. If they make a mistake, their phone privileges are put on hold for a month or so. Then as they reach the age of about 14 or 15, kids start to exhibit their own personality. The old hand-me-down phones are no longer good enough, and kids will actually pay to buy their own phones.

Group calls.

One of the strange types of "playing" with cellphones is the group call. A group of 4 teenager boys might call a group of 4 girls. Partly they are just friends, but there can easily be some bubbling romantic energy between one of the boys and one of the girls. They aren't dating yet, and this is a kind of "pre-courting" stage, when the interested boy and/or girl can be charming and funny and witty, while within the support of the close mates. He/she does not have to take the full responsibility of the phone call and get too deeply into a "relationship" but can still flirt with the love-interest. This all is of course via the speakerphone feature on the phone.

As a comment from having worked at Nokia, we never thought that the

---

35% of UK youth willing to be tracked by cellphone
Source: Carphone Warehouse Mobile Youth Life 2006

---

speakerphone feature would be anything other than a "business application" on the high-end smartphones for enterprise/corporate customers. How wrong we were. The biggest use of the speakerphone feature on cellphones today is by kids playing and making group calls. Also bear in mind, as these kids mature to young adults, they will bring this behavior to their jobs. They will instinctively say, lets make this a group call, I have Jimmy here in the taxicab with me...

Cameraphone is a toy

We adults like to think of the camera on our cellphone as being a variation of the older film-based cameras we grew up with. Back then film was expensive, prints were expensive, and cameras were expensive. Pictures were not "wasted". We took the camera to important events like weddings and holiday trips etc, and any pictures we took we would then store and expect to see years later as mementoes.

Not teenagers today. They never knew of film-based cameras. To them cameras were always digital (or at least paper pictures could be turned digital with a scanner at the techie uncle's house or at school or at the parents' office or somewhere like that). Then when kids get their first cameraphone, it becomes an instrument of immediate gratification. A friend makes a face, take a picture. The guy jumps with his skateboard, take a short clip. Tomorrow the camera memory is full, delete these images and make new ones. Most of the images taken by kids on cameraphones are meant to be consumed within the next 48 hours, shown to a few friends and deleted. Almost none are meant to be kept. Disposable memories. This illustrates how differently older generations and the youth relate to a feature on the cellphone, like the camera functionality for example. For kids it is a toy, it is used in play, daily. They also learn from a child that the cameraphone is always ready to capture images, evidence. They will not think "why" take a picture on the cameraphone; they will think "why not".

C   ATTENTION SPANS EVER SHORTER

The attention spans of current consumers are ever shrinking. They are at the lowest point ever, and still growing shorter. With the industrial revolution as mankind started to migrate to cities and live in apartment houses, the 1800s brought us the novel, the fictional story in a book, which took a couple of days to consume. This was the time before radio, cinema and TV, so for entertainment, the novel was invented. The classics were written then, from Count Dracula to Horatio Hornblower to Tom Sawyer, as the form of entertainment for a population increasingly disconnected from family and friends.

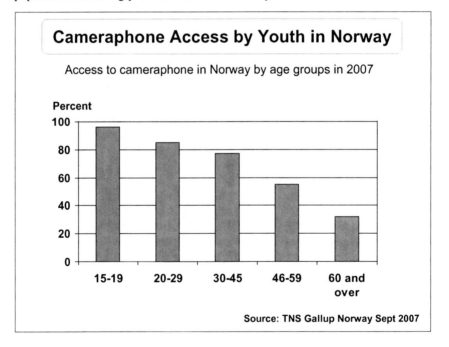

The 1930s when cinema started to get its standardized forms, the motion picture "story" was shrunk to last about two hours. The 1960s brought TV drama as a mainstream story, with detective stories and westerns as well as soap operas. The average story shrunk to one hour. The 1970s brought us the sitcom (situation comedy) on TV, which condensed the typical story to 30 minutes. Our attention spans were being shrunk.

The dramatic change was in the 1980s when teenagers were exposed en masse to music videos, via MTV and its clones. Now, suddenly a typical story shrunk to the 3-4 minutes of the length of a typical hit song. TV advertisements followed these trends, with the one-minute ad shrinking to 30 second spots, and now many stations broadcasting even 15-second ads. An interesting phenomenon is that many popular music videos from Pussycat Dolls to the Black Eyed Peas to 50 Cent have found that even 4 minutes is excessively too long to remain on one theme, and videos start to have several subplots, or interruptions such as fake advertisements, etc, interspliced to the short 3 or 4-minute video clip.

Undeniably the storylines of content in popular culture have shrunk, which has shortened the attention spans of especially the younger audiences. No wonder teachers in schools complain that they cannot compete with the fast pace of MTV.

Need entertainment

Another key element of the modern society is that all of our information and education needs to be entertaining. It is no longer information, it is "info-tainment", not education, but "edu-tainment" and not advertising but "adver-tainment" (or perhaps "adver-gaming"). Digital tools and heavily produced content, with the entertainment element weaved into the news, information, education and advertising is the desirable way for modern customers. If you do not package your message the way your consumers want it, they will simply ignore it.

A good example of edu-tainment is the docu-drama, combining traditional pure facts-based documentary with the drama effects. The facts are there but brought to life in a more relevant, contextual and understandable way. Young people will also seek relevant, factual-oriented docu-drama or even classic documentaries, if their topics are meaningful, and as long as they are made to be interesting. Whether the series of Michael Moore's documentaries or Al Gore's *An Inconvenient Truth*, young people will pay to watch factual content, as long as it is interesting.

The preference of text messaging has been discovered by politicians as well. In Canada, the Canadian Wireless Telecommunications Association launched a youth political initiative called Youth Text. Each Canadian political party agreed to respond to Youth Text messages and to reply within 48 hours. The purpose of the initiative was to get young people more active with politics, using the youth's preferred means of communication. As I was writing this, the US Presidential Elections of 2008 were the first major use of SMS texting in an American election with major candidates sending messages to their supporters in the millions and Senator Barack Obama's campaign actually recruiting more activists by asking volunteers present, to send 5 SMS text messages to friends who should also join. If SMS texting is the definitive youth communication method, anyone wanting to reach the youth should learn to communicate with it.

D   YOUTH LESSONS AROUND THE WORLD

Recently some of the most revealing youth behavior traits relating to the cellphone have been reported by Keio University of Japan professor Mizuko Ito. For example, kids use their personal phones at considerable cost, rather than the family landline phone, which tends to be free, just to avoid being overheard by their parents.

     The Japanese author on cellphones, Kenichi Fujimoto says using mobile internet content on the phone is like "refreshment" i.e. like a coffee break. In a similar vein, AirCross the South Korean mobile advertising arm of SK Telecommunications, looks at mobile not as an information vehicle, but a plaything. AirCross CEO BJ Yang says that the *"cellphone is a private fun playground"*. A fun personal playground. Not a boring executive telecommunications tool. A fun personal playground.

     To put it another way, the advertising giant OgilvyOne's Global Creative Director, Rory Sutherland says, *"SMS text messaging is an excuse to be rude in communications."* With older formats of written communications, the letter, the fax and the email, we had to compose the communication. Start with a greeting, end it with a closing. Not in SMS. With text messaging there only is 160 characters of space, so we skip the politeness, and get straight to the point. An excuse to be rude. *"Can u meet at 8?"*. Very abbreviated communication for the generation that has the shortest attention span ever. Some of the youth will complain if you use up the full 160 character space of the text message - for them 160 characters is too long as a form of communication! And yes, that last sentence was 160 characters in length. Imagine, that was "too long"?

Sharing, connecting with community

Once a young person learns he/she is not alone, but can at all times contact friends, a much more interdependent relationship starts to build. Decisions are not made in isolation, even if late at night when a phone call would be frowned upon, young kids can contact each other silently via text messaging. Experiences are not felt alone. No, experiences are immediately shared, when they happen. In Finland Professor Timo Kopomaa was the first to document this in his book *The*

                                              Tomi T Ahonen

South Korean Youth SMS Use

South Korean survey of 1,100 cellphone users aged 14-19 in 2005 found the following patterns:

Send text messages in class	40%
Send text messages when bored	40%
Hae received threatening text message	20%
Take cellphone to the bathroom	20%
Have been bullied by text message	10%

Source: Korea Agency for Digital Opportunity and Promotion November 2005

City in Your Pocket in 2000. Professor Kopomaa highlighted how differently young people behave when they have the power of the community in their pocket:

> *Nothing is agreed upon or fixed in precise terms, the spectrum of individual choice is kept as broad as possible. A certain ex tempore lifestyle becomes more widespread. Both shared and private decisions are expected to be taken rapidly, and schedules are not determined precisely, because they can be adjusted along the way.*
>
> Timo Kopomaa, *The City in Your Pocket*, 2000

This generation is used to sharing experiences and seek the opinions of friends, via the cellphone, at all times and in all situations. In addition, not only knowing that the friends are there, always, this generation can now actively seek their opinions and support at any time. I will discuss how this is turning into a whole new generation of consumers in the next chapter about Generation-C.

Who may use the phone

Steve Jones of The 3G Portal explains another key difference when he lectures

---

with me at Oxford University about mobile services and their consumers. Steve tells that for the youth they extend their concept of privacy to their cellphones. Parents, little and big brothers and sisters, favorite uncles, etc, will not be allowed to scroll through saved messages, etc. Even if it is a new phone, which the youth may be very eager to show off, such as its new camera feature or latest game, that youngster will not want the older family member to dig through messages and calling histories etc. to find out what personal communication that young person has been up to. A third of British youth admit to communicating with people their parents would not approve of, according to the Carphone Warehouse survey in 2006.

Then observe the same youngster with three of his or her best friends at a McDonald's or Pizza Hut. They will all happily put their phones in the middle of the table, and all will reach out for each others' phones, play the latest games, read through all latest messages, comment on them, etc

Even adult cellphone users have soon developed a personal intimacy with the content on the phone, so intense that in most relationships and marriages, if one partner tries to read what the other has stored on the phone, it results in a fight. Our phone is that personal. On a somewhat older age segment, Italian divorce lawyers report that in most cases of adultery the evidence is found on the spouse's cellphone.

Virtual Worlds

Another area where kids today behave differently is the virtual worlds and multiplayer gaming. It is not the first generation to grow up with videogaming. Those in their forties had videogames at arcades, like *Pong* and *Pac Man*. Those in their thirties grew up with home console games such as *Super Mario Brothers* and *Donkey Kong* and stand-alone PC games like *Tetris* and *Doom*. The twenty-somethings played with Playstations and PS2s, and Xboxes. However, even those were mostly standalone or dual mode.

What makes for radical change in the videogaming environment is the emergence of the massively multiplayer virtual worlds, online. Suddenly those who were heavily into PC and network gaming during the past five years, are increasingly in MMOGs (Massively Multiplayer Online Games) such as *World of Warcraft, CounterStrike, Lineage* and *Everquest*, and multiplayer virtual worlds such as *Habbo Hotel, Second Life* and *Cyworld*.

As the users get involved in social networking on fixed internet based services that are also available on mobile, they soon start to migrate to mobile, as the opportunity for social interaction is greater on mobile than fixed internet variants. Mark Curtis the CEO of Flirtomatic in the UK, has reported that their mobile users visit the Flirtomatic site more often, and flirt more - generate more traffic - when there, than their fixed internet online counterparts. Cyworld in South Korea has the same experience, as their parent SK Communication CEO

Dr Hyun-Oh Yoo stated in 2007:

> *We at SK Communications are extremely proud to play a part in contributing to the Digital Korea Blueprint with Cyworld, a service favorably used by more than 20 million Koreans. The fact is Cyworld is still evolving fast in a range of countries on different continents. Cyworld, as the most advanced community platform, is also converting millions of PC based users to mobile.*
> Dr Hyun-Oh Yoo, CEO SK Communications

I will discuss gaming in its own chapter later, so let me just make a couple of points about virtual worlds and the youth. Virtual worlds allow a cyberspace form of making friends - and dropping them. Some people are met in the virtual world who are literally from another part of the physical world, an American meets up with a Korean, and this friendship can flourish, and turn into a partnership and collaboration, and last for months, years even, without the two ever meeting in the real world. Kids today are comfortable at discovering friendships that are only met through a digital space.

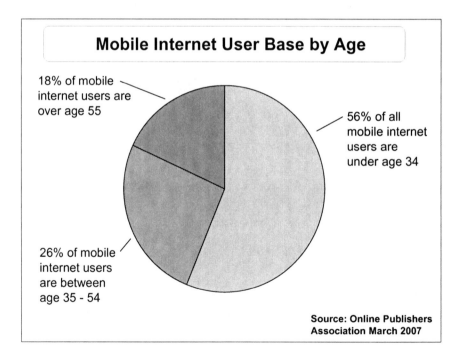

Mobile Internet User Base by Age

18% of mobile internet users are over age 55

56% of all mobile internet users are under age 34

26% of mobile internet users are between age 35 - 54

Source: Online Publishers Association March 2007

No distinction between virtual and real

Kids of today will not distinguish between the virtual and the real. Remember the 18-year-old of today was 5 when the first *Tamagotchi* appeared. The youth of today had a virtual pet - that died - before they ever had a real cat or dog. This generation lives inside *Habbo Hotel*, uses the virtual boyfriend/girlfriend to practice being a good partner in a romantic relationship; and then goes into *World of Warcraft* to earn some real dollars out of selling virtual properties. They meet up with their friends online all the time. For them there is no distinction between the virtual and the real. For them it is all real. For some very technologically oriented adults today, there is value in the emerging opportunities of "augmented reality". For teenagers, the virtual already offers full value.

Returning "back to reality" so to speak, then there is the rock concert. Earlier on, it was the classic rock concert scene when fans would raise their lighters in flame, to enjoy the moment with their rock band. Today the audience creates a glow of a different hue, as they all raise their cameraphones to the tune of the rock n roll. They will then be able to share a bit of the moment with friends, and return to the emotion of the concert in days to come.

The youth of this decade has found its gadget, and it is the cellphone. Now lets examine where this all leads, as a whole new generation emerges, which instinctively connects to friends, communities, all the time. The youth is the future and for them the cellphone is the only indispensable element to their lives and friends. As we consider the future, remember what Winston Churchill said, *"The empires of the future are the empires of the mind."*

Case Study 5 from Japan
Children's Cameraphone

I regularly advise the cellphone industry and the various manufacturers worldwide. However, if I was asked in December 2006, could I believe in a market for new *camera*phones, to be tailored for children under the age of 10, I would have laughed and said no. No, the parents would not buy new cameraphones to kids that young, they would give them old hand-me-down phones that the parents (or older siblings) no longer wanted.

So I was chairing a major wireless event in Tokyo in January 2007 and I happened to go visit the KDDI flagship store to see the newest innovations of the second largest wireless carrier/operator of Japan. There I saw a line of childrens' phones, including some aimed at the kids under age 10. And yes, these new phones were cameraphones.

So lets be clear. First of all, these were honest childrens phones. With bright basic colours, greens, blues, reds, yellows. With strong cases to withstand the shocks when the kids inevitably would drop the phones from time to time. Phones with child-friendly rounded edges. Childlike in outward appearance. Clamshell phones to protect the color screens. Childish screen greetings with cute animals like giraffes, puppies, butterflies, etc when you flipped open the phone. Clearly aimed for young kids. So cute in fact that the KDDI testing found that 11-12-year-olds would reject these phones as *too childish*, and would not want them.

So then the camera. What parent in their right mind buys a new *camera*phone for their "rug-rats?" Now we see the brilliance of KDDI understanding how advanced and mature Japan is as a cellphone market. For this age, you don't sell the phone (and service) to the kid, but to the parent. What is the biggest worry of a parent giving a new phone to a young kid. Its that the kid gets bullied and the phone is stolen. Lose money and traumatize the child.

Not with this childrens' phone. It has a built-in alarm. One that is viciously loud. But better than that - when that alarm is sounded, the phone camera takes a picture! And then - the best part - when the alarm goes off, the childrens' phone - and KDDI - immediately send the picture that the child just took, directly to the parent. This is very different from all other picture messaging services, which require the user to press several buttons, select the address to send the image, etc. No, with the children's phone and its alarm feature, the picture is immediately sent to the phone(s) of the parent(s).

If the child is in trouble, just take out the phone, sound the alarm, point the camera at the bully, and your parents immediately see who is frightening the child.

So what is the cost of adding that secure feeling to your child? And, which parent has the stomach to say no to their precious little Billy who comes home and tells about the new security phone that his friend Johnny has just received., which parent is willing to say that they don't love their child enough to get them the "security" phone?

This is a crazy industry, it constantly dumbfounds even the best of its experts and pundits. Almost all the big hits and successes are services or concepts that "according to conventional wisdom" could not have happened. And again, I am proven wrong. Yes, it is possible to sell brand new *camera*phones to kids under the age of 10. Today both rival networks in Japan already offer similar phones and services.

"Resistance is futile: you will be assimilated."
"The Borg" collective in TV series
Star Trek: The Next Generation

VII
Generation C
The Community Generation

In our book *Communities Dominate Brands* in 2005, Alan Moore and I introduced a new generation of consumers, which behaves very differently from earlier generations. We called it *Generation-C*, which stands for the *Community Generation*. This is the mostly teen aged and young adult generation that has learned to keep in touch with mates, friends and colleagues via the cellphone, at all times and in all situations.

Gen-C often learned the power of community connectedness from secret use of cellphones in school, from attempting to cheat in exams by sending SMS text messages as I discussed in the previous chapter about the youth. This kind of "secret notes" behavior very soon evolved into having the support of friends in any situation, such as a first date, or a fight with parents, or the first job interview etc. Where older generations would discuss the emotions of such situations *after* the event, say in a bar or pub with work mates or at home after a long day, Generation-C will connect and share their lives in real time, *as it happens*, and get the support and mental participation of friends instantly.

A   OUR COMMUNITY IN OUR POCKET

Generation-C stands for the Community Generation. The defining and distinguishing characteristic for Gen-C is the continuous connection to and responding to digital communities. While fluent in numerous digital technologies, Gen-C prefers using instant forms of communication, chat, IM Instant messaging and most of all, SMS text messaging.

This is very different from any other communities. You might say that mankind has always belonged into social groups, tribes, communities; it is nothing new. Nevertheless, up to the advent of Generation-C, all community interaction was only sporadic. We connected with our community only when we could.

Is real-time support relevant?

This may seem like a trivial change in timing. It is not. It is a total, revolutionary upheaval in human behavior. It has never been possible before for normal citizens to have permanent support of others literally 24 hours a day. Its value has been proven in several "mission-critical" areas like airlines - which have permanent connection with air control. Police were equipped with car radios and walkie-talkies in the middle of the last century when these were expensive gadgetry, because in police emergencies the ability to summons immediate help *while on the move* can be very critical. The military recognized this as well, and throughout the past few decades the connectedness of all units of the battlefield have brought about much more condensed firepower and battlefield effectiveness. The ability to have real-time information and data communications support was one of the keys to the decisive victory in Desert Storm.

Imagine the situation in reverse. Imagine if today you were a police officer in any major city and suddenly the police commissioner decided for some reason to remove all police radio equipment (and cellphones and pagers). The police would have to *downgrade* their collaborative effectiveness to finding a

---

Nokia Global Survey of Cellphone Owners

- 73%   have cellphone replace wristwatch
- 72%   use cellphone as alarm clock
- 44%   use their current cellphone camera as their primary camera
- 42%   want an "all-converged" device
- 33%   would rather lose wallet than their cellphone
- 20%   would rather lose their wedding ring than their cellphone...

Source: Nokia Global End-User Survey 2006

---

nearby phone booth to call the police station when needing assistance. Even then, the commanding officer could not reroute a police car from nearby (as they had no radio), but could only dispatch a new car from the police station to the trouble spot. Modern police work would immediately grind to a halt.

It is difficult to imagine a time before instant communications. Moreover, for mission-critical tasks, such as ambulances, police cars, fire engines, fighter planes, jet airliners getting ready to land at airports, etc, if there was not continuous communication, modern life would not be possible.

Humans lived alone, sharing later

Homo Sapiens has lived the same way for over ten thousand years. We sometimes moved around in pairs and groups and tribes. However, we spend considerable amounts of time doing things by ourselves, whether farming, fishing, hunting in the older times, or in our office cubicles, in our cars, at the supermarket etc. today. We encounter normal everyday situations that sometimes turn difficult or ugly or happy or amusing, etc. from narrowly avoiding a car accident to seeing a celebrity shopping at our supermarket. As we experienced those events alone, the only way to share them is to talk about them later, perhaps hours after they happened. We discuss our lives then at the dinner table, or at the water cooler at the office, and so forth.

Gen-C and permanent connectivity

This is radically different for Gen-C. Just like the modern police force or military, any member of Generation C can immediately summons contact of all friends and support. *I am lonely. I am unhappy. I want to play a videogame. Our favorite band being interviewed on MTV! I saw something funny. I think the girl I am attracted to me, just smiled at me, what do I do now.* These normal, everyday occurences. Gen-C can live those together, not alone. They find the support of their friends - and very critically as well - learn right from childhood to share in the good and the bad that happens to their friends.

Remember from the previous chapter that young people can average up to 100 SMS text messages sent per day, so they instinctively and without looking can thumb out messages. That they all carry their phones everywhere, even sleeping with them. In addition, that it is totally normal for young people to be carrying out a conversation with one person, while sending a text message to someone else at the same time. Moreover, finally that they expect responses within 5 minutes of the text being sent.

The change is no less total as was that of the police getting portable two-way radios or the military or airlines etc getting permanent connections. The individual in such a support system is *inherently* - and *always - more powerful than any individual* trying to fight such a system alone. A good example was mentioned in the ***International Herald Tribune*** on 21 March 2007 quoting a 17-year-old British youth, Lewis Heapy, about how he has direct access and support of his mates. Lewis said, *"It's the gang culture. In the past, the worst fights would get to was 'I'm going to get my big brother on you.' Now it's 'My gang's going to come and stab you up.'"*

Friends that are always available

Generation-C is the first generation to live with the friends "in their pocket" - instantly available at all times. Again, it is important to highlight how different this is from any other communications. It is not the same if the friends are there to support you, on an instant messaging system, or via e-mail, or in a chat room, or at home reachable via a fixed wireline telephone. That is not "always". If you do not have the ability to contact always, you will never discover the community support.

Even more, it is not only you who has to have access. For Gen-C to emerge, your friends also have to be permanently connected. Imagine if

---

27% of UK adults admit to sending texts while talking
Source: Carphone Warehouse Mobile Youth Life 2006

---

everyone sat at a laptop and wireless connectivity every day everywhere. They could evolve into Gen-C. If the other friends are not permanently connected, they will not be there to provide the support under all conditions. Only the cellphone or of course other cellular network "always-on" devices such as the Blackberry, allow this.

B   SHARING

Gen-C will be digitally literate and have multiple technical means to capture and generate content for themselves. They are also very apt at sharing, so they will borrow the friend's scanner, the big brother's digital camera and the uncle's faster computer or the aunt's CD burning drive to achieve what they want to do. For Gen-C content has always been digital, and could always be duplicated.

Gen-C is also very used to sharing, especially using various peer-to-peer networks i.e. Napster, Kazaa, YouTube etc. They will make good use of digital memories, so a grainy image of a friend very drunk on a party a few years ago, may suddenly emerge as part of a birthday card, etc. Gen-C is very aware of the costs of sharing, so they will happily store digital memories on cellphones,

---

Tomi T Ahonen

iPods, personal computers, network hard drives, etc., and share them when they can do it at no cost, rather than use some of the expensive networking technologies.

Is not the "Cellphone" Generation

It would be easy to assume the C in Generation-C stands for Cellphone, but this is not the case. There is a much greater part of the global population that is more or less addicted to the cellphone. Nevertheless, for them there is no radically different way of behaving as consumers, compared to what they did on fixed wireline phones, and the internet.

Let me show by example. Take the 35-year-old housewife who might be shifting the telephone conversations to go from the fixed wireline phone at home to the cellphone. This allows that housewife to for example go for a walk in the park while talking on the phone. However, it does not radically alter the consuming behavior of that 35-year-old woman. She still shops in similar stores, but does not radically alter her shopping behavior to include friends via her

---

48% of UK youth admit to sending texts while talking
Source: Carphone Warehouse Mobile Youth Life 2006

---

cellphone. She goes for a coffee while shopping, but again the cellphone will mostly stay in the purse, it is not an inherent part of the coffee break etc. For most of us older people, the cellphone only allows some efficiencies in doing the same things we did before. In other words, we try to achieve some convenience to ourselves.

With the young Gen-C, there is a radical change in behavior. Generation-Community will consult with the mates on the cellphone before and *during* consumer decisions, such as deciding, which bar, club, disco or pub to go to tonight, or while in an electronics store, a member of Gen-C will consult with the electronics "guru" friend about some new product that is on sale. This generation is accustomed to living experiences together with mates, not in isolation. If the woman in the above example were part of Gen-C, she would have told her "shopping friends" about the trip to the mall before going, and sent some messages, or made calls, while in the store. At the coffee break, again she would advise her friends what was going on, and ask for advice on what was next on her mind.

I want to be very clear, while Gen-C prefers the cellphone, it is by no means their only connection device, and in many cases, not even the predominant one. For example a heavy gamer type of Gen-C youth will sit by the

---

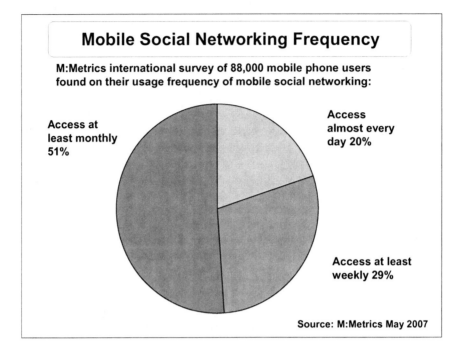

Mobile Social Networking Frequency

M:Metrics international survey of 88,000 mobile phone users found on their usage frequency of mobile social networking:

Access at least monthly 51%

Access almost every day 20%

Access at least weekly 29%

Source: M:Metrics May 2007

PC playing multiplayer online games like *World of Warcraft*. The best friends are all also gamers, so they too tend to sit by their PCs and the gang of friends gets together playing games together. They will then use the various instant messaging and chat services on their computers, as they play games, and share files, listen to music, watch *YouTube* videos etc, all on the PC. These users will also still use SMS when they are about town, but for them the primary communication channel for heavy traffic is their PC when gaming.

Is not the "Content" Generation

On *Wikipedia* by December 2007, there were several dozen definitions for Gen C, with Community Generation the one with most support, but not by any means yet a universally accepted definition. One alternate meaning that has more than slight support is the suggestion of Generation-C as the "Content Generation". This idea stems from a generation that creates digital content with digital cameras, cameraphones, music software; editing content with image editors and music editing software; creating playlists with iPods, picture and clip albums online, etc. I understand the argument and why this could be called "something-C" for Content. Nevertheless, I do not agree with the logic that it is a "generation" Content. There is no generational gap between the current and older populations. The young today use their iPods and camphones etc yes, to collect and arrange and edit their digital content.

However, we had digital content already a decade ago and it is nothing new to edit that. Our tools were cruder perhaps, but all of us had friends who had huge collections of music CD's who would make tapes to their friends, and then later, started to burn CDs. There have been digital image editing software packages before this generation, but most of those were on the Macintosh etc. Before digital manipulation tools, there were plenty of manual/analogue content manipulation tools, from the photocopier to the photography darkroom. Back in the 1970s, there were plenty of DJ-wannabes who copied songs from record albums to C-cassettes and shared these with friends. No, Generation C for Content is not by any means unique to this current generation that content behavior has existed for several decades, to gradually increasing degree.

Content is an *evolutional* change, not a new generational shift. Today's youth has easier access to many powerful content creation and editing tools, but that is simply an evolution. The radical change right now is the community aspect, something that was not possible five or ten years ago. If we saw a clever gadget in a store in the last decade, we would talk about it with our friends the next day, not immediately on the spot, calling from the store.

C   BEING PART OF GEN-C

There are several signs of whether one is part of Gen-C. Obviously, the first need is an addiction to the cellphone. Since first landmark studies about youth behavior and the anecdotal evidence of addiction to cellphones, now we actually have cellphone addiction proven in research around the world. The first serious study to suggest addiction was a Siemens study in December 2003 of cellphone users in seven Asian countries, over half of all Asians will return home to retrieve it if they left home without their cellphone.

A good sign is use of voice mail. If you leave voice mail messages, you are too old to be Gen-C. Gen-C will never leave a voicemail message. Gen-C may listen to the announcement, but after that will immediately hang up. The recipient will have seen the number of the caller and know that the call was attempted. If a message is necessary, then Gen-C will send an SMS text message instead of leaving voicemail. Why is it faster? Because the recipient has to *retrieve* voice mail but SMS is delivered instantly. Long before the recipient has even considered when it is a good moment to listen to voicemail messages, the SMS text message has already arrived. So rather than waste the time with a voicemail message, Gen-C will always prefer to send an SMS text message. A good example is the Prime Minister of Finland, whose voicemail message says, *"Don't leave me voice mail, send me a text message instead."*

Generation Text

A black and white delineation line between Gen-C and the rest of us is the communication vehicle of preference. Gen-C prefers to send text messages. They could call you, but they send a text. They could leave you a message on your voice mail, yet they hang up and send a text. You might send them an e-mail and be amused to discover the reply came via a text message. They can be speaking with you on a voice call and then send suddenly you a text message simultaneously from the same person, while the phone conversation still continues. In addition, yes, they often send text messages to someone who is in the same room. All this on the shoestring budget, knowing full well that every text message costs, typically 10 cents per message as a global average cost.

If you think, it is cumbersome to type out messages on the inefficient cellphone keypad that is only a matter of learning to do it. I will discuss SMS more fully in its own chapter later in this book. However, those truly of Gen-C can type out messages blind, literally. In other words, they can type messages with the phone held out of sight, under the table, or behind their back, or with the phone in their pocket. Moreover, no, this is not using predictive text. Predictive

---

75% of cellphone owners over age 45 want only voice calls
Source: AT Kerney Mobinet 2005

---

is definitely the crutch for us older generations attempting to keep up with the young. True Gen-C never uses predictive text. It slows them down.

Use digital feedback

Earlier generations had to learn that their voice could matter, and that they had power in writing to politicians, corporations and other entities such as through the written letter, and then more recently, using e-mail. Because of the feedback loops involved, a response might take a long time or it might never arrive. Gen-C is not accepting that. They know that SMS and IM are immediate contact methods. When they are offered a chance to interact, Gen-C will expect an immediate response. Some communities and entities that have harnessed this have taught Gen-C that instant messaging formats can deliver - and should deliver - immediate comments. This reinforces the interest to participate, communicate, give feedback, and share the experience with friends.

The word can spread incredibly fast - much much faster than was ever possible in the e-mail age. The riots in France in 2005 were mostly organized using SMS and rioters spreading the word virally from one to another. When the

---

Tomi T Ahonen

Buddhist monks in Myanmar were being beaten up and the ruling military junta tried to suppress the story in the mass media in 2007, the story spread out of Myanmar via SMS text messages. While the press could be suppressed up to a point, the story rapidly spread via SMS.

D   SMS AND DATING

Dating is a good area to illustrate Gen-C behavior as they use the power of SMS text messaging. In all countries of high SMS use, the trend is clear - young men and women prefer to use SMS text messaging in starting up a romance. Men and women both like SMS as it is much less painful, allows time for consideration and is gentler in handling rejection.

It is now common for most single girls or women in countries of high cellphone penetration to expect the man to start the courting for a potential relationship by an introductory SMS text message. This has replaced the traditional "pick-up line" in bars, clubs and discos. A woman will rather openly give the man her cellphone number, and then expect the man to come up with a

---

29% of cellphone owners under age 19 want only voice calls
Source: AT Kerney Mobinet 2005

---

creative original romantic and humorous introductory message - all this in 160 characters of the standard SMS text message.

Why not a simple phone call?

The beauty of starting the courting process with a text message rather than in person or via a phone call, is that it is more gentle to both. A man can consider his approach and words carefully and write and rewrite the SMS before sending it, whereas many men stumble upon the early words spoken to the woman they are after when nervous about making a good first impression.

Text messaging allows the girl more time to consider, she is not rushed, and this eliminates some of the hasty forced decisions that could be "no" rather than waiting, finding out about the man, considering, and agreeing. It also allows the girl to respond with a maybe, which for a man accustomed to receiving more rejections than acceptances for romantic advances, is a much better reply.

The revealing part of this process is the collaboration, which SMS allows for the girl. If a man calls the woman on the phone, the woman will need to make her mind up fast, and alone, without consultation, *during the phone call..*

However, if the man contacts her via SMS, now suddenly she can draw upon Gen-C behavior. In addition, she sends that message to all of her friends.

Yes. The woman sends the man's private, sensitive, discrete, romantic first contact SMS to all of her friends. Why? To get typical "Gen-C" type of support. To make an informed decision, of course. First of all, she wants to know if any of her friends have already received an approach from this man. If she was not his first choice, in fact. Then she wants to find out of what seemed like an original romantic message was something that her friends had seen before; maybe it is taken from some website. Not original. Third, she wants her friends' opinions on the man if they have any - some might know him, or of his reputation. Moreover, lastly, she wants them to comment on the message, is it funny, original, romantic. Should she say yes or no to this guy.

This is idiomatic Gen-C behavior - using the power of mobile telecoms to seek the assistance of the community. It is important to point out that in modern dating rituals, every first message from a man will be shared with many of the woman's girl friends. The women know this and the men know this. Of course, the message is shared.

Ease the pain

Even if the reply does arrive as a "no" to the man, it is seen as much less painful if the rejection is as a text message than said in person face to face, or on the phone. In survey after survey from Finland to Singapore, young people both women and men, say they prefer to start a relationship this way.

Studies have shown that in relationships the partners measure each others' affection by receiving at least one message per day. If the other party does not show affection, something is wrong in the relationship. In Italy for example, 68% of men and women send romantic messages to their partners regularly. 6% had received relationship-ending messages via SMS according to Tegic in 2005.

A 2006 study by Halebop and TeliaSonera of SMS use in Sweden found that 86% have flirted using SMS, 40% have engaged in SMS-sex (think email sex but actually this is more handy on a cellphone as the phone is more easily taken to bed with you and operated while in bed rather than a laptop computer).

As the romance picks up, the SMS messaging becomes intertwined into the relationship. 160 characters is a good medium to use for expressing an emotion, and creative romantics have managed short love poems in 160 characters. Romances soon develop a personal SMS language, which may differ from all other previous romantic communications by either party with unique nicknames and recurring jokes and themes. The love life itself reflects the passion and care within text messages. Both men and women expect to receive one romantic text message every day, else the relationship is heading into an argument that night.

Tomi T Ahonen

An Independent Online study in February 2006 of SMS use in the UK, found that 25% had sent a romantic message accidentally to the wrong person, like a boss, ex-partner or parent. In addition, of those who had been caught cheating on a relationship, 65% were caught because of their SMS traffic on their phone that the partner had discovered. In Italy, the biggest source of evidence for infidelity in divorce cases today is data collected from cellphones such as stored messages and traffic information.

A good example of a powerful dating service on cellphones is The 3G Dating Agency in the UK, which uses 2D Barcodes in its advertising and marketing campaigns to get new users to effortlessly connect from their cameraphones to the dating service.

Mobile communities and social networking on mobile are the next big thing for this space and there are many companies lining up to provide such services on mobile. At The 3G Dating Agency we "Take the Waiting out of Dating..." . We believe that even though 3G Video calling technology has been around for a while, there had been no compelling reason for consumers to use it, hence the low adoption and usage of this technology. Our service finally gives consumers a compelling reason to use video calling technology as a tool for social interaction. We have also been leading the way by being the first company to work with the BBC to display a QR code on a BBC website next to an article talking about Mobile Dating. This gives visitors to the BBC website the option of scanning the QR code with their mobile device and go directly to their dating site, thus truly "Taking the Waiting our of Dating..."
Romi Parmar, CEO and Founder 3G Dating Agency

This is exactly the kind of power that cellphones can provide, which totally trumps the keyboard on a laptop or desktop PC. Yes, you might be fast at typing on the keyboard, but the cameraphone clicking on the image of the 2D Barcode is far faster.

E   GEN-C CONNECTS

Younger generations often are said to be unlike their parents. This time it is more true than ever. Gen-C are not like their parents. Members of Generation C relate to cellphones and in fact all networks in a different way to previous generations. The network is there not to interrupt me, it is there to serve me. The network will not control me; I control the interaction on the network. A good example is with Gen-C and how it reacts to the ringing of the cellphone.

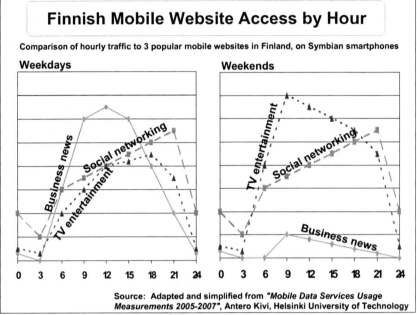

Finnish Mobile Website Access by Hour

Comparison of hourly traffic to 3 popular mobile websites in Finland, on Symbian smartphones

Weekdays

Weekends

Source: Adapted and simplified from *"Mobile Data Services Usage Measurements 2005-2007"*, Antero Kivi, Helsinki University of Technology

Why didn't you answer the phone?

A most revealing change in Gen-C behavior when compared to older generations is the reaction to a ringing phone. When the telephone network was the only connection, it was also given a very high degree of importance. Older generations were taught to keep phone conversations short just in case there is an important phone call coming in. When the technology allowed it in the 1980s, most of society bought telephone answering machines to ensure that the important calls were not missed.

When the telephone line was the only connection, it was also considered always worth answering. There could be very important information at the other end. Thus again older generations would even answer other people's phones if visiting their home or office. We were taught to identify ourselves when answering the phone, as telephones were shared instruments whether at home or the office. Nevertheless, most importantly, a ringing phone had to be answered.

Gen-C behaves totally differently. It is completely normal to them, to be at home or at work, at their phone, with no distraction such as a meeting, to see who is calling, know who it is, and still not answer it. This drives the older generations like our parents totally livid. *"You were at the phone, had the time, saw it was me calling, and didn't answer the phone?"* Nevertheless, this illustrates the difference between the attitudes to communications by Generation-C and older generations. Gen-C know there are many networks, many connections, many contacts, many reasons for calling, and that a phone call is not the most urgent contact. If that person really wants me to urgently talk, he will next send a text message. If it was just a social call, he will not send a message.

No, Gen-C will happily see his best friend calling, and not be involved in anything particularly important, and still not answer. It totally depends on the mood. Sometimes yes, I would love to talk to my friend now, but other times, no, I do not feel like it now, I will return the call a few hours later, or tomorrow. The best friend will understand. A call is an interruption, and Gen-C feels it is perfectly acceptable to reject the interruption. Remember their attitude, the cellphone is there to serve me, not to interrupt me.

My phone my money

For the Gen-C, the first financial instrument is not the credit card, a checking account or a debit card with a bank. It is the cellphone. This generation assumes it can pay for anything with the cellphone. In fact, where the phone account is a "post-pay" or contract account, it is usually the first tool of credit that Gen-C is exposed to. They may make a hamburger payment on the cellphone simply because their cash is low, and they know the phone bill will not become due until the end of the month. In effect, they have very short-term credit and learn about consumer credit and postponing payments first on their cellphone accounts before they get their first credit card.

F   SIMULTANEOUS PARALLEL NETWORKS

But let me be very clear about Gen-C. It is not a generation exclusively using cellphones. A key element of the currently connected society, is that its participants have learned to navigate multiple partially overlapping networks. The current digitally aware society is not easily manipulated. One wants a direct call, another hates the call but prefers listening to voice mails to "screen callers", a third will want the contact via e-mail - especially many Blackberry users, a fourth wants contacts to be via SMS text messaging. Even more, we may have different preferences by the time of day, or type of communication, or the person contacting us.

Similar to the multiple connectedness with networks, we also have grown very adept at maintaining multiple communities. We have our family, our work colleagues, but also friends sharing a hobby, like buddies with whom to go watch football, or play golf, or bowling or play poker or bridge or whatever. We will very likely assign different communities amidst our work colleagues, especially if working for a larger organisation. Before the cellphone, we did not have a strong selection of options to differentiate between our communities. Now we can even program our phone to ring in different ways depending on, which person calls, etc.

From *Homo Sapiens* to *Homo Connectus*

Members of Gen-C are remarkably different from older generations in how they approach digital networks of any kind, and in particular in how they use their cellphones. If you find this chapter difficult to accept, I suggest you ask that you pose these issues to any "elderly teenager" friend, say between the ages of 14 - 18 years of age, and ask if these kinds of behavior are familiar and common. You may be surprised to find that most teenagers in that age group will immediately identify all of the behavior examples in this chapter, and find them very natural to themselves and their peers. I repeatedly tell adults not to project their own behavior and values to Generation-C. We are mature. They are not. However, they are young. Moreover, they are connected. Generation-C connects at almost a telepathic level, immediately and always. Long into the night, via SMS text messages sent and received in bed.

They come into the world with the enormous power of having their community in their pocket at all times. As the idea of equipping police cars with radios early last century, Gen-C has discovered mob power and gang connectedness. Returning to the opening quotation from Star Trek and the hive mentality of the Borg collective, Peter Miles, the CEO of UK university TV broadcasting company SubTV likes to say, *"The youth? With their constant SMS text messaging, they* **are** *the Borg."*

Case Study 6 from the UK
SeeMeTV

One of the most famous innovators of TV, video and social networking on cellphones is the *SeeMeTV* service that was launched by the various 3G networks of Three/Hutchison Group in the UK, Italy, Austria, Australia, Hong Kong etc. Similar to YouTube and other video sharing services, the users *SeeMeTV* also upload videos, but in this case only from 3G cameraphones, to the service visible to other subscribers of the Three/Hutchison network.

SeeMeTV was developed by YoSpace (now part of Emap). The big innovation of *SeeMeTV* was rewarding the original creator of the video with a revenue-share every time someone viewed the video. The original creator gets a penny every time the video is viewed. A hundred viewings, you earn a dollar. A thousand people watch your video, you earned 10 dollars, ten thousand viewings and you made 100 dollars, and so forth. The people who have created the most popular content have earned literally thousands of dollars.

I should first point out that while *SeeMeTV* gets much of the attention, the first such service was actually launched by M1 (MobileOne) in Singapore as *MeTV*, so the true innovation credit needs to go to Singapore. I do not have *MeTV* user stats but the SeeMeTV numbers are often quoted in the press in the UK, so I will examine the economics of *SeeMeTV* in this Case Study. Other similar services have launched, for example In the UK, by O2, which it branded as the *LookAtMe* service.

The latest annual numbers from the UK, reported by Three UK in September 2007, revealed that *SeeMeTV* in the UK had generated 14.2 million video downloads at 50 pence (1 US dollar) per download, or 7.1 million UK Pounds (14.2 million US dollars) in video revenues. Another 6 million games had been downloaded via *SeeMeTV* and further user-generated content such as songs and pictures are also available on *SeeMeTV*.

Keeping in mind that Three UK has only about 4 million subscribers, this works out to 0.3 video downloads on average per month across the whole user base and 30 US cents of video income per month per subscriber. If this rate were to hold for the USA, the innovation has an equivalent annual revenue potential of about 810 million dollars in the USA alone.

The more relevant point is the rewards going to the original video creators. Three UK has paid out 142,000 UK Pounds (284,000 US dollars) to its members who have created those videos, as a revenue sharing "royalty" for their videos. There is no limit to how much a content creator can earn. From the first six months on the service, some of the top viewed clips included Pretzel Girl, a wedding proposal, some tornado footage, and a hot dog eating boy.

The most popular video, no surprise, was more of an adult content nature, a woman flashed her breasts in her video and that was downloaded 130,000 times. She earned 1,300 UK Pounds (2,600 dollars) in income from her video. Some anecdotal evidence among the analysts of *SeeMeTV* suggest that as much as half of the popular content is of an adult-oriented nature.

A posting at Forum Oxford in February 2008 reported that the average *SeeMeTV* video generated income of £13.33 (US$26.66) for its producer. One need not create a hit video clip to make it worthwhile; even uploading just two *average* videos would generate enough income to the original creator, to pay more than the average UK monthly bill for cellphone usage.

"SMS is a good excuse to be rude in communications."
Rory Sutherland, Executive Creative Director, OgilvyOne

VIII
SMS Text Messaging
The most counter-intuitive service of them all

Almost everyone who ever was first shown SMS text messaging reacted in the same way - its too slow, too difficult, to awkward. I think it is not for me, after all, I can make a phone call in half the time it takes to type out a short message. Why on earth would anyone in their right mind want to send a text message?

SMS is the most counterintuitive service ever to gain global success. Everything about text messaging is wrong-way-round and it has the limit of 160 characters.

(Note the above paragraph of two sentences is exactly 160 characters in length). Since we already have email with no set limit of message length, how could SMS text messaging take off at all? It is very time-consuming and cumbersome to type out messages on most cellphones to triple-tap keys to get the letters. Why not use a Blackberry or other device with a full keyboard and send a "real" email? Certainly the most damning fault has to be that each SMS text message costs. Typically, the average SMS costs about 10 cents per message in the Western world in 2007. Nevertheless, on the web the transmission of each email and IM (Instant Messaging) message is free.

Why on earth would anyone bother to even learn to send SMS text messages as the per-message costs are considerable. In addition, yes, if we do have our messaging target names stored on our phones, then why not simply hit the call button, and call the person directly?

A   SMS IS NOT FOR ME

For almost all people who are not regular users of SMS, the automatic immediate response is that they prefer to talk with people anyway, rather than attempt to write these short messages.

So let me start with the numbers. SMS text messaging is the most used data application on the planet. At the end of 2007, already 74% of all cellphone subscribers were active users of SMS text messaging according to CMG Logica in 2007. That is 2.5 billion people. This compares with 1.3 billion total users of the internet (source ITU 2008) and about 1.2 billion email users in 2007 (source Radicati 2007). In several countries the owners of cellphones have shifted their preference that their primary use of the cellphone is no longer voice calls, but SMS text messaging! Blyk in the UK, is the first telecoms carrier/operator to say publicly that the primary use of the cellphone by their customers is to send messages, and not to place calls. A shift is happening.

The worldwide average of SMS text messages sent per mobile phone subscriber is 2.6 per day (source Informa 2007). When measured against active users of SMS, they average 4 text messages sent per day. The British cellphone users average 6 SMS sent per day, South Koreans 10 per day, the users in Singapore 12 and in the Philippines 15 per day per in 2007. Even the Americans are now learning to send SMS, with two thirds of American cellphone owners already active users of SMS in 2007 and sending on average about 2 SMS per day across the whole cellphone subscriber base in the USA, according to measurements by Gartner in 2007.

US cellphone users sent 1 SMS message per day in 2007
Source: CTIA 2007

Growth

The growth of SMS text messaging is breathtaking. The first SMS short message was sent in 1991 but this was a network message sent by computer. The first person-to-person SMS text message was sent in Finland in December 1993. Just four years later in 1997, the world passed the 1 billion SMS level per year. By 1999 more than 10 billion texts were sent globally. In 2001 the world passed the 100 billion message level. By 2005 the number crossed 1 trillion messages or 1,000 billion annually. By December 2007, nine billion text messages were sent globally every day. On an annual level, that is 3.28 Trillion text messages. Or another way, 104,000 SMS text messages are sent every second somewhere in the world.

What is more, most SMS users in the industrialized world have access to email, yet they choose to send short messages from their cellphones. There is a clear measured preference of SMS over email, including email on a cellphone (such as using a Blackberry). In South Korea, the saying is that SMS is for communication with people of your own age or younger; only if you have to

---

communicate with someone *older* than yourself, you might use email.

Meanwhile about the money. SMS text messaging averages about 4 cents per message worldwide according to Informa in 2007, and total messaging traffic in 2007 generated about 100 billion dollars in total revenues according TomiAhonen Consulting. For contrast, email and IM generate under 5 billion dollars globally. We are looking at a giant industry. As large as Hollywood box office revenues, videogaming and global music revenues, combined.

Heavy texters

I discussed the youth preoccupation with SMS in the youth chapter. If you think SMS is limited to kids, consider this. Business executives in Britain on average receive 40 work-related text messages every day according to the MDA, the Mobile Data Association. Early findings in the UK revealed that the youth prefer texting to calling. Then the amazing finding was that UK *business executives* preferred SMS text messages to voice calls.

By 2006, the BBC reported that the *total* UK population had reached the point where the majority of the whole British public prefers texting to calls. This pattern repeats across country after country. For example the Irish regulator

---

Philippine users sent 15 SMS message per day in 2007
Sources: Operator data 2007

---

reported this trend in 2007. Moreover, by May 2007 the annual JD Power survey of cellphone users in the UK, had noticed the first-ever drop in voice minutes, with the corresponding rise in SMS text messages. Not only does the UK population prefer texting to calls, they also are "voting with their dollars" or moving their communication traffic from voice to text. How is this possible?

B   SMS IS ADDICTIVE

Let me start with an analogy, consider the fax today. Imagine if your company hired a new boss for you, who announced he does not believe in communicating by email, he only uses fax. You would be dumbfounded. What kind of luddite had walked into your company who does not use email.

Now hold that thought. Young people all around the world feel that way about texting and email. They think SMS texting is the natural modern way of communicating, and they prefer not to use the old-fashioned form of email. Throughout Europe and Asia, business executives, housewives, and yes, even retired people are increasingly thinking that way as well. They all are falling in love with SMS text messaging - and ditching email in favor of SMS.

Proven to be addictive

The preference of SMS was first spotted in the market where the youth first got cellphones, Finland. However, it did not remain a secret for long. Trevor Merridien reported on youth SMS behavior in his book, *The Nokia Way* in 2001:

> *As one beleaguered Finnish parent says of mobile phone-wielding youngsters: These youngsters may have a cool phone but they don't use them all the time to make calls. Half of younger users' mobile phone bills are accounted for by sending text messages rather than actually speaking.*
> Trevor Merriden, *The Nokia Way*, 2001

I already showed in the Youth chapter that SMS has been proven to be addictive in several studies around the world. So addictive that the Queensland University of Australia study in 2005 found that SMS text messaging was as addictive as smoking cigarettes.

Who does it

In leading countries, 88% of the total population sends SMS text messages. That means practically everyone who has a cellphone and who knows how to read and write. Already at the end of 2007, over half of American cellphone users were active in sending text messages according to the CTIA. A major driver of American familiarity with SMS text messaging has been the *American Idol* TV show, which has typically had 30% of its voters sending their first-ever SMS text message when voting for an Idol.

So let us examine this phenomenon in much more detail. What makes SMS text messaging so addictive?

C   SMS IS FASTEST COMMUNICATION EVER

So let me start with its speed. The speed of communication throughput in SMS text messaging is faster by several orders of magnitude compared to any other form of electronic communication, including email, IM Instant Messaging, voicemail and yes, faster than voice calls (?). Surely this cannot be? But I will prove it to you, read on.

Here every ounce of conventional wisdom screams against this premise. It is tediously slow to tap a message on an SMS keypad. The other party has to

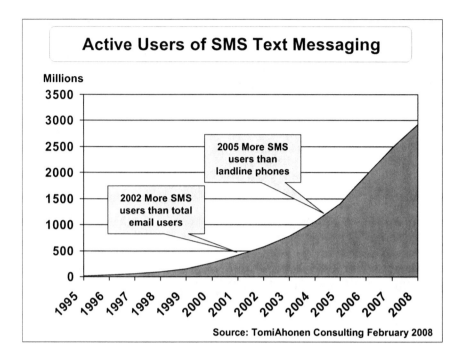

receive the SMS, open it, and read it. Of course, if I hit the speed dial button on my cellphone, and call the other person on his/her cellphone, I can deliver my matter verbally, "My plane was delayed, I'll arrive at ten o'clock" and so much faster.

Yes, under optimal and only under *exceptional conditions* a voice call can be *slightly faster* than sending an SMS text message. Only slightly faster, and only under rare circumstances. However, even under the most optimal conditions, a voice call is faster only by a factor of some seconds, never faster than one minute. Notice that I said "under most optimal conditions".

Excuse me, I need to make a call

Let us measure from the moment you want to initiate the communication. First of all, sometimes the caller is unable to initiate a call at that specific location. It may be inappropriate to call, such as being in a meeting and thus needing to step out to make the call. Or it may be too noisy at that specific location such as a noisy nightclub or disco and the caller needs to step into the lobby. Or it may be too quiet, such as a theater play and the caller needs to move outside to start the call without disturbing the others.

It is possible to start the phone call at the moment the impulse hits, but often the caller will need to move to a suitable location just to initiate the call. In these cases, we have to add half a minute or so to the "start time" before we can even make the call. Nevertheless, in all of these instances, there is nothing to prevent the person from sending the text message on the spot, giving a head-start to the person sending the text message. As long as the phone is in silent mode, you can safely send a text message from the theater, or the board meeting, or the noisy rock concert.

In the worst case, you are sitting in the opera and cannot excuse yourself for the next hour before you can even initiate a call. With this kind of delay, it will easily cost you all time saved in the optimal speed of the call.

Daddy is not home, could you call his cellphone

That is only at the call-*originating* end. How about the call recipient? Which number to call? If we call the home or office landline number, there is a good chance we do not reach our party. If we call the cellphone, some people keep them turned off, or if the person has two cellphones, which number to call? We can easily waste an extra call just to hunt the person we are calling. All the time

---

1.2 billion users of email in 2007
Sources: Radicati 2007

---

we wait for the target to pick up the phone, is time wasted, a delay, which SMS texting never has. The message would have already gotten through. Obviously, this is not every time, but whenever it happens that costs us more time.

Please hold

Does the party answer the phone? We all know more than half of all calls nowadays go to voicemail. If we call the office number, we may reach the secretary and are put on hold or if we call the home, we can reach a family member and again we have to wait. The other person can be on another call. The other person can be unable to answer the call. Maybe we call and on caller ID, the target sees it is us calling, and decides not to talk to us right now. So we rarely get to deliver our urgent message immediately if we do try to call.

I'm on the other line

So we finally have our intended target answering the call, personally. Even then it is not *in our control* to deliver our urgent matter to the party. He/she may be on

---

another call, takes our call, and puts us on hold or asks us to wait while he/she finishes the other call. This may take many minutes for us to wait. The SMS would have been delivered long ago. Or even worse, our counterpart may say he/she cannot talk right now, and asks to call us back, or asks us to call back. Now we are already many many minutes slower than if we had sent an SMS text message to begin with.

I'm sorry we got disconnected

And if our party does agree to talk with us now, there are the pleasantries, such as "how are you" and "how's your wife" etc. Some people can carry on five minutes of this even when there is an urgent message to deliver.

And still, as we have the other party on the line, we may find that the line is bad, an increasing problem with Skype and other VoIP services connecting to cellphones. Or perhaps the other person's cellphone battery is low and asks us to call another number (or at another time). In addition, then, when finally our party agrees to talk with us, we may now find ourselves disconnected in the middle of the call - probably both are on cellphones, and one might be in a

---

2.5 billion (74% of cellphone) users of SMS in 2007
Source: CMG Logica 2007

---

car step into an elevator or for whatever reason suddenly the call is disconnected due to bad network coverage. Start from the beginning.

Please leave me voicemail

But the speed advantage of SMS just keeps on growing with the remaining half of our call attempts. What if the call is not taken by our counterpart, and we are redirected to voicemail.

Now we are seriously slower than an SMS text message. While we may think that once we have left our voicemail, the matter is "out of our hands", and the message "is delivered", in reality that message has only been deposited, not retrieved. Now for us to measure the efficiency of a voice call into voicemail, we do have to measure it until the time our counterpart does listen to our message.

Voicemail is not the fastest way to reach our intended party. By now, SMS is much faster easily by a factor of hours. If our intended party is in a meeting (or if younger, in class) the delay can be an hour until the person can take calls and listen to voice mail. Note that many people will not even listen to voice mail at the first opportunity, but might schedule to listen to a series of voicemails at the time they drive home in their car for example, or another such time in their schedule, easily many hours from the time we left the voicemail.

I didn't hear the phone

If the person is asleep or for some reason has the phone turned off, the delay can be half a day or more. The person might have had the phone on silent mode from attending a meeting, and forgot to turn it back to ringing mode, and while we called the person several times, the target person never even knew that an urgent call was coming and now has several voicemail messages.

It sometimes happens that after changing a ringing tone, the person does not recognize the ringing of his or her own phone (yes, this happens to everybody). In every case where the person was not taking our call, the SMS would get through, perfectly clear as typed. Moreover, usually delivered within some seconds of you sending it, but always delivered faster than retrieving a voicemail, or returning a missed call.

My plane was delayed

If the person is on an airplane or otherwise outside cellphone radio coverage, the delay can be days until the person has the chance to listen to voice mail and know we've called. When traveling abroad many times the phone number is not transmitted by foreign networks, therefore the receiving person does not know it was us calling until listening to voice mail.

And if we left the kind of message that *"please call me I have an urgent message"* or if we had to call back, or we waited for the other person to call us back, the whole communication process reverts all the way back to square one. Start again. We're playing ping-pong with voicemail messages. The industry calls it voicemail tag.

SMS is always delivered first

SMS reaches you every time. The SMS is read before voice mail is listened to. SMS even reaches our intended target while the person is talking on the phone and there are many younger adults who actually retrieve SMS messages while talking to someone else, and tap out a quick reply on SMS while continuing on the voice call (depending on the model of the phone obviously).

Sound absurd? Bear in mind the youth survey in 2006, which revealed that 48% of British teenagers send text messages to someone while talking to someone else, either person-to-person, or talking on a phone. So yes, it is totally commonplace to speak to someone and also engage in text messaging. Again, this is not exclusive to Britain. A Disney survey of 1,500 American teens in 2007 found that 28% send text messages from the dinner table.

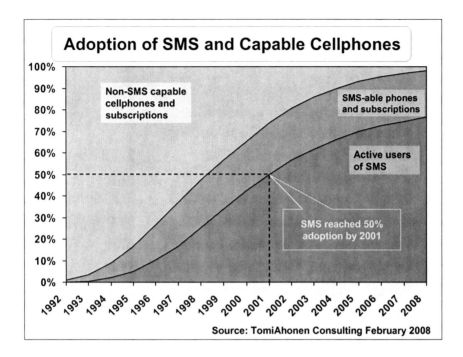

Adoption of SMS and Capable Cellphones

Non-SMS capable cellphones and subscriptions

SMS-able phones and subscriptions

Active users of SMS

SMS reached 50% adoption by 2001

Source: TomiAhonen Consulting February 2008

Reply is also fastest

All of the speed benefits *more than double* if the recipient is also fluent at SMS texting. The other person can reply via SMS while not being able to talk. If your intended person had the phone turned off, or was beyond coverage, the minute it is turned on, the SMS arrives. The recipient does not have to retrieve SMS messages and does not need to log onto any server, etc. Thus SMS is often hours, and can be days faster than a call to the cellular phone. That is why SMS is the preferred way to announce any last-minute changes of plans. A 2005 study by the Mohile Data Association showed that the most common use of SMS messages at work relates to meetings and schedules.

D   SMS IS MOST PRIVATE

While the speed part is the one that adults usually discover first, the private aspect of SMS is always discovered first by the younger users. It is like sending secret notes in class, and this kind of clandestine communications is very appealing to teenagers. There are many instances when we cannot or do not want to talk on the phone. At those times often we can communicate via SMS.

SMS Text Messaging Snapshot 2007

Total subscribers worldwide that can be reached by SMS (have an SMS-compatible cellphone & subscription)	3.2 Billion
Total active user base of SMS text messaging at end of 2007	2.5 Billion
Total SMS text messages sent in 2007	2.9 Trillion
SMS sent every *second* in Dec 2007	91,900
Average SMS sent per active user daily	3.6
Annual revenues of SMS globally 2007	$107 B
Average cost of one SMS worldwide	$0.037

**Sources: CMG Logica, Informa, MDA, Textually,
160 Characters, TomiAhonen Consulting 2007-2008**

For the rest of us this "secret notes" ability of SMS is often discovered quite by accident. It may start as receiving SMS messages while in a meeting or in a noisy stadium. Soon we notice that sending an SMS message is a convenient way to send short notices while we do not want to talk for example when in a train or bus, etc. or sharing a taxi with a colleague from a competitor and needing to send an urgent update to our boss, etc.

Secret notes

Even older people can often unobtrusively send a discreet message in a meeting while holding the phone below the table level, although few get away with it without anybody else noticing. In addition, yet another variation is sending SMS messages from the bathroom. You excuse yourself, go to the bathroom, and then send a few urgent messages. The convenience here is also that if someone else is sitting in the adjacent toilet stall, they cannot eavesdrop on your call. These kinds of bathroom break texting sessions are commonplace now with younger people on first dates, to give an update to friends, seeking advice etc.

SMS can be used where talking would be embarrassing. In open office cubicle environments, gossiping can be difficult by talking directly or on the phone, but sending SMS messages is the newest way to vent off some steam at

---

Tomi T Ahonen

the office. The CEO of UK university broadcaster SubTV, Peter Miles, says that its commonplace for British youth to send messages while in the same location. The example Peter uses is of two boys at a party. One is attracted to a girl. He doesn't dare to talk about this to his friend, who is standing right next to him, but sends a text message of the secret confession. Moreover, the friend will offer his support and advice - also via SMS text messaging, all while both stand side-by-side and engage other friends in regular discussion.

Peter Miles says that SMS text messaging to teenagers enables a kind of community "hive" mentality, almost telepathically connecting at all times. It allows friends to support each other.

SMS is also excellent for respecting the privacy of other people. It may be too late to call in the evening, but a text message can still be sent. Some send them late in the evening asking is it too late to call. The message respects private time, so on the weekend a considerate boss will not call, but rather sends an SMS asking the subordinate to call when it is next convenient. Texts can also be sent if the other person is in an unknown or inconvenient time zone, very useful for the frequent fliers.

World record for TV audience voting by SMS

Now consider this into the future. Some day most TV shows will engage with

Asian Cellphone Usage Levels

TNS surveyed 16,000 cellphone users in 29 Asia-Pacific countries and found the following usage levels of cellphone features and services:

SMS text messaging used by	88%
Cellphone games played by	71%
Camera used by	61%
(note only 62% of Asians had cameraphones at time of survey)	
Picture messaging (MMS) used by	48%
Music player on cellphone used by	43%
Internet accessed by	34%
Mobile Instant Messaging used by	11%

Source: TNS Asia-Pacific survey 2007

their audiences using cellphones (I will discuss this more in the mobile-TV chapter). Then consider this. A TV show in Norway recently set the world record for active audience participation. For a broadcast TV show, 54% of their total audience had actually participated in the TV show, using SMS text messaging of course. What was that? Must be a youth-oriented music video show?

Well, actually, it was indeed a music related show, but not for the youth. The TV show was *Danseband Jukebox*, a Norwegian TV staple, where a full brass band plays tangos and waltzes and other ballroom dance music to older viewers. The average age of the viewers of Danseband Jukebox is over 65. The TV show has no regular viewers under the age of 55. Yet this show achieved a 54% participation rate, all using SMS text messaging. If Norwegian retired folks can master sending SMS text messages to a TV show, then yes, so too can the average American consumer learn to send SMS text messages.

E   NOT DUMB LITTLE BROTHER OF E-MAIL

SMS is not like the dumb "simple" cousin of email. Comparing the two formats

---

58% of US cellphone users sent SMS text messages in 2007
Source: Pew Internet & American Life Project 2007

---

of messaging is more like comparing a bus and a private car. Email, like the bus, works on a schedule (we are not always at our email). As a bus with its regular route and bus stops, with email we have to go to a known location (like a WiFi hotspot) to access our email. As a bus on its bus stop route, email also will not take us everywhere (many people do not have email accounts).

SMS like a private car is more expensive yes, but SMS like our car is always available to us, and will deliver our messages to everyone, including those who do not have email. Do remember that every economically viable person on the planet carries a cellphone and all of those can receive SMS. In addition, like traveling in a bus where we share the resource, email is done often with others peering in, our secretary, our colleague in the cubicle next door, or our kids, family at home. Moreover, like (much of the) the private transportation in our car, SMS is always done alone, nobody else able to spy on our writing.

SMS is more private than email

SMS text messaging is also more private than email. Often the PC may be shared at home, and personal email is only semi-personal as any family member might walk in while a sensitive email is on the screen. The situation is even worse at the office, where colleagues might see what is on the screen. Various intrusions into email privacy may occur from the official as some companies in some countries have rules that all email may be read; to the unofficial where some managers or IT staff may read an employee's email without knowing that it is against company policy; to the malicious where an ill-minded colleague might break a password or in some other way gain access to your email.

SMS text messages are stored on your phone, which you carry with you. The screen is much too small for others to be able to read messages unless you show them. SMS is much less prone to hacking. Recalling the **Wired** survey, six out of ten married adults will not share their phone even with their spouse.

SMS wins on anything urgent

If given access to both methods of electronic text-based communication, all who are familiar with both, prefer SMS text messaging to most communication situations. *"I am running late because I am in traffic"* or *"Will you pick up the kids today"* or *"Do we need to pick up anything from the store"* etc type of

---

99.5% Of South Koreans sent SMS text messages in 2007
Source: National Internet Development Agency of Korea 2007

---

communication is all of the kind we need every day. These work perfectly in SMS text messaging. We do not need email to do any of those.

And finally to explore the efficiency of SMS and email, consider the reception. We hope an email to be read within 24 hours and expect it to be read within 48 hours. However, active users of SMS text messaging now expect a response within 5 minutes, according to a survey by 160 Characters in May of 2007. Five minutes vs. 24 hours, this is no contest.

And the Crackberry?

I have had many colleagues ask about the Blackberry. Will it be the future of messaging. The Blackberry is a wonderful solution for email, combining that old method of communication with cellular networks and full mobility, on a wonderful handheld device. However, consider the *lack of success* of this innovation. Blackberry was launched by RIM in 2001. Six years later, by the Summer of 2007 that number of Blackberry users was 8 million worldwide. It is easy to fall into the trap of believing in the Blackberry if you live in North America. Of Blackberry's total user base, 75% are based in North America. To put it another way, out of 220 million cellphone users in the USA at the time, Blackberry owners accounted for 2.7%. In the rest of the industrialized world, the 2 million Blackberries account for only one quarter of one percent of cellphone subscribers. Yes, six years after its launch, the Blackberry is hardly a global success story.

The Blackberry is the crutch for the digital immigrant. It gives similar benefits out of wireless email through the cellular network as existin in using SMS text messaging. Blackberrires appeal to older executives in laggard markets like the USA and Canada. Any younger users or executives in the five other continents will prefer SMS text messaging instead, rather than limiting the communication to the limited user base of email, with its delays. For the digital native, especially Generation C, SMS text messaging is the natural form of communication for the future. Yes, Blackberries are wonderful wireless emailing devices, but their total market potential is very limited. Even many Blackberry users rapidly shift the majority of their business messaging communication to SMS text messaging, using the Blackberry for that. Anecdotal evidence from Europe and Asia suggest that the growth market for the Blackberry is indeed not corporate/enterprise users, but young adults who want a high speed *SMS text messaging* phone, not email.

F   SMS IS NOT THE ONLY WAY

SMS is not about replacing phone calls and not about replacing email. They are not competitors but complements. SMS often triggers voice calls, and many busy executives have learned to use SMS alerts to draw attention to important emails in someone's inbox and the youth uses SMS to trigger IM sessions or to invite pals to join a multiplayer online game on the web.

Don't get me wrong. Yes, email itself will migrate to more wireless devices. To laptops. To Blackberries. To smartphones. To the iPhone. Moreover, other emerging devices like web tablets. Nevertheless, wireless email will not grow to dominate over SMS text messaging. No, it will be the other way round. SMS is the messaging method of choice for Generation-C. It is the inevitable winner in the messaging wars.

Not only young people. 80% of British business executives use SMS messaging daily, according to a 2004 study by the UK Mobile Data Association. After face-to-face meetings, SMS communication already comes second in preference of all forms of communication, ahead of phone calls and ahead of email, according to another study of British executives by the MDA.

Premium SMS

A specific part I have not discussed in this chapter is Premium SMS. We have

---

Tomi T Ahonen

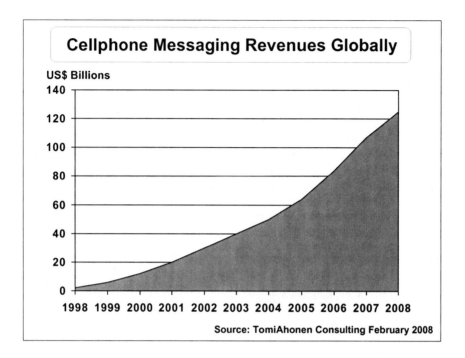

Cellphone Messaging Revenues Globally

US$ Billions

Source: TomiAhonen Consulting February 2008

lots of opportunities to use the SMS messaging method to deliver content (such as downloading basic ringing tones to cellphones) or allowing voting on TV shows like American Idol, or collecting payments of virtual goods such as internet content sold on Habbo Hotel and Flirtomatic and paid by premium SMS, or selling real goods and collecting money via mobile such as Coca Cola vending machines powered by SMS. I will discuss these kinds of premium SMS services in the following chapters on mobile TV, mobile internet and disruption.

Picture Messages i.e. MMS

Another messaging type is MMS, MultiMedia System messaging, which is commonly called picture messaging. Originally, many mobile telecoms forecasters, including myself, thought that the exhilarating adoption rates and growth rates of SMS text messaging would next come to MMS picture messaging. MMS usage pattern did not follow that of SMS, mostly because of the several unique use cases for SMS, such as the urgent update messages (I am 10 minutes delayed) and the secret short messages like a secret note in class or in a meeting. These kinds of messaging uses will not naturally migrate to picture messaging. Picture messaging is best suited for sharing an emotion or moment, and on most networks years after its launch, MMS accounts for far less than 10%

of the total messaging traffic.

Mobile Instant Messaging

Another rival is IM Instant Messaging or cellphones, often called Mobile Instant Messaging or MIM. As the youth have a strong preference of instant messaging and chat applications in their web use, this is likely to follow them to their cellphone messaging as well. A key element will be the relative price differentials between cellphone based SMS text messaging, and the costs of messages on any mobile IM services. Early user-data from leading markets suggests that mobile IM can be a very potent rival to SMS. For example Austrian carrier/operator Drei (Three), part of the Hong Kong based Three/Hutchison group of 3G wireless carriers/mobile operators, reported in 2007 on usage levels of SMS and mobile Instant Messaging, by, which MIM had 40% of their total messaging traffic. Recognize this is still triple-tapping messages on the cellphone keypad and reading them on the small screen. Messaging is going mobile, whether through SMS or IM (and not via cellphone email).

You can join the SMS revolution too

So can you do it? Yes, if the average man and woman in countries as diverse as Italy, Britain, Sweden, Korea, Japan, Singapore are all convinced this is the way to handle the most important communications - their actual love life and partnerships, the urgent messages with meetings, the secret communications whether attempting to cheat in class or carry on a clandestine relationship, etc., then is it not time for you to take the plunge. Get into texting. It is inevitable. If you have teenage kids you probably are starting to do it already. Remember my example of the "luddite" fax user in the beginning of this chapter. You would not want to like that person to younger generations. Or even if you did, do not you think you should also master the communication technology, which is both the fastest on Earth, and also the most discrete.

It is not difficult. It takes some learning. After a short time, you start to become comfortable with the keypad. There are only twelve keys, so actually "learning" a cellphone keypad is a lot faster than learning to type on a PC keyboard. In addition, as experience grows, you abandon the predictive text feature. All heavy users of SMS do it without predictive text.

I hope this chapter has helped explain SMS text messaging, what is truly the most counter-intuitive service of them all. However, also, perhaps you can now see opportunities in this space. As Charles F Kettering said, *"A problem well stated, is a problem half-solved."*

Case Study 7 from Finland
Finnair Mobile Check-in

As Finland was rapidly launching numerous SMS based service innovations in the early part of the decade, the Finnish flag carrier airline, Finnair decided to try mobile check-in as an SMS based service in 2001.

Imagine your next travel by airplane. Imagine that you are delayed, to no fault of your own, say there was an accident on the freeway to the airport. You still have some time before your flight is scheduled to depart. You rush to the check-in counter and observe a terribly long line (apparently its a busy weekend or perhaps the airline is short-staffed this morning or whatever). You can tell the line is more than 30 minutes long to your check-in counter, and you are afraid you'll miss your flight. But in your panic you then notice the sign that says you can do your check-in also via cellphone.

Wow, magic. Dial this number, enter your reservation code, select your seat, click enter, and you are done. Didn't have to stand in line for 30 minutes and risk missing your plane. So simple, yet so powerful. There is no need to stand in line (you can do the mobile check-in from the taxicab on the way to the airport, in fact) and no need for the airline to install any self-service kiosks for check-in. The phone in everyone's pocket can do the full job just as well as the automated check-in kiosk at the airport.

Traditional check-in counter space at airports is very expensive. Imogen Edwards-Jones wrote in the book *Air Babylon* that one check-in desk at London's Heathrow costs an airline 50,000 UK Pounds (100,000 dollars) per year. For an airline industry working on miniscule margins - the IATA reports that the industry made under 2% profit in 2006 - any extra check-in counter needs are considerable added costs. Furthermore, while an airline may want to try to sell last-minute seats to a departing airplane that is not sold to its full capacity, the airline cannot afford to keep its plane grounded to allow late passengers to join. At Heathrow it costs 1,000 UK

Pounds (2,000 US Dollars) for every minute the aircraft is delayed from its scheduled departure.time.

Hiring more staff for the check-in counter is not an option. Even renting space for automated check-in kiosks is an added expense and then requires maintenance. The aircraft cannot be delayed to allow more seats to be sold. So the only viable option is to allow passengers to self-service the full ticketing value system, from buying the ticket on their cellphones, to the check-in to the boarding pass. No printing, no waste. As fast as technologically possible. The future of air travel will also involve our cellphones.

Indicidentally cellphone based check-in is spreading and used by airlines from Lufthansa in Germany to Air Asia in Singapore to Norwegian in Norway to JAL in Japan. The IATA airline industry association reports that in 2007 already 2% of all airline check-in is already handled via cellphones. Meanwhile, how is mobile check-in doing with the pioneer of the service? On Finnair's busiest routes as much as 20% of the travelers use the service.

"The early bird gets the worm, but the
second mouse gets the cheese."
Steven Wright

IX
Music onto Phones
The iPod beater

A lot of the IT industry and global business press have been excited about the success of the Apple iPod and its iTunes music service. The iPod was launched in 2001 and by 2006, as the Apple iPod celebrated five years of continuous growth reaching ever more dizzying levels of sales, the Apple iTunes music store broke the billion dollar annual music sales level. Today more than 100 million iPods have been sold worldwide. Nevertheless, suddenly by mid 2006 all major record labels said strange things about digital music. Warner Music said that music would migrate to cellphones. Universal Music said music would migrate to cellphones. EMI said music would migrate to cellphones. Moreover, yes, also the fourth of the big four music labels, Sony Bertelsmann said music would migrate to cellphones.

Not to the iPod? Not to iTunes? All of a sudden, between 2005 and 2006 the whole recording industry changed its tune that the cellphone was their future. This while iPods and iTunes were breaking sales records quarter after quarter. How did this happen?

A   STARTED WITH HUMBLE RINGING TONE

A bit of background numbers on the overall business we are looking at. In 2007 the total revenues earned by all kinds of music on cellphones was worth 9.3 billion dollars according to the *Netsize Guide 2008*. For contrast, the global music industry revenues are worth under 30 billion dollars according to the IFPI. So cellphone-based music has already cannibalized 31% of the total global music industry. The vast majority of cellphone music is of course ringing tones, but included in the total are real tunes, ringback tones (i.e. waiting tones) and a staggering one billion dollars worth of full-length MP3 songs sold directly to cellphones arnoud the world. Yes, where iPods had existed for five years, and musicphones only three, already by end of 2006 more music was sold to musicphones than all of iTunes worldwide.

Most basic music: the Ringing Tone

The ringing tone business itself is ten years old. The very first downloadable ringing tone was introduced in the autumn of 1998 in Finland on the Radiolinja (now Elisa) network. Ringing tones kept on growing and dumbfounding the analysts. By 2001, ringtones had crossed the billion dollar mark globally. By the end of 2004, ringtones had passed 5 billion dollars in revenues globally.

So is it relevant? Ringtones were ignored by the traditional music industry until 2003 when rap artist 50 Cent made international news selling 500,000 copies of the ringing tone version of his hit song *"In Da Club"*. As this happened with an area of cutting edge music, rap, and the numbers were that enormous, suddenly all artists wanted their music also on ringing tones. In England the Top of the Pops charts started to track ringtone sales together with the sales of "singles" (nowadays these are CD singles, no longer vinyl records) to compile the charts. By 2004, British pop artists were earning more for the sales of their ringing tones, than what they earned from the sales of the singles. Artists today actually consider ringing tone sounds when writing new hit releases.

Crazy Frog

By the summer of 2005 a novelty ringtone hit, the Crazy Frog, actually scored ahead of the latest hit by British rock band Coldplay, and was ranked the top-selling song in England. Crazy Frog held onto its top spot for a few weeks in Britain. For context during 2005 the total global sales of iTunes was worth 440 million dollars. Crazy Frog alone sold 500 million dollars worth of its ringtone and variants during 2005 according to Jamba.

Can ringtones be real music? On one level, there have been philosophical arguments all through the ages about what is and what is not music. Was popular music by the Beatles and Beach Boys "real music" or only classical music was real music? How about rock music (*that is not music, it's just noise*). How about punk rock or rap music? There is no singing, no melody? So when new formats for music are invented, traditionalist - and usually older people - tend to try to dismiss the newer forms as not being "real" music, but over time the newer forms are accepted as had happened with pop music, rock music and rap.

If someone thinks that "no respectable" artist would do ringtones that is simply not true. The first symphony orchestra composed for ringing tones was composed by Jean Hasse and played by the Royal Academy of Music in Britain back in March 2002.

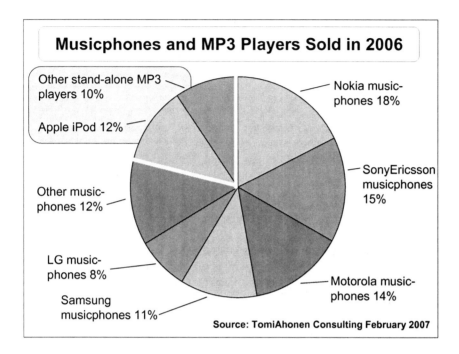

Musicphones and MP3 Players Sold in 2006

Other stand-alone MP3 players 10%

Apple iPod 12%

Nokia music-phones 18%

Other music-phones 12%

SonyEricsson musicphones 15%

LG music-phones 8%

Motorola music-phones 14%

Samsung musicphones 11%

Source: TomiAhonen Consulting February 2007

How about the fans? It is not uncommon for teenagers to get together to listen to the latest ringtone. Playing it several times, just to hear it. Can ringtones be music, of course they can. It is just a new way.

Not just the young

Many continue to think ringing tones are a silly concept only appealing to kids. However, music is a universal passion. All of us have some favorite music. While it may not be the latest rap tune, middle-aged people may reminisce fondly about music by Blondie or David Bowie or Queen or Abba. People at retiring age may prefer Elvis, the Beatles, early Rolling Stones, the Beach Boys or perhaps Frank Sinatra. Others will find their music tastes change, from pop music to jazz, classical music or show tunes for example. However, for nearly all of us there is some favorite music.

As older people notice they can have their particular music on their phones, they too become consumers of ringing tones. When the whole industry embraces the concept, from the carriers/telcos to the music industry, there is no reason the whole nation cannot enjoy ringing tones. Look at South Korea. The NIDA (National Internet Development Agency) of South Korea reports that ringing tones are used by 97% of South Korean cellphone owners. Yes, young people attracted to pop songs that are on the charts, will replace their ringing tones much more frequently than the older parts of the population, but there is no denying the appeal of music on the phone.

No longer cool

There is the trend that was observed in 2006 and 2007 in advanced markets of telecoms that the youth suddenly are abandoning the ringing tone market. It seems that they now think it is no longer cool. Perhaps they observed that their parents had ringing tones, and if it is something that the parents might do, it is no longer that special.

B   BEYOND BASIC RINGTONES

Beyond the basic ringing tone, there emerged polyphonic ringing tones (simple tunes still, but allowing several notes to be played simultaneously, think of a Casio keyboard). Beyond polyphonics came real tones (also known as truetones).

6.2% of American cellphone owners listen to music.
Source: M:Metrics December 2007

These are actual short sound file excerpts from real recordings. Now you hear the singer, the guitar, the drums, piano, horns etc. With basic ringing tones and polyphonic ringing tones, there is no royalty to be paid to the performer of the hit song, only to the composer of the song. However, once it becomes a real tone/truetone, the song's performer is clearly recognized in the song, and now royalties become due to the recording artist, in addition to the composer of the song.
     Polyphonic ringing tones ended up not being very big as a business, but real tones/truetones became very popular rapidly. The IFPI reported that over 1 billion dollars of music was sold to cellphones in 2006, which consisted mostly of full-track MP3 files and true real tones/truetones.

Waiting tones (Ringback tones)

An interesting twist on the ringing tone is the waiting tone (i.e. Ringback Tone). This extremely simple service concept was developed by WiderThan in South Korea and launched commercially in 2002. The first commercial service was called Color Ring, and the worldwide telecoms technical term - and

---

Tomi T Ahonen

unfortunately, often this confusing term is the commercial name for the service - called ringback tone. I prefer to call it the Waiting Tone, which makes more sense to the cellphone owner. The service does not ring on the "back" of the phone, nor does the service "call back" or ring back the missed calls, nor is it playing the song backwards, etc. Ringback tone is an unfortunate name for the service, where Waiting Tone makes easily a lot more sense.

Waiting Tones (Ringback Tones) are music that replaces the "brrr-brrr" network buzzing noises you hear when you wait for someone to answer their phone. Think of it as music-on-hold, *before* you are put on hold. Compare it with the ringing tone. I can use my ringing tone to play music to myself and to the people near me. Nevertheless, when you call me, I can use the Waiting Tone to play music for you, before I answer the phone (or my voicemail service kicks in).

Soon bigger than ringing tones

Exactly like with ringing tones, the subscriber purchases the song he wants, and also like ringing tones, the subscriber can change the songs as the music preferences change. However, separately from ringing tones the subscriber also

---

63.8% of Chinese cellphone owners listen to music.
Source: M:Metrics December 2007

---

pays a monthly fee, and very significantly as this is a core network signaling solution, there is no competition for service providers. The service is not dependent on the types or abilities of the handsets and much higher quality music can be delivered as waiting tones. So where on basic ringing tones you only hear the plink-plink type of basic sounds, and there cannot be guitars, drums, singing etc in basic ringing tones, on Waiting Tones you can hear the actual song as recorded by the artist. More like real tones/truetones and full-track MP3 music like on an iPod.

In just 8 months from launch, SK Telecom was earning more from waiting tones than from ringing tones. In a year, over a third of its subscriber base was using the service. Both of its domestic rivals, LG Telecom and KTF have launched waiting tones. In South Korea alone in 2003, the service delivered over 120 million dollars in service revenues. Then as the secret was out, Waiting Tones were rapidly launched in Taiwan, China, Israel, Singapore and Japan with Europe and America following later. The sales have kept growing, passing a billion dollars in worldwide revenues by 2006. Meanwhile WiderThan was bought up by Real Networks to boost their know-how in the mobile and converged music space. I will also show a case of how free music on the internet, can re-capture millions in revenues through waiting tones, in the *Mice Love Rice* example as the case study at the end of this chapter.

Ringing tone meets jukebox

Virtual worlds such as *Habbo Hotel, Second Life* and *Cyworld* are natural for the consumption of music. I mentioned *Cyworld* in the Case Study earlier and will also examine it some more in the Gaming chapter, but I want to mention the music side of *Cyworld* here.

Cyworld has been able to incorporate a lot of music features to its services. One of the innovations is the background song, which as the name suggests, is music to play on the background when a friend is visiting with you in your room. Just as you might turn on your HiFi set in your home, and put on a CD of your favorite music, similarly in the virtual world, you can play music to your friends. Except that on *Cyworld* each time you play a song, it causes a small charge to your account. This has turned into a bonanza for *Cyworld*. By 2005 background music for *Cyworld* was generating sales of 100,000 songs per day. At about 43 cents per song, the ambience nature of *Cyworld* produces music revenues of 18 million dollars annually, shared between *Cyworld* (i.e. SK Communications) and the rights holders in the recording industry. Now for example in India, background music is also offered for cellphones while you talk on the phone. Again, this may seem utterly idiotic - do not we have enough noise and disruption on our calls - but apparently, the early feedback from India is that the background songs are a big hit. Perhaps it is a cultural thing?

Returning to *Cyworld's* music. The latest variant of the music in *Cyworld* is yet another variant of the ringing tone concept, called the Welcoming Tune. The owner of a Miniroom in *Cyworld* can designate a given song to be played whenever someone enters the room. It may take a little while for the owner to come to the room to keep company to the visitor, so the welcoming song is a good sign you are a good host, are on your way, and give something nice to your guest just upon entry. Waiting Tunes are full-track MP3 files that are played once, and each time they are played, they generate a charge (43 cents per play). This is like the modern re-incarnation of the jukebox. Every time you play the song, a charge appears on your phone account. Another big hit inside *Cyworld* and provides a new way to enjoy music digitally.

C   MP3 FULL-TRACK DOWNLOADS

In June of 2003, as a trial, Sony Music recording artist Ricky Martin pre-released several tracks from his newest album as MP3 files sold directly to cellphone owners six days before the album was released. As only South Korea had the penetration of suitable cellphones at the time, this trial was limited to South

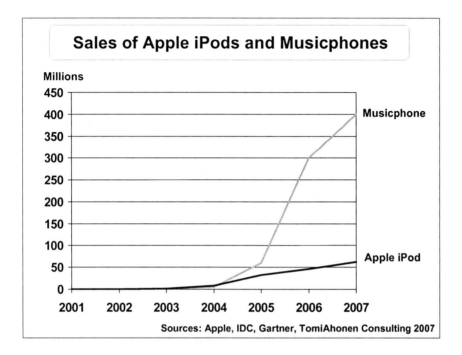

Sales of Apple iPods and Musicphones

Millions

Sources: Apple, IDC, Gartner, TomiAhonen Consulting 2007

Korea. In six days, Ricky Martin sold over 100,000 songs. Since then music consumption has grown explosively. Two years later, by September 2005, 45% of all South Korean cellphone owners downloaded full track MP3 songs to their cellphones, as reported by NIDA. For contrast, five years after launch in America, the total Apple iPod penetration was about 15% of the population, and users of iTunes downloads obviously less than the total installed base of iPod users, as the majority of iPod music was transferred from music CD collections rather than downloaded from iTunes music store (Apple does not provide the exact breakdown). Yet even in 2007, approximately 10% of all music sold in the USA was sold on the internet according to the IFPI.

Songs as MP3 files are reasonably priced in South Korea, nothing like the 2.50 US dollar prices on some networks. A single MP3 full-track download of a South Korean artist to a cellphone typically costs about 45 cents per song, and MP3 full-track downloads by Western artists cost about 80 cents to download directly to the phone.

Musicphones

South Korean phone manufacturers were among the leaders in developing musicphones. Samsung was first to release a cellphone with more capacity than the iPod Nano, at 5GB. Not to be outdone, its rival LG released its Chocolate music phone, which in Europe become the best-selling cellphone model of all time, according to Europe's largest phone retailer chain, Carphone Warehouse. During 2007, SonyEricsson reported that its Walkman branded phones were driving its phone sales; Motorola reported its latest musicphone variants of the Razr were its best-selling model. In early 2007, Nokia said it had sold more musicphones during the year 2006 than all Apple iPods ever made. The cellphone industry was slow to wake up to the musicphone, but once it became interested, they soon came to dominate the MP3 player market, just like they did against the PDA market and digital camera market earlier.

By early 2006, senior executives from each of the four giant music labels - Warner Music, EMI, Sony BMG and Universal Music had come out during 2005-2006 all echoing the same theme: the natural future home of music will be on cellphones with direct downloads of full track songs. Not stand-alone MP3 players like iPods nor online music stores like neither iTunes nor separate music CD sales whether in stores or online:

> Warner Music's Chairman and CEO, Edgar Bronfman, said, *"Wireless will become the most formidable music platform on the planet."*

> EMI Vice President of Digital Development Ted Cohen admitted that the cellphone will win out over stand-alone music players as he put it *"The cellphone will become the digital music player of choice."*

> The General Manager of Universal Music, Rio Caraeff says it like this, *"Music is inherently mobile and something you enjoy on the go."*

> While Sony BMG Senior Vice President of Digital Business, JJ Rosen says it like this, *"Everyone likes music, and everyone has a cellphone."*

In May 2007, Bill Gates said musicphones would kill the stand-alone MP3 player like the iPod, and even Apple's Steve Jobs finally admitted this was true, in January 2007 at Macworld as he launched the iPhone. Steve Jobs said that the future of MP3 players belonged to musicphones.

Apple's iPhone, not revolutionary in Korea

While the world was very amazed at Apple's unveiling of the iPhone in early 2007, a very similar, large screen, touch-screen phone of almost identical form factor, had already been revealed by South Korean manufacturer, LG, which won an industrial design award in 2006, before the iPhone was even announced. The commercial product, which this evolved into is known in the West as the LG Prada fashion phone.

Where the West Coast of America is waking up to fashionable cellphones and with Apple's considerable marketing presence and leadership, in South Korea this type of innovation is commonplace. The iPhone, at least by its superficial outwardly appearance, was not seen as revolutionary at all. A clever tweak of the concept, perhaps, and time will tell what the user interface and "multi-touch" screen and various sensors will do, but where the Western press was overwhelmed by the iPhone launch, the Asian reviews were quite underwhelmed. Perhaps that is why the iPhone will launch in the USA first, and in Europe before Asia. It is an advanced smartphone for a laggard market but a far more advanced 3G version is needed for the more advanced Asian market.

Convergence in MP3 services: Melon Music

Melon Music from South Korea is perhaps the most advanced music service in the world, being the first fully convergent music service. Melon features over-the-air music downloads; web-based downloads; real-time music listening (streaming); and the whole service is available on cellphones, personal computers and stand-alone MP3 players. There are buy-to-own models and rental models to music. Developed by WiderThan and being part of the biggest carrier in South Korea, SK Telecom, Melon Music also reaches most of the South Korean users. By 2006, already 21% of SK Telecom's total cellphone subscriber base had signed up to Melon Music.

D   MAKE YOUR OWN MUSIC

But wait. The phone is not only a consumption device like the iPod. As I have shown throughout this book, the cellphone is a multi-purpose multi-Channel device. An *interactive* media channel, the cellphone is the optimal tool for user-generated content, available at the point of inspiration. Its ability to expand music experiences extends far beyond what is possible on a stand-alone MP3 player like the iPod.

Want to compose a ringing tone? The first commercial application to allow normal consumers to create ringing tones that others could download, was launched in Finland by Radiolinja. When was this? Ten years ago, already in 1998. Longer than Apple has made iPods, user-generated music has existed for cellphones. That idea has now evolved into such innovations as mashing ringing tones to create your own, such as with the service called *Tonemine* in the USA.

Compose serious music? Some advanced musicphone models allow MIDI (Musical Instrument Digital Interface) connectivity - meaning professional musicians can use a phone to play synthesizer sounds, from the drums to guitar to piano to the violin, and you cannot tell the difference to any other professional MIDI synthesizer say from a Korg, Moog or Yamaha.

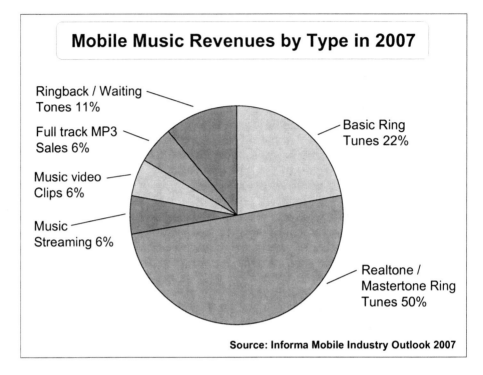

Mobile Music Revenues by Type in 2007

Ringback / Waiting Tones 11%

Full track MP3 Sales 6%

Music video Clips 6%

Music Streaming 6%

Basic Ring Tunes 22%

Realtone / Mastertone Ring Tunes 50%

Source: Informa Mobile Industry Outlook 2007

From sound of music to music video

Not only listening to music, but also watching it. Where MTV was previously limited to cable TV offerings, today music videos can be always with the listener through music video services on cellphones.

Again early numbers bear this out. In the UK, the 3G wireless carrier, Three of the Hong Kong based Hutchison group, has attracted about 4 million subscribers to its 3G in its first three years, out of the UK total cellphone population of 60 million. Three/Hutchison launched music video downloads to its 3G phones, which were priced at £1.50 (about US$3.00) and in its first year sold 15 million music videos.

If given the option of buying the digital song, or buying the same song and its video, most of the MTV generation will buy the video, and clearly are willing to pay a little bit more for it. Meanwhile in South Korea, music video has been a staple of the music market for the youth on cellphones.

Do-it-yourself music video

What is the end-state? If we merge video camera-phones with the passions of bloggers and citizen journalism, and give digital tools, why not shoot your own music video? Seattle based rock band, Presidents of the United States of America have done that already in 2005. They shot the music video for their hit, "Some Postman" using only the simple videocams on their SonyEricsson cameraphones.

The issue then becomes one of content rights and mindset. The old media mindset is one of controlling media, and thus maintaining a high price. As it is exclusive, we can charge more. In the internet and mobile phone economics, this is extremely shortsighted, as Ajit Jaokar and Tony Fish argue in their book *Mobile Web 2.0*. They point out that this is a fundamental difference in old media thinking and the web experience when user-generated content is involved, writing:

> *Indeed, we believe that the requirements of the media/content industry are in contradiction to the 'network effect' application. In the former (media industry), you must restrict the free flow of content in order to make it more valuable. In the latter (applications benefiting from the network effect), you must actively encourage the free flow of 'user generated content'. Note that this is not an argument for the 'Napster mindset'. We are not advocating swapping of 'Hollywood' content but rather seek to encourage the free flow of 'user generated content'.*
> Ajit Jaokar & Tony Fish, *Mobile Web 2.0*, 2006

That phenomenon of user-generated content is already in full swing, influencing the success of music artists and soon all media. Today hundreds of bands have already used cameraphones to capture video for their music videos and often then upload these to video sharing sites like *YouTube*. The British dance label Ministry of Sound actually invites fans to submit user-generated versions of videos, which they pioneered in 2006 with the dance hit "Put your hands up for Detroit" by Fedde Le Grand.

E   ENJOY LIVE MUSIC

Again, the extent of how far music can be enjoyed on the phone is not limited to replicating what is possible on CD or DVD (or iPod), You can also *view* live concerts on 3G phones. Robbie Williams was the first major rock artist to multiply hundredfold the audience of his premiere rock concert broadcast live in Berlin at the launch of his album in October 2005. His concert was simulcast live on 3G phones in several European countries. He attracted a live paying audience of 100,000 fans aroound Europe on 3G cellphones, in addition to the 7,500 paid live audience in Berlin where he performed his concert.

Learn to dance

Dance is a significant part of enjoying popular music. Yes, you can dance while wearing your stand-alone MP3 player or iPod. Nevertheless, that MP3 player cannot *teach you to dance*. However, since it was launched in South Korea, the virtual dance tutor is on the phone in many countries. Select your favorite song, set the tempo, and a stick figure will guide you through the steps. As you learn your dance moves, you speed up the tempo. The virtual dance tutor has been on South Korean cellphones for three years already. Rihanna the American hiphop artist was one of the first western artists to adopt this idea in 2006 with her music videos online. Moreover, if you think of yourself as a choreographer, you can capture your dance moves and share your skills with others with a 3G phone. Again, thousands of clips on *YouTube* validate this concept.

User-generated dance moves

The British pop trio Sugababes was among the first Western bands to invite its fans to submit video of dance moves that the Sugababes would then perform in their stage act during their international tour of 2006. The Sugababes fan experience was developed by Endemol together with O2 the British wireless carrier formerly part of British Telecom and now part of the Spanish Telefonica Group. Think how innovative this is. Almost every child has at some point pretended to perform the moves of their fave band, in make-shift stages at home. Before, if a teenager was gifted in dance, and wanted to send dance moves to a pop band, it was for all practical purposes impossible. The child would have to draw stick-figures, set the moves to the rhythm, and use some bizarre notations to show how the dance moves should be executed. A hopeless task.

The video recording feature on a cameraphone makes this literally child's play. A group of three teenage girls can pretend to be the Sugababes, ask their big brother to shoot the dance moves on his cameraphone, and the girls then send the moves to their favorite band. In addition, as this was something the band had invited, the band will have an assistant view all submitted videos, and select a few of the best to show the band and choreographer, for consideration. The band selects the best moves and the fans are elated. Yet another example of media experiences that were impossible prior to Mobile becoming the Seventh of the Mass Media.

Long Tail: 8 cents per song

The concept of the "Long Tail" has been popularized by Chris Anderson in his book of the same name. One of the applications of the long tail in the 7th mass media space is in music. Tre (Three, part of the Hutchison Group) in Sweden has introduced a very advanced cellphone music service. One of its remarkable

Tomi T Ahonen

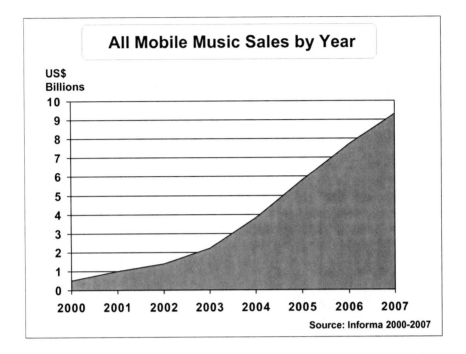

All Mobile Music Sales by Year

US$ Billions

Source: Informa 2000-2007

elements is that prices of MP3 songs can be as low as 8 cents per song. How is that possible where iTunes prices are in the 79-99 cent range? In Sweden, the catalog of songs includes many old and relatively obscure Swedish songs from decades gone by. These still have some fans who like the songs but they are too few for the record label to consider releasing a new CD with the music. However, cellphones allow a powerful sales and delivery platform for digital music. For such older songs, even at prices as low as 8 cents per song, the content owner and network can share the revenue and make some income from this back catalog to music.

Fan Clubs

With music and cellphones, it does not end with listening to the songs, or even to seeing the songs. The cellphone is an inherently *interactive* media. If it is the preferred means to consume music (and videos) and as it is carried always everywhere, it automatically becomes the preferred channel for fan interaction.

The first band to fully capitalize on this concept was the Hong Kong based pop duo The Twins, with their cellphone based fan service, Twins Mobile. I wrote about the Twins with my co-author Alan Moore as a Case Study in our book *Communities Dominate Brands* in 2005 so let me just summarize. Twins fans had messaging chat services, fan club newsletter, collected loyalty points to enjoy premium services and the band offered exclusive tickets and passes to concerts and the service includes games with chances to win concert tickets. Furthermore, the service was an MVNO (Mobile Virtual Network Operator) so Twins fans would get telecoms services with Twins, from basic voice calls and text messages, to premium voicemail announcements by the Twins, to custom phones featuring the two singers.

Testing hit potential

In January of 2006, the soul/urban band the Fugees announced that it will release three new songs to the Verizon MP3 service. These are not previews of upcoming songs to their next album. The Fugees said they are not committed to releasing these songs in any other formats as of yet, only that they wanted to make the songs available to their fans. If any of them turn out to score big, they can release that song or songs also on other media like on their next album.

Thank you for the music

So today 9.3 billion dollars are generated by mobile music. Ten years from the first ringing tone, nearly a third of all music is now consumed on phones. Much more than just listening to songs, the cellphone as the 7th Mass Media Channel allows users to enjoy music in more ways and more instances than ever before. Music on cellphones. Yes, it will be bigger than anything you ever imagined on iPods. Then the question becomes are you ready to capitalize on this opportunity? Johnny Carson had a good observation about talent and opportunity, when he said: *"Talent alone won't make you a success. Neither will being in the right place at the right time, unless you are ready. The most important question is: 'Are you ready?'"*

Case Study 8 from China
Mice Love Rice

A good example of how Waiting Tones/Ringback Tones are changing the economics of the music business comes from China. Plus Eight Star (+8*) an Asia and China-focused research consultancy explained about the Mice Love Rice phenomenon in their Inside QQ report in January 2008.

A Chinese music teacher, Yang Chengang who lives in Hubei Province of China, decided to release a pop song in 2004, called Mice Love Rice. Like most music in China, his MP3 song was offered on the internet, for free.

The MP3 version of Mice Love Rice became a big hit and generated over 100 million downloads, most of, which were free downloads. This would seem like the suicide formula for the traditional music publishing industry worldwide. A case of perfect evidence of how bad the economics in music are nowadays in a Post-Napster file-sharing environment.

However, in China the record company did have a way to monetize the popularity of the song. They released the song as a Waiting Tone (ringback tone). These are songs that are played on mobile phones, similar to ringing tones. Except that with Waiting Tones, the song is played to that person who is trying to call you, before you answer. A bit like music-on-hold, before you answer. And like music-on-hold, the quality of the music is far better than basic ringing tones.

Waiting Tones/Ringback Tones were invented in South Korea by WiderThan (and the Korean version was initially called Color Ring) and are already a two billion dollar industry worldwide, spreading into most markets.

As the song Mice Love Rice was becoming popular and it was available for free, many of the fans who liked the song, wanted it also as their Waiting Tone. As the Waiting Tone is a network service enabled by the wireless carrier/mobile operator, and cannot be delivered through independent third parties without the express technical connectivity by the carrier/operator, there are no free Waiting Tones to cannibalize the revenue potential.

Now the record label was able to monetize the popularity of the song. Mice Love Rice generated 170 RMB in licencing revenues (21 million dollars) on its Waiting Tone version. Or to put it in another way, the equivalent earnings of bonus 20 cents for every free web download !!

This is the way of the future for music in the digital space. Yes, we can offer music for free under certain circumstances, if we can then make money from the same songs in other ways.

Tomi T Ahonen

"Mobile gaming has introduced the 'rental concept'
to consuming videogames."
Graeme Oxby, Marketing Director, Three UK

X
Wireless Gaming
The virtual girl friend on the cellphone

Videogaming had its humble roots in the 1970s. The first successful videogame, *Pong* (crude ping-pong on arcade videogaming machines) gradually gave way to *Pac Man, Donkey Kong* and other early hits. Some expensive consoles appeared for home use, allowing some of these games (often only *Pong* and its derivatives) to be played at home. After the personal computer industry emerged in the 1980s, videogaming found a robust business, and gaming platforms such as Nintendo and Sony's Playstation helped make videogaming mainstream. All along, many games or their clones appeared on the rapidly growing PC market.

Videogames were considered a techno-nerdy little niche market much through the 1990s until someone noticed that towards the end of the decade, that videogaming rivaled Hollywood movies as a global industry. Videogaming had come of age. Today towering over Hollywood, videogaming is also a larger industry than the global recorded music business.

A   ENTER THE *SNAKE*

An impressive industry, but what of the cellphone? Nokia opened the door with the gutsy introduction of a simple videogame to its cellphone line in 1998. The Nokia *Snake* became a huge hit, and in terms of a single gaming title (and its newer variant, *Snake 2*), it is by far the most played videogame of all time having been played by more than a billion people worldwide. *Snake* soon brought a youth-appeal to phones as advanced markets saw the cellphone enter the teenager market. Youth would often say, they did not care, which brand of cellphone they received, as long as it had *Snake*. Nokia was building its first generation of loyal fans among the youth from the late 1990s.

Early cellphone games were mostly added as time-killer applications, to allow people to do something when in a bus or train, etc. Today most phones ship with at least one time-killer game pre-installed. Moreover, if those are not enough, most phones can take simple downloadable games such as *Tetris, Pac-Man, Solitaire* etc.

Next came the simple interactive network game. An early variant was the *Who Wants to be a Millionaire* game, by, which new questions could be sent to the phone through the network. These involved the user to pay for some data charges typically with WAP based interactive games. Other quiz games were set up to work with SMS text messaging. As phones became more advanced, Java based games also emerged. These would typically all be single-player games. Even such games as the *Formula One* game offered by Vodafone in 2005 were the single player games, driving the racecar against other cars but only against the computer game, not against networked gamers.

That all changed with the N-Gage, Nokia's second major contribution to the evolution of gaming on cellphones. Released to great industry fanfare and with a massive Nokia PR push, in the end, the N-Gage was seen as a flop, a marketing failure. It is true that the N-Gage was flawed, both as a phone and as a

---

20 Million Playstation Portables had been sold by 2007.
Source: Sony 2007

---

gaming platform. As the two N-Gage phones sold only in the low millions in their lifespan (out of 1 billion cellphones sold annually), and where gaming platforms like Playstation, X-Box and Nintendo Wii sell in the several dozens of millions every year, certainly N-Gage was not a significant market success. Nevertheless, the relevant point is that when the N-Gage was released, it energized the whole worldwide videogaming industry to consider cellphone-based games and gamers.

Even though the dedicated N-Gage phones are no longer made, the N-Gage platform and games live on with some of the more advanced Nokia phones today on the N-Series. However, you do not need to have a specific Nokia N-Gage handset to play videogames on cellphones. In fact, the vast majority of all games are the kind that they would play on most mid-range cellphones, and indeed, would play on most obsolete PCs and laptops. Today videogame developers are all getting into the cellphone-videogaming dimension.

How big is it

Let me look at the money. The videogaming industry, worth about 45 billion dollars can be divided roughly in two, little under half is the sale of the consoles like the Sony Playstation 3 and PSP, the Microsoft Xbox 360 and the Nintendo Wii. The rest, or about 25 billion dollars is software sales, the sale or rental of the actual gaming titles like *John Madden's Pro Football*, or *Grand Theft Auto*, or *Tony Hawke's* skateboarding games. Videogaming software sales are divided roughly into internet/PC games, console games and cellphone games. The fastest-growing part has been cellphone games, which reached 5 billion dollars of annual sales in 2007, according to *Netsize Guide 2008*. Thus, out of all videogaming software sales, 20% was generated on games on mobile in 2007.

Bearing in mind the theme of this book, one should not try to simply copy the content from a previous media format; mobile is as different from the internet as TV is from radio. Thus we should also explore unique, better gaming experiences on cellphones. It is important to remember that the videogaming experience on the small screen of the cellphone will be inherently different from that of playing a game online on a PC screen, or on a Playstation hooked up to the TV set. The screen is smaller, the keypad often less robust for severe gaming play, and the controls often less user-friendly than the "Playstation-style" gaming controls on consoles or the full keyboard on PCs, not

---

1 billion people had Nokia *Snake* on a cellphone by 2007.
Source: Nokia 2007

---

to mention those on dedicated gaming control devices such as steering wheels for cars, handguns for shooting games, etc. In spite of the limitations of screen and keypad, the cellphone based videogaming segment delivers one in every five dollars for the videogaming software industry.

As game developers noticed the trend, they started to understand cellphones and their users. As we have seen in the Youth and Gen-C chapters, cellphones are the gadget of choice to young people. Videogame developers now work with this. One of the obvious uses is to build a title for cellphone use as the launch or introductory title for a new console game. *Urban Freestyle Soccer* became the first console based videogame in 2003 to be released as a mobile game first before the console version to follow. Now console game developers regularly have trial versions for cellphones both to build the buzz among the hard-core gamer community, and to generate early revenues.

Gen C is also a gaming generation

The biggest single influencing technology for the previous generation was television. While TV is also of interest to younger generations, TV especially how it was consumed in the past, is passive. Gaming is active, the gamer will

---

enter the imaginary environment of the game, and take an active role in playing in it, with it, living it. Very similar to how older generations related to TV when they were young, young videogamers today will have dreams, even nightmares, based on the latest games they play. The game characters are introduced into the "regular play" just like previous generations brought favorite TV characters into their play such as playing "Cowboys and Indians" in the 1960s or "Cops and Robbers" in the 1970s etc.

Furthermore, videogaming is immersive; it requires our full attention. If we do not take an active role in a game, nothing happens. The story narrative of the game will not proceed unless the gamer participates. This is the total opposite of traditional TV, where the story will continue whether a given member of the audience was sitting in front of the TV set or not. On both broadcast media, TV and radio, we can consume the content in background mode, such as preparing dinner in the kitchen while having CNN news on the background, or driving our car and listening to the drive-time talk show, etc. As to its intensity and interaction, videogaming is massively more appealing to young people than passive media like TV. Nevertheless, let's look at cellphone gaming in more detail. Jump in...

B   OH NO, NOT THE *TAMAGOTCHI* AGAIN

Yes it is back. We all remember that horrible toy that our children bought a decade ago that had to be fed and played with on a regular basis or else it died.

Did you notice that the *Tamagotchi* has returned? First at the start of this decade, there were the obvious cellphone adaptations in Asia, such as the sumo wrestler game in Japan and the kickboxing game in Hong Kong. As with the *Tamagotchi*, the gamer has to feed the fighter, and play with it (train it) so that the fighter could grow strong. What the cellular networks added, was the ability to play one virtual fighter against another: networked *Tamagotchis*.

As word spread of the strange mobile network fighting games in Japan, the game idea spread to Europe. The mobile operator/carrier Orange in the UK, and France adapted the idea but targeted the game for younger users who were interested in dinosaurs, by releasing the *Dino Island* game in 2002. Again, the players would grow, feed, nurture and play with their dinosaurs. There was a fighting element for those who wanted to fight dinosaurs. Orange reported that two years later, in 2004 the game was still a top revenue-generator among its target age group. Now there are similar games from penguins to polar bears.

Virtual friends

Meanwhile in Hong Kong and Japan the *Tamagotchi* idea was developed even further as the virtual girlfriend/boyfriend. Rather than feeding food to the "pet",

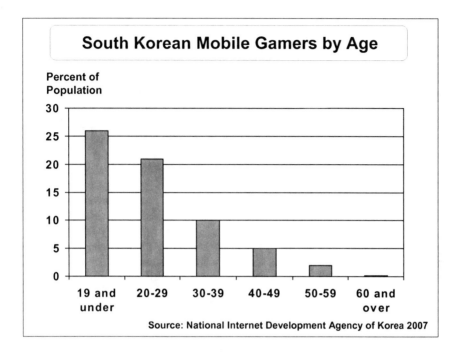

South Korean Mobile Gamers by Age

Percent of
Population

Source: National Internet Development Agency of Korea 2007

now the virtual girlfriend of boyfriend needed caring SMS text messages on a daily basis. These could be love poems and other shows of affection so that the relationship would grow and flourish. The virtual partner would react in predictable ways, so if the gamer has annoyed the virtual friend or ignored the partner too long, then the virtual girlfriend/boyfriend would become annoyed. To fix matters, the gamer would then need to send virtual flowers, chocolates etc. to make the partner happy again. The concept is still the *Tamagotchi*, only the setting is a bit different, and the target age group obviously teenagers.

For those who think this idea is so silly it can only work in the Far East, it may come as a surprise that the British version of this game generates tens of thousands of premium SMS text messages per month in the UK, alone. The Hong Kong developer of *V-Girl*, Artificial Life has already released its more advanced version onto 3G phones.

The real story is who plays this game. It is not the 30-year-old computer geek that you might think. The big user group is actually young teenager boys and girls - an almost even split between boys and girls. When asked why a 12 or 13-year-old might spend so much of their money on this strange hobby, they say it is for practice. They have not had a real relationship yet, but see their bigger brothers and sisters already dating, and are of course terrified they will not know how to behave.

A virtual partner is a perfect playground to practice. The idea is not far fetched, in some of mankind's most intense areas of capability, such as fighter pilots, submarine crews, tank crews, etc., simulators are used to train the required skills. Young people today are very astute, will naturally gravitate to anything that could give them the "edge" or to help them overcome what to them is the most traumatic near future scenario, the first real romance.

Yet another interesting variant of this idea is *Metronerd* from Finland. This is the "dating coach" game for adult computer engineers. Finland has the highest per-capita ratio of engineers out of the total population (Germany is second, Sweden is third) so among any college educated adults, to find the person's job as an engineer is very common in Finland. Engineering is a male-dominated industry, and for those who have spent most of their youth studying the demanding disciplines of math and sciences well enough to be accepted to the engineering universities, these kids were not the typical party animals of their generation. It is a common joke in Finland to assume the engineers are clumsy at romance. So enter *Metronerd*. It takes the virtual girl friend idea, and helps (mostly male) engineers in what it takes to be romantic. To coach them into sending flowers and romantic messages and candle-lit dinners and so forth. However, returning to our theme, this interesting relationship tutor is actually just a variation on the *Tamagotchi*: a virtual pet.

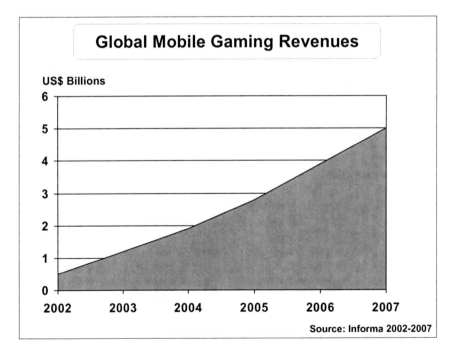

Bees and horses

In Austria in 2002 the *Tamagotchi* reappeared as the network game *Killer Bees*. In this game, the "Tamagotchi" was not a live pet as such, it was the beehive (castle) that gamers would build with worker bees, and then gamers would grow an army of killer bees to attack the beehives of other networked gamers. The game soon became popular with teams such as colleagues at work. The idea was that colleagues would know when one of them was stuck in a meeting and unable to defend the beehive that was the ideal time to attack. With a national leader board displaying who are the national masters, these were the continuous targets of rivals, which meant that there was also a lot of variation with the top rankings as the best players got to be attacked more often than the rest.

While *Killer Bees* was mostly an entertainment game, in Hong Kong the local more money-oriented culture developed the *Tamagotchi* idea into a money-making and gambling opportunity in 2004. *Super Stable* is an online massive user cellphone video game where gamers breed and groom their virtual racehorses, so that they can race against other virtual horses. In horseracing mad Hong Kong these virtual horse races are broadcast, just like races involving real horses. Fans of *Super Stable* can place bets on the horses, and yes, they can breed new horses. *Super Stable* is a big hit in the passionate horse racing community of Hong Kong and has become so popular that its users spend more on their mobile phone than heavy business users spend on regular voice and messaging.

These videogamers are not teenagers. These gamers are adults, who are passionate about horses, but cannot afford owning a real horse. Through *Super Stable* these owners get many of the benefits of owning a real horse at only a tiny fraction of the cost. I will look at *Super Stable* more in the Case Study at the end of this chapter.

Pop Kids

Perhaps the ultimate reincarnation of the *Tamagotchi* is the reality TV game show variant of the *Pop Idol/American Idol* TV format, called *Pop Kids*, and developed in the Netherlands. I will discuss *Pop Kids* in a Case Study after the Mobile TV chapter, so I will just briefly mention that in *Pop Kids*, cellphone owners give virtual birth to avatar kids who will grow up to eventually enter a reality TV contest against other virtual *Pop Idol* contestants. The kids will go through various types of preparation by their parents, enter singing, dancing and music classes to prepare for the contest, and so forth. Again, it is the *Tamagotchi* reborn, but now to eventually be seen on broadcast TV.

The main feature of the *Tamagotchi* on cellphones, is that we carry our phone everywhere, so the user can "play" with the *Tamagotchi* at all moments of idle time. The two main improvements over the stand-alone *Tamagotchi* is the network element, which allows the service to grown and evolve beyond what was initially installed onto the device; and obviously the networked play element of multiplayer gaming. For the game developers, cellphone games add the ability to charge per play or per transaction.

C   HABBO HOTEL AND CYWORLD

While little games are built for the cellphone, totally different virtual worlds live on the web. There are so-called MMOGs, Massively Multiplayer Online Games. Some are fantasy and wargaming worlds like *Everquest, Worlds of Warcraft, Lineage, Counterstrike* etc. Others are virtual worlds for playing, socializing and blogging like *Second Life* and *Cyworld*. *Habbo Hotel* was one of the first of these, introduced in Finland in 2000 as *Hotelli Kultakala* (the Goldfish Hotel) by Finnish social networking developer Sulake, and released internationally under the *Habbo Hotel* brand. It is now available in dozens of countries around the world. Aimed at the teenager age segment, *Habbo* rapidly spread and had over

---

9.1% of US cellphone users downloaded games in 2007.
Source: M:Metrics 2007

---

80 million users around the world by December 2007.

Habbo Hotel was the first internet game to feature micropayments via cellphones. Access to *Habbo Hotel* on the web is free for all, but to pay for content, you use your cellphone and pay premium SMS as the payment mechanism. As *Habbo Hotel* is aiming for the 12-15 year age segment, these do not have credit cards, and premium SMS is a natural way for them to have electronic payment options.

So what do they do in *Habbo Hotel*?

On a sunny day, kids might go out playing baseball. However, on a rainy day they will go visit with a friend's house and play indoors. This was what *Habbo Hotel* was designed to capture. Kids can go to the web and meet their friends online, invite them to their room and play. The *Habbo Hotel* rooms are similar in concept to for example the islands on *Second Life*. So each kid has a room in the hotel. Then each kid has his/her virtual persona as an "avatar" or a digital puppet, called a "Habbo". You can customize your Habbo, select the hair style, skin color, dress, etc. Make it a reflection of you, or perhaps an alternate you, or an aspiration of you.

In *Habbo Hotel* kids then mingle and do things together. They play

---

Tomi T Ahonen

videogames, they chat, they listen to music, etc. As what teenager kids do in real life. The behavior shows remarkable consistency in teenager youth behavior. Mark Curtis described *Habbo Hotel* in his book ***Distraction***:

> *Much behaviour on Habbo is recognisable and predictable: girls tend to set up businesses, boys form gangs to take over rooms. 12 year olds aspire to be close to16 year olds, who take advantage by employing them as accolytes to work in virtual hairdressers. The real difference that Habbo symbolises is that knowing someone is so much easier, the opportunities to socialise infinitely extended around the world, 24 hours a day. Digital technology removes the physical constraint on how many relationships one can form. The average amount of time users spend on Habbo in a session is 40 minutes. 40% spend two hours or more at a time. From this adult's point of view that is an unthinkable amount of time to spend on a web site, but apparently users do not see it as just a web site. The spatial environment is critical to this illusion. For*

51.1% of Japanese downloaded cellphone games in 2007
Source: Mobikyo Japan Mobile Internet Report 2007

> *instance one can see users speaking in other rooms, but not overhear what they are saying. This is social immersion, digital style.*
> - Mark Curtis, ***Distraction***, 2005

These are all very typical of young people outside the virtual world. Similar behavior as can be observed in any gathering of teenagers from the high school to the playground. *Habbo Hotel* has become the largest multiplayer online environment with over 80 million registered Habbo characters (and yes, Tomi Ahonen has his own Habbo as well, I must be one of the oldest users on that service). Contrast that with about 2 million active users of *Second Life* or 8 million on *World of Warcraft*, and you can appreciate the scale. While the original *Habbo Hotel* concept was strictly an internet environment, played on a PC, its developer Sulake has released their *"Pocket Habbo"* cellphone version.

Korea and *Cyworld*

An even more advanced converged virtual world is now in Korea, called *Cyworld*. As in *Habbo Hotel*, on *Cyworld* gamers can create their own rooms in their home pages (called minihomepi or mini homepage) and like on *Habbo Hotel* they can create their own avatars (minime, like the character in the *Austin*

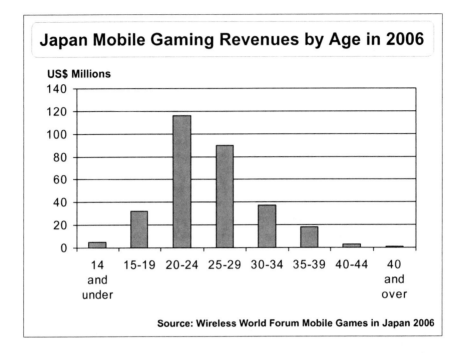

Japan Mobile Gaming Revenues by Age in 2006

US$ Millions

Source: Wireless World Forum Mobile Games in Japan 2006

Powers movies). Nevertheless, on *Cyworld* members can also upload pictures, blogs, share diaries, listen to music etc.

Where *Habbo Hotel* targets only the youth, *Cyworld* has managed to cross the age divide. As I explained in the *Cyworld* Case Study earlier, *Cyworld* is already used by over 50% of the total Korean population, and over 90% of the youth of the nation. Politicians post their policies on *Cyworld*. Housewives share cooking advice on *Cyworld*. It is a completely new social phenomenon; like blogging on speed. Just like *Habbo Hotel*, you can do your activities on *Cyworld* through the fixed internet (broadband) connection. However, also capitalizing on Korea's over 90% penetration of advanced 3G phones, all of *Cyworld* can be enjoyed and accessed through cellphones, but obviously at added cost. Mobile blogging alone generates 3.40 dollars per user per month of data revenues to the carriers in Korea.

Massively Multiplayer

As to true massively multiplayer games on cellphones? Some are going in that direction. Nokia's *Pocket Kingdom*, for the N-Gage was one of the first. In 2007, Disney released the multiplayer game around *Pirates of the Caribbean* as an MMOG for cellphones. Meanwhile Nexgen of Singapore offered its dwarf battling game, *Elven Legends* as one of the world's first 3G cellphone and broadband internet cross-platform MMOG experiences, which has launched in many Asian countries from Malaysia to South Korea and already expanding to Europe.

Today many MMOGs have interfaces to cellphones, such as receiving gaming alerts, leader board information and news updates. Nevertheless, into the near future it is likely that many multiplayer gaming environments such as *World of Warcraft, Lineage* and *CounterStrike* will continue to thrive on the PC platform, as a gamer can achieve considerable gaming benefits from a large, high-resolution screen and better gaming interfaces possible on PCs.

However, the screen size or keypad need not be an obstacle if the right gaming experience is developed. It is possible for a game to be developed to capitalize on the smaller screen. If you are a submarine captain, all you really need to see is the periscope view - something that is quite similar to the view on a small screen of the modern cellphone.

Location-based gaming

Then there are games that take advantage of the location of the gamer. One of the first successes was the *Mogi* game in Japan, a virtual treasure-hunt with team play. Virtual treasures were located in various places around Tokyo, and clues given to teams who then needed to move around Tokyo to discover the treasures.

Another location-based game around the principle of real people interacting with each other is *Phone Tag* by LivePlanet, a game that is promoted by Hollywood actors Matt Damon and Ben Affleck. The game is the cellphone network gaming variant of the children's playground game of "tag" (also known as "you are it"). The game where one person has to chase the others until he/she catches someone, who then is "tagged" or "becomes it" and starts to chase the others.

In *Phone Tag*, the phone display will show on a map the dot of the person who is approaching you. In addition, it will show the location of your target. In this game you can both be chased by someone, and simultaneously be tasked to chase someone else. However, you will not know about the other gamers, if someone is getting closer to you, is that person really chasing you, or if that person is by coincidence getting to be near to you.

However, the location-based game need not involve humans. A clever game on that line of thinking is *BotFighter* from Sweden. In addition, a location-based game, here the gamers build battle robots on their PCs on the internet, but their combat depends on the location of the phone of their owner. If you happen to visit a certain shopping mall or a school or office, then random other *BotFighter* gamers will be in your proximity. The network will alert you of the rival's presence and allow the robots to do battle.

This is a great idea for a game, generating a million premium SMS text messages per week in Sweden, a country of only 8 million people. When comparing to a game publisher who prints gaming DVDs or CDs and ships to videogaming stores, etc., this kind of cellphone based opportunity is a radical change in how to market the games and collect revenues more directly.

A million SMS per week, if we assume the game developer ends up getting perhaps 5 cents per message after the revenue-sharing etc that means about 200,000 dollars per month or 2.4 million per year. The money in online cellphone games adds up rather fast in gaming.

Of course, the basic gaming models are possible on cellphones. A game can be sold as a download. A game can have a monthly or annual subscription. A game can be sponsored - in India a major part of the mobile advertising industry is innovating with "advergames" - where a game is used as the marketing vehicle for a given brand or product. Coca Cola's India brand Thumbs Up for example released a game involving virtual climbing of Mount Everest in 2005. Moreover, the Indian movie industry, Bollywood, already uses cellphone advergames for new release publicity, first tested with a sliding puzzle game for the movie *Jurm* in 2005.

However, perhaps the biggest potential of cellphone gaming economics comes from micropayments and gaming customization. Much like a *Habbo Hotel* user or *Cyworld* user can customize their room and avatar with small items of a cost of about 30 cents per item, future gaming environments can build their business model around this kind of pricing mechanisms.

Kart Rider uses cartoon logic

South Korean online game *Kart Rider* is one of these kinds of innovators. *Kart Rider* is a multiplayer car racing game and has a lot of conceptual similarity to an early *Super Mario Brothers* car racing game. *Kart Rider* is a multiplayer car racing game with a fascinating twist - it adds an element of "Tom & Jerry" style cartoon violence and cartoon competitiveness. Just like cartoons as "Tweety and Sylvester the Cat", "Bugs Bunny", "The Road Runner vs. Wily E Coyote", and "Tom & Jerry" - in *Kart Rider* the gamers can employ what I call "cartoon logic" and cartoon violence to try to win their races.

For example if your opponent is drawing near you and threatens to pass your car, you can slip a banana peel to the road. In reality, obviously, a car will not be affected much if running over a banana peel. Nevertheless, according to cartoon logic, if you go over a banana peel, your car will go into a spin. That is what happens in *Kart Rider*. On the other hand, if you want to catch the guy in front of you, you can shoot a rocket at the car in front of you. The kind of logic that does not work outside of cartoons and *James Bond* movies. However, it works in *Kart Rider*. In addition, if you see the rocket coming at you, if you were well prepared, you can launch your balloon - and float above the rocket, safely hanging underneath the balloon. In reality, a balloon could not inflate fast enough, and it would need to be an enormous balloon to be able to carry the weight of a racecar - but this is cartoon logic. In *Kart Rider* you can take a temporary float above the other racers if you prepared and bought yourself a balloon before you started your race.

These kinds of gimmicks and gadgets are of course all separate low-cost purchases in *Kart Rider*, worth about 30 cents per item. Then there are the usual customizing items such as selecting racecar colors and stripes and flashy wheels etc. You can also customize your race driver such as the helmet and color of your driver overalls etc. All of these are small cost items. This way the game developer can afford to give the basic game away for free, and make all the revenues from the extra cost items and customization.

The popularity of *Kart Rider* is so great in South Korea that already 25% of the total South Korean population have participated in races in *Kart Rider*. Two cable TV channels are devoted to real-time game-play. Moreover, in a national survey of cars by popularity, the top most popular car in South Korea was the Porsche 911, but the second most popular car was not another real car like a Ferrari, Aston Martin or BMW. The second most popular car in the survey was the "Super Pro" car of *Kart Rider*. Imagine that, a virtual car came second in this national survey, ahead of almost all real cars. In addition, "Super Pro" is the

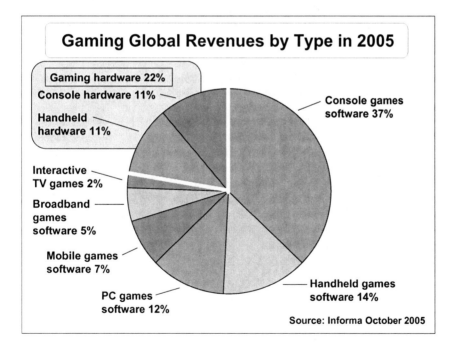

most expensive item in *Kart Rider*, costing about 10 dollars. You do not need to be rich to play *Kart Rider*.

It is too early to tell if this can sustain the whole gaming industry, but many games and virtual worlds are moving to this model. Rather make the cost items very small, below the pain threshold, and get heavily addicted users to make many of these small purchases weekly or even daily, rather than charge them a couple of dollars monthly as a rental fee. A good indicator of how profitable this can be is the British online dating service *Flirtomatic*, which went from a subscription model to a customization model in 2006 and dramatically increased its revenues and profits. In late 2007, Electronic Arts announced that it is also going to use the business model of "Asian" multiplayer gaming, where the game itself is free, but the money is made from the customization, gifts, and virtual items for sale.

Do not pass go

Gaming is an industry larger than Hollywood movies. Gaming is not passive, it is immersive and takes the full attention of its customers. Clearly, a preference of youth customers, often young people will rather play games than watch TV or movies. Now the big shift in gaming is from console gaming to internet/broadband games and wireless cellphone games. As game developers learn to take full advantage of mobile as the 7th mass media channel that will also help make cellphones the biggest platform for gaming. Was Nokia's N-Gage cellphone gaming platform ahead of its time? Yes. Nevertheless, will cellphone gaming become big. Definitely. Already today, the iPhone is driving added interest into cellphone gaming, as we will see in the MyNuMo Case Study a bit later in this book.

How long until Sony's Playstation Portable (PSP) will be incorporated into SonyEricsson cellphones, probably not very long, as SonyEricsson has already capitalized on its Cybershot brand for cameraphones and Walkman for musicphones. Moreover, the Nokia N-Gage, it has already re-emerged on top end Nokia N-Series smartphones. Now the industry needs to move into this space and forget about earlier platforms. Alexander Graham Bell put it well, when he said about technology transitions, *"When one door closes another door opens; but we often look so long and so regretfully upon the closed door that we do not see the ones, which are open to us."*

Case Study 9 from Hong Kong
Super Stable

The national sport of Hong Kong is horse racing. For many local residents the dream of success is to one day own a real race horse. Hong Kong is even the venue for the competitive horse riding events of 2008 Olympics held in China. The people of Hong Kong are also keen gamblers.

So in 2003, one of the local cellular telecoms carriers (mobile operators) New World Mobility launched a multiplayer cellphone game to capitalize on the horse racing mad population and their willingness to gamble. The game is called *Super Stable.*

Similar to the *Tamagotchi,* the starting point for any gamer is to join the game with a baby horse, distributed (with its pedigree heritage information) on a SIM card (Subscriber Identity Module), which is typical of all GSM networks. The SIM card will hold the virtual "DNA" for the baby horse, and then act as the gaming identity for the new horse and its owner.

Much like the *Tamagotchi*, now the new horse owner has to start to train and groom the horse for racing. There are decisions on, which (virtual) horse feeds to give to the horse to eat, and when to take it to training, which jockeys and trainers to hire, etc. All of this costs, and the payments are handled via the cellular network's billing system. Just like premium SMS votes for *American Idol*, or buying clothes for your avatar in *Cyworld* or virtual red roses in *Flirtomatic*, you can buy virtual services to your *Super Stable* horse.

Then what happens? Once the horse is old enough and ready, you enter your horse in a contest against other virtual horses, of course. These are broadcast, live on radio (just like real horse races in Hong Kong) and yes, you can bet on the races, and you can even breed your horses with other virtual horses to create virtual offspring. The game became so popular it soon spread to other neighboring regions, with *Super Stable* gamers in Macau, Taiwan and Shanghai. The game then added the ability to have virtual horse races across international boundaries.

These videogamers are not teenagers. These gamers are adults, who are passionate about horses, but cannot afford owning a real horse. Through *Super Stable* these owners get many of the benefits of owning a real horse at only a tiny fraction of the cost.

Meanwhile the game developers and network operators collect all kinds of service fees from special horse feeds, grooming, training etc. services they offer to the gamers, always of course at a fee. *Super Stable* has become so popular that its users spend more on their mobile phone than heavy business users in Hong Kong spend on regular voice and messaging.

"Everyone has a purpose in life. Perhaps yours
is watching television."
David Letterman

XI
Cellphone TV
Is not viewing highlight clips or live TV

The world's third largest advertising agency, BBDO, ran a survey of user preferences in 2005, and found that TV finished a distant third behind cellphones and the internet. The *Financial Times* reported the story with the front-page headline "Mobile Phones will replace TV as most important medium" on April 7, 2005.

Broadcasters in leading cellphone countries from Korea to Italy have been on the march to get TV onto the cellphone. Italian cellphone carrier Three bought TV broadcaster Canal 7. Japanese wireless giant carrier NTT DoCoMo bought local broadcaster Fuji TV. Yes, we will be watching content on cellphones, but as I have been saying at my mobile-TV and video short course at Oxford University since 2006 that *"TV will not be primarily consumed by pocketable 3G cellphones."* I then always add, *"It will be 'TV-related' content and services that will deliver the success of mobile TV."* Obviously I believe in the success of TV-related content on the cellphone, why the distinction?

A   UNDERSTAND DIFFERENCES

It is vital to understand how the consumption of existing TV content will evolve, and what will be successful on what is commonly known as the "fourth screen". As I have discussed before, Cinema, TV and PC are the first three screens and now cellphones offer us the fourth screen.

We need to recognize that TV content has been fine-tuned to fit perfectly the roughly 25-32 inch screen sizes of TV sets at home. Our content, services, and programming formats have all been built to fully capitalize on that box at home. Differing from content on radio and cinema, current TV hits are formats that would not be sustainable on cinema or radio, such as reality TV, chat shows, game shows, etc. These were all formats that were invented after TV was introduced. There obviously are also TV formats that are direct copies or developed from cinema and radio, such as live sports broadcasts, news, "made-for-TV movies", soap operas etc. Where a format works well on multiple media, it has a better chance of also working on cellphones.

As the cellphone has a far smaller screen and its viewing times often brief, any video content should be shot by cinematographers and directors who understand the medium. Actors should be mostly in close-up. There should not be much movement of the camera. Large mass scenes that fill movie screens do not work well on cellphones. Luciana Pavan of MTV explained at the Forum Oxford Conference that MTV currently uses two separate camera crews when it records its own programming like *Jackass*. One camera crew shoots for TV and the other crew for the cellphone and other small screens like video iPods etc.

Note there are such differences in the Third (Cinema) and Fifth (TV) Mass Media as well. TV content is mostly designed to allow casual viewing, in other words, we do not miss out on a typical TV show even if our viewing is interrupted and we miss out on a part of it. With series having standardized plot elements and very familiar stereotypical characters, even starting from the middle of most TV shows a viewer familiar with the show can enjoy it to its end without missing the plot. This is quite different from the cinema where often critical plot elements are introduced early in the movie.

We have TV sets already

The biggest issue with mobile vs. TV is not a contest of two rival *new* media (such as was with videocassette recorders, Betamax vs. VHS). It is a contest of an existing dominating delivery platform (TV) and a new one (cellphone). In every home in the Industrialized World, we have a TV set already. In America, there are more TV sets than people and worldwide there were about 1.4 billion TV sets in 2007. Therefore, for the existing TV content we have a perfectly suitable platform that is fully deployed. In addition, nobody will argue the point that for typical TV content, the viewing experience is better at our flat screen TV at home, than on the best screens of cellphones such as an iPhone or Nokia N96.

Traditional TV and its content formats are evolving to more convenience, such as using TiVo, Sky+ and other PVRs (Personal Video Recorders). We will get ever larger plasma screens and projection TV sets at home. We will also have increasingly the ability to view our movies and DVDs on the go, such as on our laptop PCs, PSPs, video iPods and yes on cellphones.

Cellphone TV will be emergency TV

For viewing our common episodes of popular TV shows such as *Desperate Housewives*, the *Shield* or the *Sopranos*, or our soaps or baseball and football

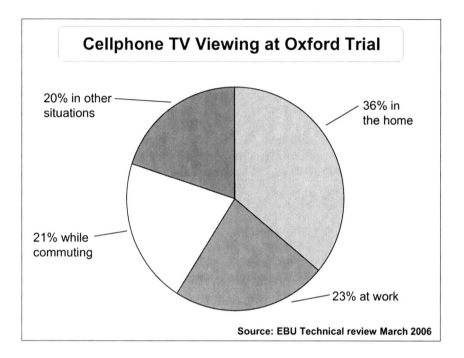

Cellphone TV Viewing at Oxford Trial

20% in other situations

36% in the home

21% while commuting

23% at work

Source: EBU Technical review March 2006

games, we will always prefer to be at our large screen TV set. Rather than try to squint at the game on the tiny screen, we will attempt to get home in time, or else set our recorder to time-shift the game, until when we get home. For the mainstream TV broadcast content that we already have access to on our home cable, satellite or broadcast channels, we will not readily use our cellphones.

There will be the occasional exceptions of course. Maybe we forgot to set the PVR, or we are suddenly caught in an unusual traffic jam on a route, which usually has no congestion. Then if we are about to miss our TV show, we could pull up the TV on our cellphone and view it on the small screen. As an exception. However, not as the rule. Nevertheless, this is for the TV formats that have been perfected for the traditional TV screen.

The other typical use is to have the cellphone TV as the *alternate* TV set. Therefore, if the main TV tuner with the family plasma screen TV is used by dad to watch the football game, and the kids want to watch *Jackass* on another premium channel (MTV), and cannot use the old TV set for that, they can use a premium TV service on the cellphone to watch their preferred channel. This is one of the lessons learned in South Korea and Finland with digital broadcast TV tuners embedded into cellphones. The kids often use them as the second premium TV tuner when the parents "hog" the main TV screen.

B   COMPELLING MOBILE TV

As I said, we will continue to consume most of our television on the large plasma screen TV at home, not the cellphone. To find our successes, we should not try to copy the existing formats to the cellphone. As I have been repeatedly saying in this book, we should capitalize on the unique benefits of cellphones. This is also true of television content and services. So yes, we will consume a lot of TV and video content on the cellphone that is "TV-related". What do I mean by that? Lets use the Six M's to build some billable value to mobile TV services, as we introduced in the chapter on Creating Magic. I will map out some of the successful innovations in cellphone-TV with the methodology of the Six M's.

Movement in mobile TV

The first of the Six M's is *Movement*, escaping the fixed place. Few broadcasters are expecting to launch "Location-Based Variations" to television content, so this might seem like there could not be much on Movement. By this, I mean that if you are watching the *Sopranos* in Chicago, we cannot allow you to select to kill

---

2.5% of Germans watched video on cellphones in 2007
Source: M:Metrics 2007

---

off its lead character, the mafia boss Tony Soprano, while another viewer in Atlanta prefers to let Tony live. I do not mean we cannot have viewers vote for plot lines and characters, as we do already with *American Idol, Big Brother* house etc. I mean that we typically cannot have a localized variation of a continuing plot-line show. As the shows are continuing storyline episodic TV, there cannot be practical regional variations. We might have some regional variation with issues such as language and subtitling, say in Quebec Province in Canada, there could be French versions of programs that are in English in other parts of Canada; or in Belgium, there could be Dutch and French variants in regions of the country.

Lapland TV

That is not what they decided in Norway. Up North in Lapland lives the indigenous population of the Saame, who wander across the borders of Norway, Sweden and Finland, herding reindeer and making a nomadic living. (Think of the Inuit Eskimos of Alaska and Northern Canada). The area of Lapland is vast and extremely sparsely populated - roughly the size of Montana. What is worse,

---

Tomi T Ahonen

the Saame people do not stay put, they roam around the region.

Like any modern people, the Saame do have needs to consume television content. Their language is different to that of the Norwegians, and much of their culture and interests are quite different from mainstream Norway. Because of the enormous expanse of area and sparse population, it would be prohibitively expensive to set up television broadcasts to the whole of Lapland, just to meet the needs of the very few Saame population that amounts to a few tens of thousands of Saame in Norway.

Here is where cellphone technology can help. Norway has been deploying its cellular coverage very deep into Lapland. Since the cellular coverage is there already - admittedly not quite in every nook and cranny, but much more extensively than broadcast TV. Now Norwegian TV together with the wireless carrier Telenor they have launched TV programming exclusive to the Saame population, available via cellphones using the cellular network. There is no need to install a separate broadcast network and a TV frequency will not need to be allocated to the occasional viewing by this small population.

And the added bonus is that the Saame population can get their "regional" programming actually anywhere in Norway, meaning all of Southern

---

20% of South Koreans watched video on cellphones in 2007
Source: TNS Global Telecoms Insights 2007

Norway as well, when a given Saame travels say to Oslo the capital. Again, full national coverage of Saame language programming is now available, but without dedicating scarce national TV broadcasting spectrum for this small population. This kind of localized programming can be delivered quite efficiently via 3G networks as long as there are not large numbers of simultaneous viewers.

Moment and mobile TV

The second of the Six M's is Moment, expanding the concept of time. One of the most powerful elements of the cellphone, the Moment attribute is multitasking, doing more than one thing at the same time. Obvious uses include TiVo and PVR style pausing live TV and recording shows to watch later, etc. However, we can go much further on the Moment attribute around mobile and TV.

Spycams to Live TV shows

A big opportunity of "TV-related" content is the concept of "spycams" within various live and reality TV formats. The idea is not to show the broadcast feed variant to cellphone users when they are not at home - even though some may consume this content also in this way. The idea is to show the cellphone content *in parallel* to the viewing of the main show on broadcast TV. We want the TV viewer to consume simultaneously two broadcasts of the same show. How is this possible? By using shows with exclusive premium-cost spycam.

The cellphone based spycam idea was introduced in Sweden and Italy in the *Big Brother* house reality TV show. Six exclusive cameras were installed into the *Big Brother* house, which could only be accessed by 3G cellphones, and at a premium cost. The idea was not that a fan of the show might watch one of these exclusive spycams when moving about town; rather that this viewing would be done at home, in parallel to the broadcast TV show being televised live. Say you noticed on the main TV show that two of the house members left the others in the living room, and went to the kitchen. Moreover, that the broadcast feed stayed on the six other housemates still in the living room. You could now use the 3G cellphone to "spy" on what was going on in the kitchen.

This is what I mean by a "TV-related" service on the 7th Mass Media. We enhance the viewing experience with the cellphone, while people sit at home watching TV. Just in Sweden, the wireless carrier/mobile operator Tre (Three/Hutchison) reported that they sold half a million premium video live sessions to 3G phone users in the 2004 run of *Big Brother*. Bear in mind that the

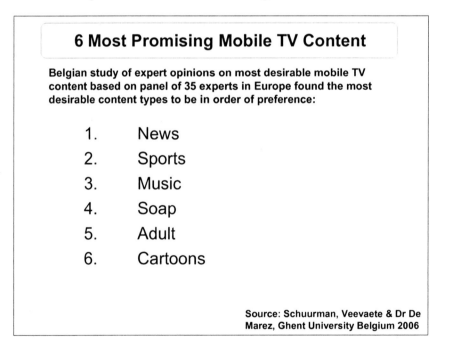

6 Most Promising Mobile TV Content

Belgian study of expert opinions on most desirable mobile TV content based on panel of 35 experts in Europe found the most desirable content types to be in order of preference:

1. News
2. Sports
3. Music
4. Soap
5. Adult
6. Cartoons

Source: Schuurman, Veevaete & Dr De Marez, Ghent University Belgium 2006

total Swedish population is only 8 million and back then the 3G cellphone penetration in Sweden was around 100,000 handsets.

MTV used the idea of the spycam in 2005 with the Video Music Awards for Europe. MTV Europe offered premium 3G viewers a backstage pass to the same show. So while one artist was making an acceptance speech, the spy cams could used to see what gossip was happening backstage, etc. In effect, cellphone users were sold a VIP backstage pass.

Me and mobile TV

The third attribute is Me, expressing oneself and personalizing the phone. The phone allows us to interact and engage with our content. One of the most powerful parts of the mobile-TV proposition is the voting in reality TV shows. This is such a big element that I will make it a separate section of this chapter.

C   SMS TEXT MESSAGES AND LIVE TV

American readers will be aware of the tremendous success of SMS text messaging voting of *American Idol, which* received national attention already in 2004. TV voting actually goes back to 2001, when MTV introduced its revolutionary TV show, *Videoclash*. It was the first TV program where viewers could select what to see next, in real time, by sending text messages to the show.

The *American Idol* TV show is based on the *Pop Idol* format originally developed by Fremantle Media in the UK, together with 19 Management. By the summer of 2006 had been run 67 times in 32 countries, from *Australian Idol* to the *Brazilian Idolos*, from France's *Neuvelle Star* to Germany's *Deutschland Sucht den Superstar*, and so forth. Many copy-cats have also run, such as *China Idol*, where more votes were cast than in any political election in the world.

A White Paper by SMLXL entitled ***Pop Idol***, discussed the *Pop Idol/American Idol* reality TV format in 2006. The White Paper revealed that the 67 *Pop Idol* contests that had already been completed, had achieved a total of 3.2 billion viewings worldwide. The more amazing number is that these viewings had generated viewer votes of 1.9 billion, mostly via SMS text votes. Bearing in mind that the *Pop Idol/American Idol* format shows tend to be the most-watched TV show in each of the countries it has run, thus achieving large TV advertising revenues; the 1.9 billion televotes have produced the owners of the show a windfall income of 600 million dollars by the summer of 2006. This amount was split of course between the broadcasters and telecoms carriers (operators).

Multi-user and Mobile TV

The fourth M is multi-user or the community dimension. Recently various social networking and digital community services have emerged in the mobile TV space, from user-generated content to SMS-chat boards broadcast on night time TV. Let me show you user-generated content for mobile TV.

User-generated plots

The Dutch TV innovator, Endemol (who created the *Big Brother* format)launched a cartoon serial of "mobisodes" to cellphone TV, which aired in Spain in 2006. The gimmick of the show is that viewers were asked to vote roughly once every three episodes on what direction the show should next take. As the shows were mobisodes - short clips - and on cartoon - i.e. no contracts to renegotiate if a lead character was killed off too early etc. - this could be done rather easily. As TV broadcasters become ever more familiar with the new medium, they can incorporate such innovations.

SMS Chat

SMS-to-TV chat was invented in Finland where the services launched in 2001. SMS-to-TV chat boards run on all commercial TV channels all night generating about 1,000 premium SMS text message chat comments per hour.

You might wonder that why do not these people use internet chat boards? After all, Finland is one of the world's highest penetration internet and broadband countries. Nevertheless, on an internet chat only a small part of the population might be exposed to your comments. On TV, the content is broadcast to every home. It feeds the ego of the chat-crazed TV viewer and SMS-to-TV chat boards now are emerging in most countries. That is the enormous addiction to SMS-to-TV chat. Alan Moore and I discussed this in our book *Communities Dominate Brands*:

> *The level of the premium paid on SMS-to-TV chat grew to nine times that of person-to-person text messaging by the end of 2003. With three channels all offering this service, even that did not curb the appetite of Finnish TV viewers, and avatars were introduced to read the message in its robotic voice, the price premium was 18 times that of regular person-to-person SMS. The programming was incredibly addictive and profitable.*
> - Tomi T Ahonen & Alan Moore, *Communities Dominate Brands*, 2005

The inventor of the SMS-TV chat format, Finnish broadcaster MainosTV3 said in 2006 that it earns 10 Million Euros ($15 Million) out of its share of the TV chat revenues annually. Also bear in mind that Finland's total population is only 5 million, so the TV chat income for just one of Finland's

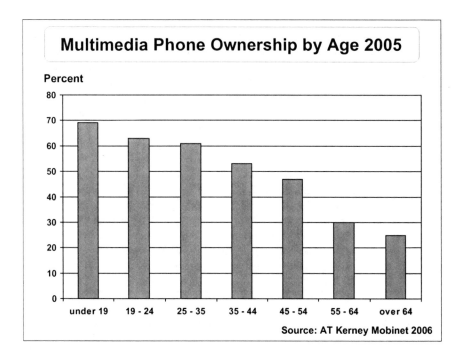

Multimedia Phone Ownership by Age 2005

Percent

Source: AT Kerney Mobinet 2006

broadcasters averages 3 dollars per person per year of bonus revenues beyond advertising and subscription income. If we assume the same level of spending, the value of this idea in America could easily be 900 million dollars for just one of the major national network broadcasters like CBS, ABC or NBC.

The shows are so profitable that overnight they replaced the half-hour length infomercials such as dieting miracle cures, super kitchen appliances, wonder-cleaner fluids and self-help seminars that used to run in night-time TV.

SMS-to-TV Games

Another variant of multi-user cellphone services is interactive multiplayer gaming on broadcast TV channels. The first SMS-TV games were simple crossword puzzles and similar games where participants were asked to send premium SMS messages to be the first to figure out the puzzle on the screen. Often the prizes were nothing more than seeing your name on a leaderboard.

Since then the industry has developed dozens of gaming formats. For example, soccer and ice hockey goal-scoring games where the TV screen shows the goal overlaid with a grid of numbers corresponding to the cellphone number keys. In front of the goal is one or even two live hosts acting as the goal-tenders, who try to block the virtual soccer balls or hockey pucks being shot at them by the TV viewers. What may seem moronic when described in words, does in fact deliver lots of interactivity on such TV shows and channels.

Another typical SMS-to-TV game is a kind of killer-car/robot game in Malaysia where gamers control robot-cars that try to crash into each other in a demolition-derby, until only one is left as the winner. Imagine gladiators with cars, but controlled by the gaming viewers on their cellphones. The game is so entertaining just as car-crashing competition that it is highly watched content even by those who are not paying to play the game.

SMS-to-TV rap

The latest variant from Finland is *"SMS-to-TV rap"* - by, which young rapper-wannabes send their rap lyrics in 160 characters to the rapping avatar on TV. You get to select the appearance of the digital rapper - what kind of hair, skin color, dress, etc., and then have the avatar read out your rap lyrics. Two live DJ's comment on the lyrics. In addition, the kids cannot get enough of it. They are thinking. *"Perhaps there is a record producer watching the show, maybe I*

Average creator of video for YouTube was paid 0 dollars
Source: YouTube 2007

---

should send my rap in **again**, *to be sure it was noticed..."*
SMS-to-TV rap premium SMS in Finland is charged at over 26 times the regular rate of SMS text messages or about 2 dollars per rap. The cellphone has made it possible to fulfill Andy Warhol's prediction of 15 minutes of fame. Except that on SMS-to-TV rapping it is more like 15 seconds of fame.

D   HOW MUCH MONEY?

The fifth of the Six M's is Money, expending financial resources. A good example of a mobile TV service generating money is TV voting used in hit reality and gaming shows from *Big Brother in the UK*, to *American Idol* to *Who Wants to be a Millionaire* in India. Premium SMS text messaging revenues are rapidly becoming a significant source for whole networks. Endemol says its *Big Brother* formats deliver 25% of revenues from cellphones in Europe, while Asian broadcaster Star says already out of its total earnings over 5% in many of its markets come from SMS revenues. In An Italian SMS dating service on TV generates 5 million Euros ($6 Million) per year. Already a 900 Million dollar

---

business in its own right worldwide in 2006, SMS-to-TV is also the most profitable TV format of all time.

The TV industry worldwide is in transition, as it noticed starting with the USA and UK in 2004, and the world following in 2005 that the industry earned more from subscription revenues (cable TV) than advertising. However, because of SMS-to-TV, Finland is ahead of that, and Finland became the first country where the domestic commercial television industry earned more from wireless revenues than advertising according to Digita in 2004.

Its not all fun and games with cellphone participation. With money come also problems. British broadcast TV was rocked in 2007 with several scandals involving viewer vote-in shows and other interactive programming. Some TV quiz shows with premium SMS text messaging as the contest vehicle were accepting messages - and taking payments - after the contest itself was already closed. Some TV shows awarded prizes for bogus winners etc. The British telecoms and broadcast regulator, Ofcom took strong action in the Summer of 2007 to weed out the problems and several TV shows were given large fines for running fraudulent games.

Average creator of video for SeeMeTV was paid 27 dollars
Source: Three UK 2007

The Machines attribute in mobile TV

The last of the Six M's is Machines, empowering automation and gadgets. Remote control and remote monitoring. I have often said that the cellphone is the perfect remote control for any device that is beyond line of sight, like controlling and monitoring our home, our office, our car, etc.

From TiVo to Network PVR

Now some broadcasters are introducing what they call "Network PVR's" (Personal Video Recorders). TiVo is a PVR, so this is a kind of evolution beyond basic TiVo. The first such service was launched in Italy and the type of technology is being developed also for example by Korean mobile TV innovator OnTimeTek and British broadcaster Channel 4. With a network PVR, you do not need to buy a hard disk video recorder like a TiVo box. You can pause and rewind live TV, skip past ads, and do just about any kind of recording and repeat viewing of content but the "TiVo box" sits at the network side of your cable connection.

What makes Network PVR so unique is that you are not limited to viewing your preferred TV content at home on only your own TV set. If you have to pause a live TV show, you can continue watching it at the office, at a friend's house, and obviously also on a 3G phone if you want. Nevertheless, here is the killer - if you forgot to set the recording, yes you can control the network PVR with your cellphone! Stuck in an unanticipated traffic jam while the game is about to start, no problem, take your phone and start to record. When you get home, some 15 minutes too late for the beginning, no problem! Just do the time-shift, and watch the game from the very beginning, in almost real time. As you skip the ads, you catch up to the real time broadcast before the end of the game.

The Magic of Innovation

The TV related converged cellphone-TV industry is still a child, at only seven years of age. Most innovations are arguably only baby-steps into a much brighter future. However, there are plenty of exciting examples from around the world.

I want my MTV... on a cellphone?

MTV has been developing the mobisodes type of custom programming even further. Their *Head and Body* cellphone TV show episodes were all designed to be very easily enjoyed on the small screen and also developed to work without spoken words - thus the mobisodes could be shown in the various European countries some, which have language groups measured only in the few millions. MTV understood that subtitling would also not work well on the tiny screen.

Today MTV's European networks are used as a testbed for programs and concepts that could be considered for the main broadcast channel. Meanwhile back in the USA, MTV's parent has released MTV *Mobile Junk 2.0*, a 3G cellphone content channel by, which MTV can test out new programming concepts on small loyal MTV audiences, and then bring only the most successful ones to the broadcast channels. Then in the most advanced cellphone market, Japan, MTV has introduced a service of user-generated video content, where the benefit is that 3G cellphone users watch the user-generated content and vote for what they think is best, and those videos that are voted best get to be seen on the broadcast version of MTV Japan.

Digital broadcast cellphone TV

In the summer of 2005 a new type of broadcaster launched its service commercially in Asia. Tu Media became the first to broadcast digital cellphone TV content in South Korea, on a broadcast technology called DMB. In America two rival broadcast technologies of ability will launch, one on a global standard called DVB-H and another on a more USA-centric standard called MediaFlo.

We have had broadcasts to pocket TV for two decades, with little Casio

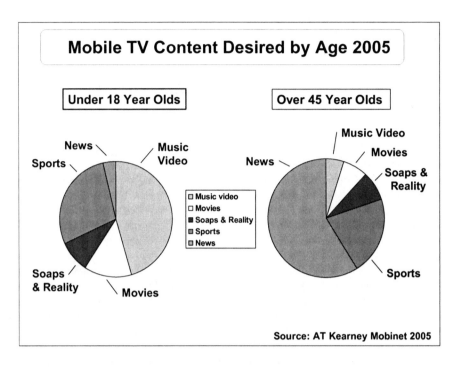

Mobile TV Content Desired by Age 2005

Under 18 Year Olds

Over 45 Year Olds

News
Sports
Music Video

☐ Music video
☐ Movies
■ Soaps & Reality
▨ Sports
▨ News

Soaps & Reality
Movies

Music Video
Movies
News
Soaps & Reality
Sports

Source: AT Kearney Mobinet 2005

and other pocket TV on small screens. These suffered from poor reception and fuzzy images due to the analog transmission technology and were limited to the few TV channels that were visible on standard analog broadcast TV. Now digital broadcast to cellphones will bring both the clarity of digital broadcasts and a much wider range of TV channels to pocket TV.

With digital technology optimized for the tiny screen the picture is brilliantly clear and differing from 3G cellphone TV, the digital portable TV is completely jitter-free. The best way to imagine it is to think of integrating the cable TV or satellite TV set-top box directly into the cellphone. Depending on the memory and capability of the phone, various TiVo type of Personal Video Recorder (PVR) functions can be incorporated into the TV-phone, such as pausing live TV etc.

South Korea was first to launch such full digital broadcast on DMB technology in the summer of 2005 and by the summer of 2007 in South Korea over 6 million DMB capable handsets and other portable digital TV receivers such as TV screens in cars and TV receivers for laptop PCs had been activated on two rival DMB broadcast systems. The South Korean cellphone population is about 40 million, so just in two years, about 15% of all Korean cellphone owners had migrated to digital pocket TV on their phones, cars and laptop PCs.

E   PARTICIPATE IN THE TV SHOW

TV participation is not limited to votes on *American Idol* or sending in videoclips to a TV show. With TV-related content, there is a lot of innovation and we see signs of successes from various countries around the world.

Star Text

One of the first ideas was launched in the Philippines in 2003, called *Star Text*. With *Star Text* various celebrities from the Philippines agree to be available via *Star Text* to their fans for a limited time. Various TV and movie actors, talk show and game show celebrities, pop and rock stars, athletes etc have participated. The vehicle of interaction is of course premium SMS text messaging. The messages cost about five times the regular rate of text messaging. Fans are very happy to be able to communicate directly with their stars, and this premium is not seen as prohibitively expensive.

The incentive to the celebrities to participate, is that they get a cut of the premium payments - they get paid for every response they make. As being one of the featured celebrities on *Star Text* is a short-term limited time by, which any one star is on the system, the stars will not be overly burdened, and also the stars can limit the "exposure" their persona gets in the media. Yet they get invaluable direct feedback from their devoted fans. A direct dialogue with them.

There are filters to eliminate rude messages and stars will not reply to inappropriate messages that will simply be rejected by the system. The stars will naturally not respond to the messages using the clumsy text input of a cellphone, but rather will have a comfortable personal computer keyboard and screen by, which to respond. The system will have many automated standard response templates like "thank you for writing" etc, but the star will typically include one or two lines of real responses to each fan.

Include your jokes with American Idol stars

As TV show producers become more familiar with the cellphone, its abilities, and the personal nature of it, they will continue to innovate further. For example, the British variant of *American Idol*, called *Pop Idol* in 2004 launched MMS picture messages of its stars. It used cartoon-like "speech bubbles" that the cellphone user could then fill in with text. There was a premium charge of course, but now the fans could send the image of their star, with a speech bubble and a custom message, to a friend. This allowed fans of the show to create their own jokes and personalize messages, to have the Pop Idol stars "talk" to their friends.

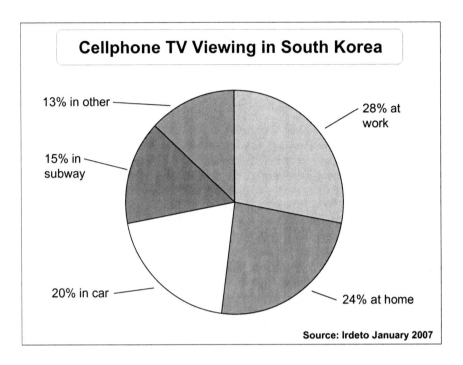

Cellphone TV Viewing in South Korea

13% in other

28% at work

15% in subway

20% in car

24% at home

Source: Irdeto January 2007

Measure viewers better than with Nielsen ratings

Another variant of viewer participation was introduced in New Zealand, on what they called *Power Points*. Whenever you saw a special *Power Points* logo on the screen you were to send a text message to the prescribed number. Each message was charged at SMS charges, but viewers who did participate, would gain points that could be used for buying cellphone content like ringtones and pictures. As a further incentive, all who participated in *Power Points* would get a chance to win one of several cars.

The TV channel received real-time accurate information on its viewers. Much more accurately than Nielsen ratings and diaries and boxes of what is on. As cellphones are personal, the accuracy of this measurement was very precise on, which family member was watching. Did people who watched the beginning of the show stay to the end. Did viewers of the lead show follow onto the following show on a given night, etc.

Linear content, non-linear advertising

For decades radio and television broadcasters have learned that advertising needs to be embedded into the linear flow of the programs. Therefore, a TV show would have ads at the beginning and end, and often in the middle: within the same linear experience as watching the content. With mobile TV, this need not be the case. As mobile phones allow tracking of money, and phones are personal, we can split the viewing consumption from the advertising consumption.

Less advertising?

For example, we could have an allowance of programming that could be consumed in exchange for a set number of ads. As the ads are targeted and personalized, many less ads would be needed per TV episode. The internet TV service *Joost* shows only 3 minutes of ads per hour of programming (5 percent of the time), in stark contrast with traditional formats when 12-15 minutes of ads are shown per hour (20%-25% of the time).

Now the mobile TV provider could have for example a weekly allowance of ads, a handful, perhaps up to a dozen, which would then create a balance of free viewing time for the mobile TV consumer. Now you do not need to interrupt the movie or show to force viewers to watch ads. The show can begin directly, without forcing viewers to watch an ad first. The linkage between linear programs and their related advertising will be broken. In Japan on the 1Seg technology based digital TV broadcasts to cellphones, a separate parallel interactive channel allows for this kind of advertising to run totally separate from viewing the programs.

Watch this space!

TV and the cellphone will converge. There will be hundreds of variants of clips, live TV, interaction, voting, user-content, remote control etc. What is important to understand, is that traditional broadcast TV content will not be viewed primarily on cellphones. Yes, some will, but the majority of our TV viewing will be on our new plasma screen TV at home. What the cellphone-TV will do, is to help introduce new formats and concepts that were not possible before.

The convergence of mobile and broadcast television is inevitable. One of the first broadcast executives to confirm that vision was the CEO of the largest South Korean broadcaster KBS, Yun-Joo Jung, who said in November 2005, *"The mobile will be the main device to enjoy radio and TV programmes anytime, anywhere."*

Case Study 10 from the Netherlands
Pop Kids

Pop Kids could be summarized as *American Idol* meets Tamagotchi. Yes, the future of reality TV will come from the virtual worlds. Dutch digital content developer Ex Machina has developed a variation on the *Pop Idol/American Idol* reality TV format that has added on online and mobile element, and in effect merged the childrens toy Tamagotchi with the *Idols* reality TV show. Here is how it works.

In *Pop Kids* two parents are needed, with cellphones, to create their Pop (Idol) Kid. This is a virtual baby, which grows in the form of an avatar. Much like the tamagotchi toy - or indeed a horse in the *Super Stable* case study before - the Pop Kid will need to be nurtured, trained, played with and developed - by both parents ideally - to become a fully rounded contestant in the eventual *Pop Kids* reality musician contest.

The system takes the parents' music tastes into account when creating the baby's virtual DNA - as if merging the genes of the parents. If the father likes rock and roll, and the mother likes classical music, the kid might develop a music taste in something like Apocalyptica's heavy-metal-meet-symphony-orchestra style of music.

Parents also have to decide when to enter the growing child into music classes, dancing classes, singing classes etc. All of the training will cost, of course, paid for by the parents as premium SMS charges onto their cellphones. Any conflicts among the parents, for example disagreements over what area of music the kid should focus in, will also reflect in the "character" of of the *Pop Kid* (*"I had a troubled youth, my parents were arguing all the time"*). As the child matures there are plenty of opportunities to enter childrens' contests as further preparation for the eventual big national TV contest. Of course, in the end of the 18 days' incubation there is a national contest on TV among all *Pop Kids* that will then allow the winners to be determined, by public SMS voting.

This kind of involvement puts a new twist on the *American Idol/Pop Idol* format. No longer is the producer of the show in charge, selecting who are the participants. Now the viewers can become participants themselves, by becoming parents to their *Pop Kids* and joining in co-creating the show.

"Mobile phones will replace TV as most important medium."
Andrew Robertson, CEO of BBDO

XII
Mobile Advertising
Lets go mAd

The cellphone can receive messages. So will it have advertising? Of course, it will. As all other media before it, advertising will be part of the content we will consume on cellphones. There already are a vast range of advertisement, sponsorship and other marketing messages delivered to cellphones. The first mobile advertising (mAd) was served onto cellphones in Finland in 2000 to enable SMS news headlines delivered for free. By the end of 2007, Informa reported that mobile advertising worldwide was worth 2.2 billion dollars. So lets get mAd: mAd as in mobile Advertising.

A   ALL PREVIOUS ADVERTISING WORKS ON PHONE

The cellphone has a speaker and screen, can access the internet and display static pages, video clips and audio files. The cellphone can therefore transmit most existing forms of advertising and marketing communication. From single page advertisements and classified ads to TV and radio spots to web banner ads and "interstitials" - the kind of ads that appear briefly on screen as a longer web pages load. Let me start with basic messaging.

Simple coupons and messages

In its simplest form, advertising on cellphones can be discount coupons and various alert messages. All around the world little ad campaigns have been built around delivering advertisements via SMS text messaging and WAP pages. Some are like banner ads on the internet, where a bit of news content or a sports score or map is delivered, sponsored by McDonald's or Nike or Coca Cola. It could be a discount coupon that you can receive by dialing a certain number, or received as part of a promotion, or forwarded by a friend, in what is called "viral marketing". In advertising campaigns in many European countries, SMS and WAP are becoming common elements of new media elements in advertising.

Admob, billions served

A great example of how "cellphone economics" play on any hit service is the international wireless advertising company Admob. Launched in 2006, a year later Admob was delivering 1.5 billion cellphone ads per month and by the end of 2007 was delivering 2.5 billion banner ads per month. Yes, you read it right, from zero to 2.5 *billion* ads monthly in under two years. Admob serves its cellphone ads in about two dozen countries including the USA and the UK.

Sending a coupon, a map, a menu, a listing of movies, or nearest locations to access some product or service is quite predictable as advertising on cellphones. A more advanced option is capitalizing on the *location information* of cellphone users. Already today, even at its crudest level of accuracy, the carriers can track within a mile, or often within a few hundred feet, the rough location of every cellphone in their network. You do not have to be speaking on the phone, as long as it is turned on, and finds a network signal, its location is known. Then depending on the technology deployed in the network, the accuracy can be as inaccurate as a mile, to as precise as ten feet (3 meters). Advertisers early latched upon this prospect, and invented location-based advertising.

B   LOCATION-BASED SPAM

The idea behind Location-Based ads is an old one. It was widely discussed in the industry around 2001 when I chaired the world's first conference on wireless advertising and marketing. The basic concept behind Location-based ads is easy to get, but fatally flawed. So much so that there will be no significant business out of so-called location-based (spam) advertising. Let me explain first what it is.

What location-based advertising will not be like

The original idea was that a main street store or some shopping mall would notice a given target customer "within range" such as walking within a few minutes from a given store, or inside the shopping mall. These could be personalized to each individual consumer and such ads could greet the visitor to a mall for example, such as the actor Tom Cruise experienced in the movie *Minority Report*. For example, a florist might have an extra supply of roses, and send an alert to every person within walking distance of the flower shop that they have roses on sale at a dozen for the price of six, or something like that. We can include a map to my store, a coupon for discounts, etc.

Willing to Receive Mobile Advertising

Survey of 1,500 UK youth aged 11-20 by Q Research in 2007

32%   of UK youth said they were willing to accept mobile ads in general

71%   said they were willing to receive cellphone ads if they were personally targeted

76%   said they would welcome mobile advertising if that consisted of coupons and discounts

82%   said they would be delighted to receive top-ups to their pay-as-you-go/prepaid accounts through cellphone ads

Source: Q Research February 2007

Conceptually it makes sense and engineers tend to love this idea. I could advertise to those prospective customers who are near me. There is likely some novelty value to this type of advertising, so early on some may even be welcome by some random pedestrians. Merchants also may feel that this is a way to increase the traffic i.e. "footfall" to their stores. Nevertheless, much like the reaction to junk mail at home, and spam e-mails at work, very soon unsolicited generic push ads will be rejected by consumers. All early attempts at this have failed and I strongly discourage building mAd concepts around this idea.

Proximity based ads, such as those using Bluetooth, are actually just a variant of this interruptive location-based ad. Rather than using the cellular network's location identity, they use the proximity of a Bluetooth enabled phone. However, the idea is the same, and it is as pointless. Yes, location-based spam has some academic appeal to those who love technology. Nevertheless, for practical purposes, this concept is pretty much as dead as it can be.

C   MADONNA GOES "mAd"

I have been critical of the basic location-based spam advertising ever since my first book was released in 2002. However, I have always added that there is a big opportunity in location-based ads. Not location-based unsolicited spam relating to nearby shops and stores. Rather location-based *event* ads. So already in my second book *M-Profits*, I described the Madonna Concert mobile ad proposition. It is worth repeating. Imagine Madonna performing at Yankee Stadium in New York. As her fans walk in, they get a personalized message like this:

> *Dear Mr Ahonen, thank U 4 attending my concert. Here is a coupon for 20% off on my new CD. Download it directly or forward the ad. Enjoy the concert. Madonna*

The beauty of the cellphone ad starts from the mass event and location-based services. We know anyone attending Madonna's concert is a dedicated Madonna fan. With an ad like that, every fan of hers will love to receive a personal greeting from Madonna. It could include a response link where the fan is asked to join Madonna's fan club - for free - and to receive free gifts exclusive to that concert, such as a free screen saver of Madonna from that evening's concert at Yankee Stadium.

17.2% of US cellphone users received ads in 2007
Source: M:Metrics October 2007

Fans will love this type of direct contact

Almost 100% in the audience are true Madonna fans. These will all opt for joining the fan club. They will be so proud of this contact by their favorite star that the next week they will be showing the message - and the various freebies of the fan club - to all of their friends who also like Madonna but who missed the concert. So what is in it for the star? In fact, here is the driver of the whole proposition. Madonna gets much more from this than any other marketing tool she could ever expect to use.

How the artist wins out of this

Now Madonna has used location-based advertising to gain permission to market directly to 20,000 of her most loyal, paying fans in New York City. She repeats this across her global concert tour of 50 cities and she will have the cellphone numbers of approximately one million of her best fans worldwide. If the fans were willing to pay 50 dollars for the concert ticket, then these fans will be wanting to buy Madonna's next album.

It is very expensive to promote new music. Just the costs of making the

---

Tomi T Ahonen

music videos run into the millions of dollars, not to mention heavy advertising and sales support in the pop and rock magazines, appearances on all kinds of TV shows, pushing the music through radio stations, trying to get onto MTV playlists, etc. Much of the 30 billion dollar global music industry is marketing, trying to push the music to the buying public.

Would it not be so much easier if we knew exactly who are the biggest fans, and just sell directly to them? Without all the wasted marketing effort, such as Madonna's video playing to fans of heavy metal or rap or country who all will not buy her music.

Now she can. When Madonna releases her next album, she can send a message to her fans to pre-order the album or even buy the songs directly downloaded to her phone as I explained in the music chapter, is reality in South Korea today.

What is her cost? After just one such world tour, she has the cellphone numbers of one million of her most loyal and dedicated paying fans around the globe. To send an SMS to each of her 1 million fans even if they have no discount, and we assume 10 cents per SMS, gives a total marketing cost of

---

75.4% of Spanish cellphone users received ads in 2007
Source: M:Metrics October 2007

100,000 dollars. Assuming this is a pre-release offer of her new album that only her registered fans could buy, with this miniscule cost, she'd sell probably close to a million copies of her next album, with no other marketing costs at all.

With the smallest amount of planning and design in the campaign, it should also spread virally from the most passionate fans to the next tier of Madonna fans, perhaps to four or five million more, and many of those would also buy her next album very soon after it was released. This would be the lowest cost music marketing campaign to reach million sales of a music album, ever.

Would you like the same seat for the next concert?

But it is not only selling the next album. How about Madonna's world tour a year later. Then, when Madonna returns to New York, she can now contact each of her fans two months earlier, and offer discounted prebooked seats to Yankee Stadium. This time she can say that for a short time her fans can get two seats both at a 10% discount. By talking directly to the fans, each fan knows of at least one other close friend, who missed last year's concert, but who is enough of a fan that he/she would enjoy it. Make the fans sell the seats. Rather than selling out Yankee Stadium once, by repeat sales to those who attended last time, now she

---

gets two sell-outs. With the price of one text message. If we say 20,000 seats at Yankee Stadium to keep the math easy, and if we say 10 cents per SMS, she gets two sell-out concerts of 40,000 tickets sold, for a total marketing communications expense of... 2,000 dollars! (This is too easy...)

Engage with fan club

This process would build a virtuous cycle – those who attend her concerts get music first – and those who buy music first get early warning of upcoming concerts. Nevertheless, it would not stop there. Madonna could release her newest hits first to these registered fans for example as ringing tones. Note that she need not give away the song, as it is a new release, and nobody has any version of the song yet, Madonna can sell a million ring tones in just one day. It would not end there. Madonna could expand her brand through this channel. Almost anything she would want to release as a "Madonna product" such as t-shirts, books, fragrances, etc., could be marketed to these fans, as long as she kept giving some exclusive benefits, and did not over-expose herself via this channel.

As I discussed in the music chapter, artists are already moving into this direction setting up fan clubs around cellphones following the innovation of the

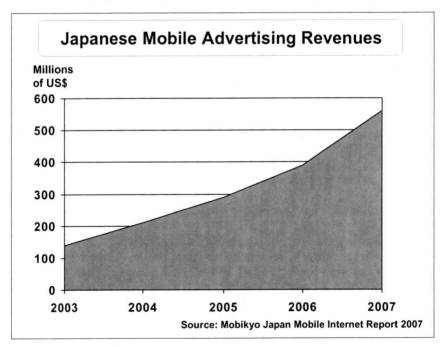

Hong Kong based pop duo, the Twins. Now artists such as Sean "Diddy" Combs the USA based rapper (formerly known as Puff Daddy and P Diddy) and CEO of Bad Boy Productions are developing ever more such tools to interact with fans in real time and via the cellphone.

Not just Madonna, obviously

This is the future of location-based advertising. Moreover, it does not stop with pop and rock music. How about all other events arranged at stadiums. Football. Baseball. Hockey. Basketball. Golf. Tennis. Motor racing. The Kentucky Derby, etc etc etc. Anywhere that people gather in the thousands to one venue for one purpose, for, which there is a charge for attending, these are all ripe for location-based ads. In addition, the fans will love the advertising, not hate it.

D   CAN ADVERTISING BECOME CONTENT

While the location-based ad is one possibility, an even bigger one is the innovation that is possible with advertising becoming content. Why not make advertainment or advergames as I showed in the gaming chapter. Combining entertainment and advertising i.e. advertainment, or combining videogames and advertising i.e. advergames. Make advertising so appealing that the target recipient values the advertisement inherently, as if it were paid content. *"Cannot be done"*, you say? Yes it can, and has already been done several times.

The art of music video grew out of advertising

MTV gives us a fantastic example of what any advertising/promotion should strive for. Back in the 1970s the music recording industry was trying to capitalize on the emergence of pop music TV shows. In the 1970s, huge worldwide artists like the Rolling Stones, Queen, David Bowie and Abba were being invited to every little local pop music show on hundreds of TV channels in a hundred countries. They simply did not have the time to tour the world to appear on Top of the Pops in England, Musicladen in Germany, American Bandstand in the USA, etc to promote each new hit every two months and new album every year.

The record producers discovered that they could send "film clips" of their latest hits to be played on the shows, even when the artists themselves did not have time to fly all around the world. These precursors to the modern music video were very clearly developed as the promotional tools for new music. They tended to feature the band performing on stage, lip-synching to the music.

My point is that these "film clips" of pop music artists performing their songs were *advertisements*. Their aim was to sell the hit song of the day, and help promote the sales of the latest album.

MTV took these three-and-a-half minute "film clips" of music, and started to play them in rotation when they launched on cable in 1982. They called them "music videos" and a new art form was born. What MTV was doing was a fantastic innovation. They took what had been built as advertising, and what was definitely free content to MTV - the music film clips - and turned these into the content shown on their 24 hour music TV channel, MTV.

And then - here is the part that always makes me smile - to a show already consisting 100% of advertising, MTV had the nerve to *sell advertising*. Now Pepsi, Nike, Levis and Pizza Hut were all fighting for paid advertising slots between the MTV videoclips, which themselves were obviously advertising. In the process, MTV became the most desired youth brand in the world. This is what I hold as the example when I lecture to the mobile telecoms, wireless content, and advertising industries. Lets take the MTV example, and try to build advertising content, which is so compelling that users will want to receive it.

The Nightlife Guide to the City

I discovered the first wireless service that fit this criterion, back in 2001. I wrote about it in my second book, *M-Profits*:

> *The Nightlife Guide to the City is a service of free content consisting totally of ads also has been pioneered already for the wireless telecoms environment. In Helsinki Finland, in the late Spring of 2001 the local youth magazine "City Lehti" with a strong mobile and internet presense, decided to launch the nightlife guide to Helsinki, targeted at the bar-hopping, disco-chomping night-life. The users have to sign up for the service - for free - and then they receive several SMS or WAP ads over the weekend. These are of course ads from the major bars, pubs and discos of Helsinki; advertising their specials, hours, visiting DJ's and bands, special theme nights, etc. The service was drawing a lot of initial interest from the club-hopping nightcrawlers of Helsinki.*
> Tomi T Ahonen, *M-Profits*, 2002

Notice that this kind of service might appeal to only 1% of the total population. Most people do not want to receive a series of five ads every Friday and another five every Saturday promoting the local night spots and their specials, DJs and bands. We simply do not go out enough every weekend to appreciate this. However, for those single people in their late teens and early 20s, who literally do go out every weekend club-hopping, for them this is a godsend. They will not even make decisions on where to go, before these free ads arrive. After that they decide, and as these are the influencers, and the "cool people" - where they go, their friends will follow. Clubs and bars know they can dramatically increase their business, if these trendsetters decide to make that bar

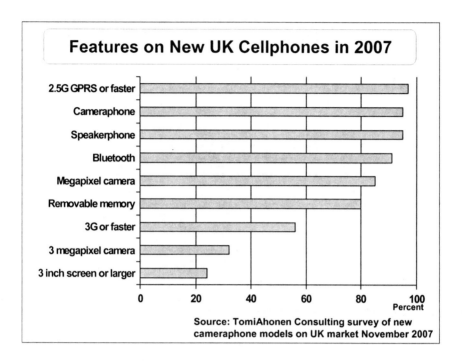

Features on New UK Cellphones in 2007

Source: TomiAhonen Consulting survey of new
cameraphone models on UK market November 2007

the spot of choice for that night.

The sales gimmick is that the five slots are auctioned based on their scarcity. Only five slots on a given Friday and only five slots the Saturday. If you want to be on this service and want to reach the heavy partying nightcrawlers, bid what you think this service is worth to you this weekend.

Yet another great example of advertising becoming content is advergaming with the October 2007 launch of two new spicy snack brands by Japanese snacks maker, Tohato. The company set up a massively multiplayer online game (MMOG), where gamers selected the brand of preference and joined its "Evil Army" and then fought in the *"World's Worst War"*. Signing up required purchase of a bag of the snacks. Gamers were encouraged to recruit friends to join, which earned them promotions in the army. The games were soon a national sensation and had 100,000 daily hits on the mobile internet in Japan.

E   LETS MAKE IT VIRAL

A major opportunity for mobile advertising and marketing is the ability to forward ads via viral marketing methods. If you liked the ad, you can forward it to your friend. There are many variants to this, including forwarding a link where your friend would then click on the link to receive the coupon or game or whatever is involved. The reason why forwarding a link is preferable to the advertisers, is that when your friend clicks on the link, then your friend's phone information can be captured by the advertiser as they now have direct contact from the cellphone of your friend..

Viral marketing

We carry our cellphone in our pockets every day everywhere, but not a separate pocket TV or portable radio, because of our need to remain connected. We want to be able to communicate. Yes, the cellphone can be used as a media channel to deliver content, but our addiction to the cellphone is based on the need to be connected, or more precisely our need to be reachable; it is not because of a need to be entertained.

This is where viral marketing finds its opportunity. We want to share our content on our phone(s). If the advertiser makes it easy (one click) and cheap (ideally for free) to forward ads, then the best fans of our products or services, can become their best promoters and evangelists. Jupiter Research revealed in September 2006 that 64% of consumers will try something that is recommended by a friend. Moreover, 69% of consumers will forward something they like, to

---

Effectiveness of Internet Ads vs Mobile Ads

Comparison of effectiveness of advertising with UK consumers

Selecting a credit card, mobile ads more effective than internet ads	38%
Selecting a car, mobile ads more effective than internet ads	41%
Selecting a bank account, mobile ads more effective than internet ads	42%
Selecting a TV set, mobile ads more effective than internet ads	54%
Selecting a supermarket, mobile ads more effective than internet ads	68%

Source: M:Metrics February 2008

---

their friends. Typically the number of people they will forward to is anywhere from 2 to 6 friends. Rudy de Waele, the industry guru who blogs at *M-Trends.org* says we should *"think global, act viral."*

Sufficiently contagious

I think we can be guided by what Mike Beeston, the CEO of Fjord, the UK based user interface specialist firm for cellphones, calls "sufficiently contagious". It should be the goal, the objective of any mobile service - and definitely for any service in the mobile advertising space. The mobile advertising must be so well done that the recipient not only likes it himself/herself, but is so much impressed by it that the recipient feels compelled to forward it to at least one other person. That is "sufficiently contagious".

Note that sufficiently contagious does not mean "totally contagious". Obviously no cellphone user will find everyone on their phone list of 150 names to want a given item of content. If our best friend likes it, probably our mother does not etc. However, if I get a really good game based on the Superbowl, I will know, which of my friends are also that much into football that they would probably like it. Sufficiently contagious. That is the standard.

Free guided video tours of hotels and resorts

The Greek travel industry has introduced free hotel advertisements with video clips and full interactivity, on cellphones. The Greek hotel industry to submits videoclips to the online cellphone based hotel guide. The cellphone users get to view the ads for free but the hotels are charged for the video traffic, by every time a clip is downloaded.

This is similar to the concept of toll-free (freephone) calls. It reverses the payment model and allows cellphone users to access content that is free to the users. In addition, why not, for any possible holiday destination, is it not better to pre-view it by cellphone before you decide on, which hotel to book. The service includes direct links to the hotel online sites for checking on availability and prices, allows direct online bookings and includes the ability to talk directly with the hotel receptionists etc. All free to the prospective tourist, all data transfer costs are picked up by the hotel in question.

F   ALPHA USERS THE ULTIMATE INFLUENCERS

Once we have compelling mobile marketing and advertising projects, then a further power boost is possible, mainly only via cellular networks, by using what are called "Alpha Users" (not to be confused with Alpha Males, the aggressive must-win type of Alpha Personality). Alpha Users are the people who want to tell their friends about the newest (coolest) services and ideas. Thus Alpha Users are far better than "Early Adopters" because Alpha Users both want to use new technologies (like Early Adopters) but they also are instinctively capable of spreading the word on anything they like.

This is an important point. Alpha Users are not the same as Early Adopters. There is some overlap and some very obvious Alpha Users are also Early Adopters. Nevertheless, Alpha Users were impossible to physically identify until the advent of cellphones, so understandably this radical marketing innovation sprung from Finland, only four years ago. My book *3G Marketing* was the first to introduce Alpha Users based on research by Finnish customer analytics specialist firm Xtract, in 2004.

To be clear on their differences, there are many Early Adopters who are not very social, so they rather prefer technology and new gadgets and can be isolated as people (the stereotypical techie geek). An Alpha User is naturally connected and connecting, very social. Also there are many who are not at all Early Adopters by technology orientation, but are still Alpha Users for a given community or group. We explained the Alpha User rather thoroughly with Alan Moore in my fourth book *Communities Dominate Brands* where we discuss Alpha Users in two chapters.

When we combine viral marketing (at a "Sufficiently Contagious" level) with Alpha Users, we get the best of all worlds for a wireless marketing or

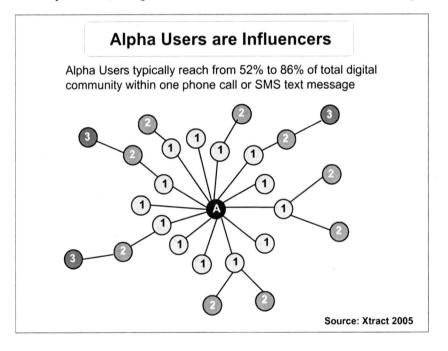

Alpha Users are Influencers

Alpha Users typically reach from 52% to 86% of total digital community within one phone call or SMS text message

Source: Xtract 2005

advertising campaign. Studies of Alpha Users have shown that less than 2% of the total group will know personally over half of the total group. These are the ideal viral marketing targets.

The method is what could be described as "social contagion". Driven by relevant content, put into context that pulls its audience and potential customers that then creates word of mouth and a viral spreading of that information digitally, which ultimately becomes buzz or PR friendly articles and columns – with credibility. Your customers have seeded and marketed your product for you. They are happy to do it for you, as long as your product is worth talking about.

Interruption to interactive to engagement

We introduced *Engagement Marketing* with Alan Moore in our book **Communities Dominate Brands**, for several chapters. Alan coined the term Engagement Marketing. Most current advertising is interruptive advertising. On TV and radio interrupt the programming we want, to play advertisements we mostly do not want. Thus people use technologies such as PVRs (Personal Video Recorders) like TiVo and Sky+ to skip past ads. We also get bombarded by interruptive ads in our magazines and newspapers, on billboards, before the movies start at the cinema, and as the banner ads and pop-ups on the internet.

A newer form of advertising is interactive advertising. If we have an interactive link such as for example Google Ad Words on the internet, we can now selectively click onto an ad, and be brought to the company (or web page) that the advertiser would want us to see. It is an improvement from interruption, brings the choice to the user (many talk about shifting from "push advertising" to "pull advertising").

Marlboro interactive

A good example of what can be done with cellphones in the interactive advertising space, is a campaign by Marlboro in Japan. They had a unique messaging code on the inside flap of every pack of Marlboro cigarettes. The Japanese smoking consumer was invited to send that code to the number and increase a chance to win Marlboro merchandise like T-shirts, caps, sweaters, etc.

The point of the campaign was that Marlboro in Japan knew that cellphone users worldwide do not share their phones. The same smoker would be the same cellphone user. So now they could collect an individual perfectly accurate record of how their cigarettes were consumed., which customer sent two codes per day (smoking two packs per day on average) and, which customer sent one code per week (smoking thus only 2-3 cigarettes per day) etc. The wireless marketing campaign on cellphones became a very powerful customer behavior measurement tool, and certainly could not be replicated on any other mass media channel.

Beyond that is *engagement marketing*. With engagement marketing, the user - the recipient of the advertising - becomes personally involved in co-creating the advertising experience. The examples of ad campaigns running on an engagement marketing principle are still rare but are starting to emerge. I will discuss Blyk in the Case Study at the end of this chapter as one of the best ones so far. Engaging with customers is a radical departure for most advertising and branding executives around the world. Coca Cola Chief Marketing Officer Stephen C Jones explained in 2005:

> *Wireless technology has enabled the consumer to review and reject much of the one way messaging they receive and resort the dialogue that's relevant to fit the way they live. Experiencing a Coke or interacting with an enthusiastic Coke employee on line or in person has always been far more motivating than 30 seconds of anthemic brand worshipping. Its not that TV and radio programs are irrelevant. Its the lack of ability to develop a relationship with an ad that makes the medium a less viable marketing tool.*
>
> Stephen C Jones, Chief Marketing Officer, Coca Cola

1.2 billion TV sets in the world in 2006
Source: ITU Digital Life 2006

A simple early example of Engagement Marketing comes from Italy. Vodafone Italy launched its picture messaging (MMS) service with a campaign of "My dream". Cameraphone users on the Vodafone network were invited to send in pictures of their dreams, which were showcases on the Vodafone website. Vodafone would then award the best daily dream to the customer, up to a limit of 15,000 Euros (about 22,000 US Dollars). Therefore, if your dream was a fancy mountain bike, or a fashionable leather sofa, or a designer dress, or a vacation or whatever, this dream might be the daily winner.

To understand how powerful marketing can be on cellphones, lets look at some statistics from Japan. I mentioned earlier that 54% of Japanese cellphone users consume ads on their phones. That alone is an impressive number. However, a more eye-opening statistic comes from a survey of Japanese cellphone users by Mobile Research and Goo Research from July 2006, which found that 44% of Japanese cellphone users have clicked on ads on cellphones.

Four out of ten Japanese cellphone customers are so happy with the advertising they receive on their phones that they click on the ads? This is the future. Ads on Japanese (and South Korean) networks are so advanced that they do invite users to click on the ads, to interact with them and to *engage*. On the

---

Tomi T Ahonen

web campaigns are considered great successes if they achieve 1% or 2% response rates. On well designed mobile ad campaigns, far greater success rates are common. On Blyk over six months, the average response rate was 29%. The world record was set by a very well targeted Gillette campaign in South Korea by AirCross that achieved a response rate of 98%!

Immediate call to action

The most potent ability of the cellphone, as opposed to any other advertising media, is its chance for immediate call to action. The cellphone is personal. It is an interactive media. It also can have the payment method in-built into the service. On the cellphone, every time, the user is only the one and same person. If the payment is enabled by the network (or charged via premium SMS) then all you need is to click once and your purchase has been authorized and charged. The billing is automatic, to your phone bill (or deducted from your prepaid/pay-as-you-go account).

The power of this is immense. We as an industry have not even scratched the surface of how big the immediate call-to-action can be. As

---

2.9 billion data-capable cellphones in the world in 2007
Source: Morgan Stanley 2008

---

advertising becomes more compelling on the cellphone, and advertisers learn that they can sell direct via the cellphone, it will dramatically accelerate the transition of advertising revenues from the earlier mass media to the Seventh of the Mass Media, the cellphone.

G   WE KNOW WHO YOU ARE

The last big benefit of cellphones for advertisers, and many consider this the holy grail, is the customer data. Every cellphone, whether on post-paid/contract account (with names, addresses etc registered) or on a pre-paid/pay-as-you-go account (which might have a dummy name like Donald Duck or no name and address at all) is individually tracked, at all times. Every phone and every network activity done by the phone (making calls, receiving messages, surfing the net etc) are logged to the system. Every one, every time, for everyone. This for 3.3 billion cellphones worldwide.

The cellular industry billing systems (or actually the charging and rating systems used to generate the billing information) are the most complex.billing

---

systems of any industry. They collect an immense array of data on transactions often worth only fractions of a penny, and do this for dozens of transactions daily across millions of customers. Compared with credit card companies and banks, the telecoms billing systems are a whole order of magnitude more deep and complex in the data they collect. Moreover, telecoms carriers of cellular networks have the most data to collect and sort.

Cellphone data is the next Intel Inside

Any media owner will appreciate knowing the media audience or customer. AMF Ventures measured the relative accuracy and completeness of data about audiences and customers that can be collected across three media in the summer of 2007. On TV they found that only 1% of audience data is captured. On the internet, a much more complete picture is formed, as 10% of audience data is collected. However, AMF Ventures found that only on mobile, is 90% of audience data collected, making it the media, which by far has the best information about its audience and customers.

Analytics 2.0

But it is not just collecting information on what I consume on a cellphone. This industry actually allows a radical new way of measuring relevant data on customer, the social aspect of our consumption. Much like "Web 2.0" or digital communities and social networking is radically altering the internet experience, now with the accuracy offered by cellphone data mining, we can actually identify our *social context*, of not *what* we consume, but *with whom*.

Lets take ice hockey as an example. Its time for the NHL to play for the Stanley Cup, the annual championship of professional ice hockey based in Canada and the USA. I have been a long time NHL fan. If a network were to measure my SMS text messaging behavior during a given game in the series of the Stanley Cup finals, there would be a clear spike in my messaging traffic.

Next, the network could identify, which phone numbers are those to, which I send messages. Then by examining the patterns of those people I am communicating with during a game, rapidly a network of NHL-related messaging starts to form. A circle of perhaps a dozen friends of mine, but most of those will have some other friends that also exchange these messages, and so on, and so on. Soon it becomes possible to isolate essentially all NHL fans within the customer base of one wireless carrier.

Note that we cannot do this accurately on any other media. If our TV set is turned on, we do not know, which of the family members is actually watching the game. On the internet our identity is easily masked by corporate firewalls, multiple accounts, removing cookies periodically, etc. Nevertheless, on cellphones we know each phone is unique, and thus the messaging will be

US Consumer Device Preferences

Tracking survey of which consumer devices US respondents say they cannot live without by Pew American Life Project

In 2002:   In 2007:

63% Landline phone   51% Cellphone
47% Television   45% Internet
38% Internet   43% Television
38% Cellphone   40% Landline phone

Source: Pew American Life Project 2007

definitely between the two persons.

When such accuracy is possible, only then can we map out communities of interest by tracking the calls and messages between members of a community. Xtract reports that analyzing two months of cellphone data usually reveals most communities within the network. Bearing in mind a typical cellphone owner is a member of several interest groups and communities, family, work, hobbies, etc, the total number of communities that can be mapped is enormous.

Still, this is the dawn of the next age of customer insights. The analytics of not *what* we consume, but *with whom*. This could be called Data 2.0 or Analytics 2.0 in line with Web 2.0 for the internet. In addition, much like Web 2.0 brought great new business opportunities for services and companies such as Skype, MySpace, YouTube etc, so too will Analytics 2.0 bring radical new information and actionable customer insights to the data analytics side of mass media.

Must Request Permission

Finally, I want to end on the permission issue. All mobile advertising has to be permission-based. The mobile phone is the most personal mass media, and any intrusive unsolicited spam will be very strongly rejected by consumers.

The Mobile Marketing Association has issued guidelines and many carriers around the world have endorsed them. The primary overriding guideline is that all cellphone-based advertising must be opt-in, actively approved by the subscribers. Not passively, where the phone owner would have to "opt out" of it. No, every single customer needs to expressly give permission before ads are delivered. However, if we do that, we will build a new advertising media that has incredible potential for accuracy to advertisers, and value to recipients.

Early numbers

Many of the major players of the industry have recently talked of developing mobile advertising, from Nokia's Adserve to Google's passionate push into mobile, to Vodafone setting up even an annual conference for mobile advertising, or Ogilvy providing mobile workshops to its creative teams and its customers. Still today, most mobile advertising campaigns have been modest: trials, tests and mobile add-ons to other digital campaigns. So most of the data is still quite preliminary.

However, early data is coming in. In the UK, Q Research interviewed 1,500 youth about attitudes to mobile advertising. On the unqualified question about willingness to receive ads on cellphones, 68% said no i.e. only 32% said yes. Nevertheless, when the question was changed to offer targeted ads to personal tastes, 71% said yes. If the youth were offered coupons and discounts, 76% were willing to receive ads, and if the ads would fund top-ups of prepaid (pay-as-you-go) accounts, 82% of the British youth said yes, they would like mobile ads.

The first comparative analysis of mobile advertising and internet advertising was reported by M:Metrics in February 2008, and they revealed that mobile campaigns were typically between 30% and 70% more influential than internet campaigns in consumer decisions. Some of the categories measured were selecting credit cards (mobile ads 38% more influential than internet ads); automobiles (41%); TV sets (54%) and supermarkets (68%).

Mobile Advertising, mAd, will soon become the leading method of marketing communication, promotion, advertising and branding. The important thing to bear in mind is to go from interruption to engagement. To bring the target audience into the mix and make them part of the marketing process. To engage. For as long as there will be business, there will be promotion of goods and services, whether in the form of "advertising" or "marketing". To quote the economic statistician Roger W Babson, *"To stop advertising would be to stop growing."*

Case Study 11 from the UK

Blyk

Blyk is an invitation-only, youth-only virtual cellphone telecoms carrier, what is known as an MVNO (Mobile Virtual Network Operator) in the UK. The trick with Blyk is that the service is totally free to its members, who must consume ads on their cellphone to get minutes and SMS text messages to use. They get a modest balance of 217 free SMS text messages and 43 minutes of free calls as their monthly allowance (which works to an average of 7 SMS text messages and 1.4 minutes per day per day). In exchange, the Blyk customer agrees to receive and consume up to six advertising messages per day. Beyond these, the UK users can top-up the account at normal UK competitive top-up rates similar to any pay-as-you-go (prepay) cellphone account.

Blyk breaks telecoms taboos in many areas. One is its focus. Practically all telecoms operators in the world, including those with youth-targeted propositions, will sell their services to almost anyone. Blyk is very specific, they will only serve the 16 to 24 year age segment and will use legally acceptable proof of age for validating that the customer is of Blyk's intended age. If you are 15 or 25, you cannot get in. Furthermore, Blyk will not let just anyone join, you have to be invited to even sign up.

There have been many carriers who have tried an advertising based telecoms carrier business. Most were based on the idea that just prior to your call you had to listen to an ad. Blyk is quite different. Blyk is built around the idea of *user co-created advertising*. So rather than forcing its customers to be interrupted by intrusive ads, Blyk engages with its customers so well that it entices them to join in co-creating the marketing experience.

What is **"user co-created advertising"**? In Blyk's case it works like this. On first sign-up to the service, the Blyk user is asked to fill out a profile of interests. Based on this profile that customer's advertising will be targeted.

Then the companies who do the advertising - and Blyk has landed global giants such as Coca Cola, Buena Vista, MasterCard and L'Oreal among its first advertisers - will start to engage in dialog with the customers. So for example, if a 17-year-old girl says she has an interest in make-up, then L'Oreal could ask her on one day, what kind of make-up she is interested in, and offer choices of eye makeup, lipstick, nail polish, etc. Lets say the girl is interested in lipstick. The next day L'Oreal could ask her, which colors and shades she likes. And lets say she likes bright red. After that L'Oreal could ask, which celebrity the girl likes, and offer a choice of six celebrities. She might pick the actress Eva Longoria.

Each of these discussions counts as a daily message sent by L'Oreal, and each reply to the girl. Blyk charges each outgoing and incoming marketing message to L'Oreal, naturally, not deducting these from the 217 free messages allowance of this customer.

Now L'Oreal has a far more accurate picture of this 17-year-old girl's interests and preferences. Next time L'Oreal wants to communicate with her, L'Oreal can send a video clip of Eva Longoria with the new hot red lipstick, and offer the girl a trial coupon for that lipstick. For the girl this is the most precise, personalized and relevant advertising she had ever seen.

The first numbers from Blyk are in. Blyk was on target to reach 100,000 customers during the Spring of 2008, in half the time of its stated goal of that amount in one year. The more telling number is response rates. Where most internet campaigns achieve response rates of less than one percent, and even most early mobile banner campaigns tend to get responses in the single digits, over the first five months, Blyk was averaging response rates of about 29%. This for a company that *bombards* its customers with 6 ads per day. But most revealing is the attitude of Blyk users. Their number one complaint to Blyk? They *want more of the ads!* We embrace what we create. If the advertising channel can transcend the interruption model, and become an engagement marketing channel, it will transform advertising as we know it.

Tomi T Ahonen

"Within a few years, all content creators will
be paid for their content."
Tomi T Ahonen in book *m-Profits*, 2002

XIII
Mobile Internet
Mobile internet is not fixed internet on phones

The internet has become so pervasive and relevant that it may seem to be the obvious digital platform "forever" into the future. Having appeared out of the obscure military and university networks in the early 1990s, today the internet has well in excess of a billion users. Certainly that is a power that will prevail?
Or will it? Or will it...
First, we must remember that before a new paradigm is introduced, it is easy to fall into a false sense of security about the current way having some permanence. I have been doing a lot of thinking of this "mobile internet" space, since I authored the first White Paper for Nokia to discuss the internet on mobile phones and cellular networks, in 1999. So my thoughts have nearly ten years of reflection and evolution. However, to get us going, let me examine a few transitional and permanent innovations to give us historical context. While the internet will keep on growing in size and relevance, the dominant role of the internet may be surprisingly short-lived. Nevertheless, let us look at a historical example first from aviation.

A   TRANSITIONAL TECHNOLOGIES

In the 1920s there was intercontinental air travel, but the prevalent form of aircraft for civilian transport was... the airship (!) i.e. the dirigible, the "zeppelin" like the Hindenburg - the huge cigar-shaped "balloons" that carried people over the Atlantic.
Most people in the world expected in the 1920s for air travel to be based on airships, not the fidgety small uncomfortable and "short range" airplanes. Yet in little over a decade, airplanes replaced airships. Ever faster and more comfortable airplanes appeared for passenger travel and as a few spectacular air

disasters caused fear of airships, the transition was complete by the time of the mid 1930s. Just because one technology has become the dominant one in any one point of time, does not preclude a superior technology from taking over.

How the internet came to be

So let us turn to the internet. Only twenty years ago, the majority of all computers connected to the internet were not PCs. They were mainframe computers from universities, government and military. Most PCs were stand-alone units, few had network cards, and even those only connected to small office networks only, not the internet. There were slow modems for PCs, but these were mostly used only to access "BBS" or Bulletin Board Systems. It was not until 1994 when *Time* put the Internet on its cover that the mass migration of PCs to the internet started. Even then most modems and network cards were added cost peripherals, *options* to the specifications of PCs. Today essentially all desktop and laptop computers are sold with built-in connectivity to the internet.

Therefore, in the early 1990s, most who worked on any data or applications for the internet, did not even bother to think about any personal computer users, the systems, data protocols and storage hierarchies were built with mainframe users in mind. In fact, the dominant storage format was something called "Gopher" by, which internet data was stored and searched.

To explain, Gopher was superceded by internet browsers *Mosaic*, *Netscape* and now Microsoft's *Internet Explorer*. Imagine today. As the dominating majority of all internet users use browsers, nobody bothers to think of how does the data work with Gopher. We think only of *Internet Explorer*, maybe give a bit of thought for *Netscape*, and that's it. Gopher - the dominant internet data storage and search protocol of only fifteen years ago, is totally forgotten.

Introduced advertising

As the internet migrated from the mainframe-based university and government "research internet", to the PC-based "consumer and business" internet in the 1990s, another major change took place. *Advertising* appeared on the internet. I was there to witness that transition, working as the Director of Marketing and Sales for OCSNY a PC networking company that became the first Internet Service Provider listed in the New York *Yellow Pages*. Being a recently graduated creative marketing guy, I was seeking for new ways to reach customers. The majority of our advertising was the *Yellow Pages* and classified ads in some New York area newspapers.

There was no advertising on the internet. However, the Nynex *Yellow Pages* made an experimental online version that they published on the Genie service, a walled garden BBS (Bulletin Board System). As we were a major

Tomi T Ahonen

First Computer Company Ad on Internet

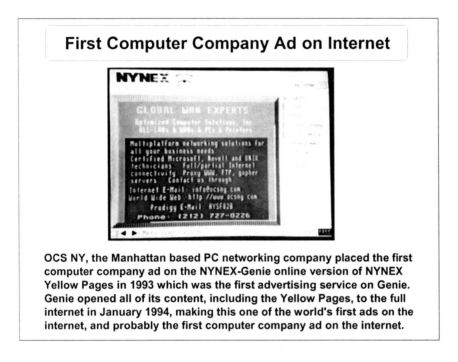

OCS NY, the Manhattan based PC networking company placed the first computer company ad on the NYNEX-Genie online version of NYNEX Yellow Pages in 1993 which was the first advertising service on Genie. Genie opened all of its content, including the Yellow Pages, to the full internet in January 1994, making this one of the world's first ads on the internet, and probably the first computer company ad on the internet.

computer industry advertiser of the New York *Yellow Pages*, they approached me, if we might be interested in an experimental ad on the Genie-Nynex *Yellow Pages*. This was the first type of very simple advertising that Genie was willing to trial. I jumped at the opportunity. We created the ad, which you can see on this page. There were several dozens of ads from miscellaneous businesses, but ours was the only computer company ad on Genie. Then by pure stroke of luck, a few months later Genie decided to open up all of their pages to the internet. This meant that also our ad would suddenly be exposed to the "full internet". It made us one of the very first advertisers on the internet, and as far as we could see, the first-ever computer company to post an ad on the internet in early 1994 half a year before *Time* and *Newsweek* ran the internet on their covers.

What we were not prepared for, was the hostility of many random contacts from the internet. They felt we were *corrupting* the web. That it was *unholy* to create ads onto the internet. That it was all supposed to be free, and non-commercial. Moreover, that if now advertising would be allowed onto "their" internet, soon full commerce would follow and that would *corrupt* the *purity* of information on the internet.

Obviously, in the big picture, I had almost nothing to do with this trend of commercializing the web, other than being in the right place at the right time. It was Nynex's decision to trial *Yellow Page* ads on Genie; and independent of that, it was Genie's decision to open their walled garden fully to the internet. However, I did authorize the original ad on Genie and did "design" it, for what little creative effort that did take one afternoon at the office. In addition, we were indeed one of the very first companies to start to break that barrier, to bring first advertising, and soon also actual commerce onto the internet.

From this experience, I felt first-hand the trauma of a change in the paradigm for the internet. Before web browsers the internet was populated by mainframe computers. Before web browsers the internet users were governments and universities. Before web browsers the internet was organized by Gopher. Before web browsers there were no ads on the net. Before web browsers there was no commerce on the internet.

After the shift to the PC based internet, the browser became the basis for the format. The majority of the users were individuals and companies. The worldwide web would become searchable and search engines surpassed the structural hierarchy. Moreover, advertising appeared, which led to commerce appearing on the web.

Now onto the shocking news. The fixed internet model is about to change again. Away from what we know, and onto the cellphone.

---

211 million North Americans accessed internet in 2007
Source: Morgan Stanley Technology/Internet Trends 2007

B   HOW BIG

Lets start with the big picture. TomiAhonen Consulting tracks the different methods to access the internet and for 2007 has found that of the 1.3 billion active users on the internet, approximately 67% use a cellphone some of the time to access the internet. Only 33% of all internet users access exclusively by PC or laptop. 30% access exclusively by cellphone, and 37% use both cellphone and PC. I do want to point out that the cellphone based use includes access to WAP services, which some purists do not count as "proper" internet access. However, as most cellphone access to internet service provider sites such as Google, Amazon, Yahoo etc is via a WAP site, and the end-users themselves do think of WAP experiences as being "the internet on the cellphone", it is a fair definition to include WAP access as cellphone-based internet access.

In several countries the majority of all internet users are now cellphone users, such as those in Japan, South Korea, India, South Africa etc. In many European countries like Italy, UK, and Scandinavian countries between 30% and 40% of internet users already use cellphones to access the web. Even in America today more than 10% of internet users access via cellphones. Bear in mind that

---

the first internet access cellphone, the Nokia 9000 Communicator, was launched only twelve years ago in Finland, in 1996. Another example is Yahoo's Go portal, their effort to enter the mobile internet. The recent trends have been accelerated with the hype around the Apple iPhone. So a transition to a cellphone internet is already underway. Similar to how airships gave way to airplanes in the 1930s, and how the internet gave way from Gopher to browsers in the 1990s. Now the PC based internet is clearly shifting to a cellphone based internet.

Not exclusively cellphone

When defining it at the basic browsing level i.e. "WAP users" and above, but excluding SMS text messaging users, already more than half of all internet users accessed the internet at least part of the time via cellphone. I also need to be clear. The user *number* count is not the same as *usage*, nor *data traffic* (nor content *revenues*). The users on cellphones are often in a hurry, multi-tasking, and the usage on cellphones tends to be of shorter duration than on the PC. Also many applications and services with heavy data loads, such as playing multiplayer games, downloading movies etc, tend to be done of course on

---

215 Million Asians accessed the mobile internet in 2007
Source: Asia Digital Marketing Yearbook 2007

---

broadband internet connections rather than cellphones. However, Japan has already seen the transition of total user access times by cellphone internet users to grow past PC users in 2006, according to the national regulator data.

So while access devices and users do come via cellphones, the heavy usage is still on PCs, as is most of the heavy data load. However, on the data *revenues*, the mobile internet is already far larger than the PC based internet content revenues.

Why the shift

What is driving this change. First, there is the rapidly improving power of smartphones. Think iPhone. The screens are getting to be large enough, the connection speeds and network availability is becoming good enough, and the pricing models of the carriers is getting ever more user-friendly with many carriers around the world offering all-you-can-eat types of unlimited use pricing plans for wireless internet access. Lastly, the content owners are discovering this opportunity.

What is accelerating the change is shrinking handset replacement cycle.

Our PCs are replaced roughly every 3.5 years. Nevertheless, our cellphones are replaced every 18 months. It also helps that cellphones cost a small fraction of the price of a laptop today, and that cellphones mostly are subsidized (you buy a contract and then get the phone at a great discount, or even free) while laptops are not. The price differential is even more relevant in the developing world.

Many people who do not have a PC or PDA, are looking to the latest smartphone as their first internet connected device, whether to get an e-mail account or to visit some websites that they may be interested in. At the other extreme, many laptop users found that for example a Blackberry would be sufficient on travel, to give access to the email and the web, and thus many are abandoning laptops in favor of handheld smartphones, including Palm Treos, Nokia E-Series and iPhones.

Meanwhile, in developing parts of the planet, most users cannot afford a personal computer, but can afford a simple mobile phone. With very limited fixed internet connectivity and lack of broadband, and both unreliable and very expensive internet access, the mobile option is even more compelling, even at very basic WAP service standards.

Is the wireless internet different?

Our thinking is guided by what we know. We know the current fixed wireline PC based internet, increasingly on broadband speeds. When we hear of a new development relating to the internet, we naturally tend to think of it as an *extension* of our current understanding of "the" internet. In most cases this is of course quite valid. It is only when a radical departure from the status quo is happening that this kind of thinking may cloud the true potential of the development. This usually happens at a disruption point at the introduction of paradigm-shifting new technology.

When we consider technologies that have truly revolutionized society, many of those transitions have had names for the new technology relating to existing ways. For example in the horse-and-buggy days, when the automobile was introduced, it was called the horseless carriage. As Henry Ford said, if people were asked what they wanted when cars were being introduced, they would have said they wanted a *faster horse.* Clearly they could not see a need for a four-person fully enclosed horseless carriage.

When telephones first emerged, the existing paradigm was the telegraph, so phones were called "voice telegraphs". Television came into a time of radio, so it was first called "picture radio". Each of these was a valid way for people to come to terms with the new technology supplanting something they were accustomed to. However, each of these descriptions seriously underestimated the true potential of the emerging technology.

With telephones the first reason for any residence to acquire a telephone connection was for fire alarm use. Telephone wire connections and the actual

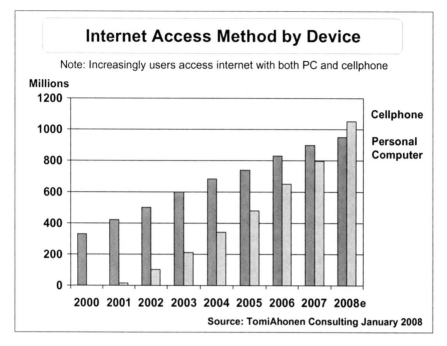

Internet Access Method by Device

Note: Increasingly users access internet with both PC and cellphone

Cellphone

Personal Computer

Source: TomiAhonen Consulting January 2008

telephone devices were very expensive and only the wealthy could afford them. The early use of telephones was much like the telegraph, with short, urgent messages such as *"your aunt has died"* but on the telegraph nobody "chats" for hours with a friend just to stay in touch. On the telephone a whole new culture of keeping in touch with friends evolved. In addition, of course vast amounts of new infrastructure were needed to connect every household to the telephone grid, whereas the telegraph was needed only at few distinct points.

The new cellphone based mobile internet may seem similar to the familiar current fixed internet, but the mobile internet is actually quite different. The two are not the same. They have considerable overlap but also considerable own domains where the other is not a strong substitute. The mobile internet will grow remarkably fast over the next decade. Over the next ten years at least, both will co-exist and grow, and a healthy business can be built upon either - or both.

The internet on cellphones

The current fixed internet - the sixth mass media channel - with mostly free content, has numerous strengths that make it a very potent information channel, entertainment platform and media outlet. The amount of content and data is bewildering and most of the content is free. It has been estimated that during the next two years more information will be placed onto the internet - counting

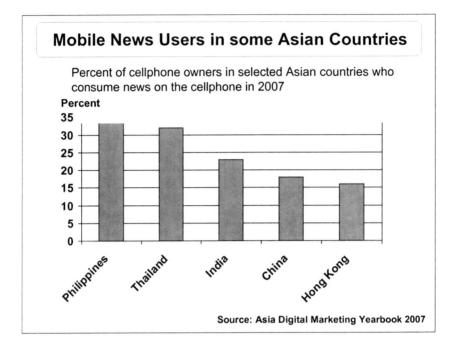

Mobile News Users in some Asian Countries

Percent of cellphone owners in selected Asian countries who consume news on the cellphone in 2007

Source: Asia Digital Marketing Yearbook 2007

internets, intranets and extranets - than all information man has created up to today in any form.

The fixed internet reflects its roots as a research tool. Many of the services and applications available on the internet can be had for free. As it was built to be a multiple-redundant data network capable of sustaining a nuclear attack on any of its centers, the network is robust and reliable with redundancies built in. Most modern PCs have the software needed to access and view content on the internet, and the predominant internet protocols for basic content, like HTML (HyperText Markup Language) for words and various picture standards for images, are relatively simple to use and most current software support them.

It is fully possible to provide "full" access to the "real" or legacy internet on any advanced cellphone, as long as the carrier/operator enables this. The iPhone is a good example of it, and this has been technically possible for twelve years, since 1996 when the first Nokia 9000 Communicator was launched in Finland. Nevertheless, to construct content and services on the 6th mass media channel, to be consumed on the 7th mass media device, is quite *pointless*. It is similar to looking at a car - a horseless carriage - and deciding that what that automobile really needs today, is adding a real horse for its engine *horse*power (in addition to the petrol engine it already has).

If we have the 7th of the mass media, as inherently capable of

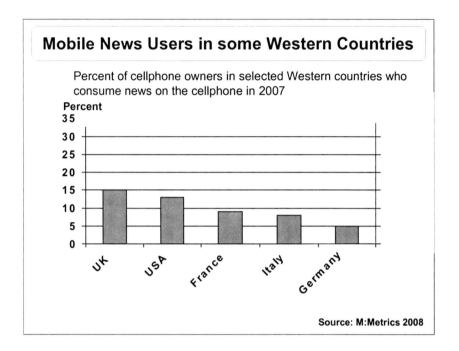

replicating all previous six - including all of the "real" PC based internet - but that mobile adds seven new elements not available on the internet; then it is folly to try to limit any mobile internet experience to the "crippled" options of the 6th of the mass media. Moreover, as the ability to charge per click is impossible on the fixed legacy internet, and built-in to the mobile internet, it is economically short-sighted to bring all legacy internet services to the cellphone.

C   UNDERSTANDING MOBILE INTERNET

The most profound difference between the current fixed internet and the new mobile internet (on cellphones) is money. I want to first make a clarification in terminology. The "mobile internet" is not the same as the "wireless internet". The wireless internet can be enabled on any wireless technology such as WiFi and WiMax as well as cellular 2G and 3G networks. However, the "mobile internet" is distinctly cellphone based. Cellphone based. So when I say "internet on cellphones" that is accessing the legacy fixed internet through a cellphone.

So I will not bother discussing the wireless internet in this book. That has its own opportunities, at far smaller scales than the mobile internet. Nevertheless, from this point on, in this chapter, I will no longer discuss accessing the "real" internet via a cellphone, but rather the newer "mobile internet" that utilizes the full benefits of the 7th mass media channel. Only the mobile internet has the 7 new benefits: Personal, Permanently Carried, Always-On, Built-in Payment Channel, Available at Creative Impulse, Best Audience Info, and Captures Social Context. The "real internet on cellphones" is the dumb idea similar to sqeezing a real horse into an automobile.

Money money money

Therefore, the mobile internet is naturally able to handle money and payments. The cellular network can handle large payments like the credit card companies, as well as track (and accurately bill) payments worth only a fraction of a penny.

It may be difficult to initially comprehend how dramatic this difference is. Imagine trying to set up a modern banking system in the times of bartering trade. What is the exchange rate for beaver skins to live chickens, how about potatoes, and does their price fluctuate between summer potatoes when they are fresh and winter potatoes when they are not. How could a modern utility like an electrical company collect its payments when every household would offer different goods. How about handling the value of intangible services such as

---

Value of paid content on the internet was $25 billion in 2007

Source: The Guardian 24 May 2007

---

insurance or the interest on your bank deposit? Even in that system, many agreed forms of bartering quickly would be developed and some common good, be it beaver skins or seashells, would emerge as a currency substitute.

Yet the current fixed internet *has no system to handle money*. The mobile internet does. On every cellphone, each and every caller is always identified. That includes all the "anonymous" customers on pay-as-you-go/prepaid accounts. The network does identify every single cellphone account explicitly and exclusively based on the unique cellphone number and subscription, even if it does not know that person's real name or address. That caller's cellular phone subscription is definitely known in every case, and the phone number is globally unique. So if caller x visits my WAP site and then visits the Playboy site, and then makes a crank call to the police, each of those transactions is fully logged and known by the network. In addition, that phone can be identified whenever it is turned on, no matter, which country it is in, even if the user never places or receives calls on the phone. Just turning it on, reveals the unique phone subscriber identity, and its location.

On the legacy internet there is no way to know who is who, from where any given contact has arrived, or where some data is sent, unless we force our customers to identify themselves by registering to our website. The internet was *designed* to allow anonymous contacts and a wide latitude of freedom for all users. One of its features is the *repeated attempts* to deliver data. The money economy does not work that way that I give some money to my friend, who hopefully gives the same amount to his friends unless he is busy, and eventually you might get yours. *"Just tell me if the cash didn't arrive and I'll send it again."*

The legacy internet commerce cannot create payment transactions by its own structures, and lives by credit cards and external means like Paypal to handle payments. There have been numerous initiatives to develop e-cash and e-money and various other methods of electronic money transfers on the internet, but no uniform system has emerged and people are using things like Paypal accounts to get around the money limitations of the fixed internet. For example Paypal had achieved 105 million registered accounts by July 2006, or roughly 10% of all internet users at the time. Yes, that is very impressive for Paypal, but it did leave 900 million internet users without a registered payment mechanism.

Beyond the mere money issue is the anonymity of the internet and the potential for fraud. Almost anyone can set up a web host and put traffic and copy files on the internet. So the free part of the internet is remarkably insecure. That

---

Value of paid content on mobile was $31 billion in 2007
Source: The Guardian 24 May 2007

---

is why practically all business websites have limited access through identities and passwords, and/or install cookies onto the visiting computers to identify them later, etc.

Mobile internet is exact opposite

For the internet economy this has revolutionary effects. The very same content, which is near impossible to bill for on the fixed side of the internet, is automatically tracked and charged - and billed *on the mobile internet.* Every page click, every search, every view, every download is tracked and can be billed. The charge can go to your account, or could be charged to an advertiser, or could also be charged to a family account for example, paid by the parent.

If a content provider wants to assign a value to the web page, it is naturally possible on the mobile internet. If the same content provider wants to assign a different value to various elements of content, links, downloads, etc., all of that is possible and requires no registrations, no credit card numbers, no authorizations, no permissions, no pin codes - and potentially even no age

---

verification, etc., unless the content provider wants to set some such added security or verification of purchase. Let me be very clear about this. If the carrier/operator so chooses, every customer can be billed at a given click. No credit card numbers needed, no PIN codes, no authorizations. The mobile internet is so powerful at handling money that potentially every individual page can be charged for. Moreover, the billing system is so efficient that technically it is perfectly possible to bill for content in increments of fractions of a US cent per page, if the content owner - and the carrier/operator - so desire.

D   VALUE OF CONTENT

The big issue with the legacy internet is the value of the content. Yes we all admit that the internet brings some utility to us, but what is the marginal value of one page? For most of the pages, to most of us, most of the time, the value is very near zero. Even a page, which is on our bookmarks list and a page, which we visit frequently, may have near zero value or more realistically we might be able to measure its value as about one or two cents at most.

Not so on the mobile internet. The content tends to be billable. This brings about several benefits. First of all the content provider gets direct payment. No longer is the content provider dependent on advertising revenue, based on an aggregation of "eyeballs" as they are on the fixed internet. Secondly it brings about an *expectation of value* for the user. If I pay for something it better be good. The natural laws of the economy can start to function. Today on the fixed and free internet, it is pointless to argue about a lack of quality or outdatedness of information on any given website, as the content is free to begin with. However, when the content is billable, the content provider is then responsible for maintaining quality.

Very soon the good quality pages will get growing amounts of traffic and the bad quality pages will get diminishing traffic. The bad quality pages must upgrade their quality of content or suffer the consequences. This has been a key for example to the popular video submissions at *SeeMeTV* on the Three networks of the Hutchison group. As the average video generates 13 UK Pounds (26 dollars) of income to the original creator of the video, there is a strong incentive to make sure the video is as good as possible, updated when necessary, etc. As I showed in the Case Study on *SeeMeTV* earlier in the book, top content owners can earn 1,000 dollars or more for popular videos.

Analogy: selling water

"Tomi you live in a dream world. It can't be done." Those who suggest that charging for content is impossible with the fixed and free internet, it is good to recall a marketing challenge from a few years ago. There was a time when water

Fixed Internet vs Mobile Internet 2007

Devices	900 M PCs	3,300 M phones
	(45% laptops)	(80% 2.5G data phones)
Ave cost/device	$700	$125 ($25 if subsidy)
Replacement	3.5 years	18 months
Access	hotspots	always-on
Content revenue	$30 B	$45 B
Messaging users	850 M	2,400 M
Messaging revs	$5 B	$105 B
Content	mostly free	always costs
Billing	difficult	built-in
User preference	expect free	willing to pay
User age	adult	youth
Regional leadership	North America	Asia

was free throughout the Western world and nobody "in their right minds" would think of charging for plain drinking water. Of course, there were mineral waters, sparkling waters etc., but just for regular tap water the concept of selling it was pretty much pointless. During the 1980s and 1990s as environmental issues rose to the forefront, in many developed countries legitimate worries emerged about the taste of tap water and arguably a market opened for branded spring water.

That does not cover some countries of exceptional cleanliness, hygiene and purity of nature, which also were blessed with an overabundance of pure spring water from glaciers. The two examples I would draw are Switzerland and Sweden. Countries of mountain springs, clean lakes and rivers, very highly advanced water filtration and purification systems, a high degree of engineering, very advanced medical care, and a culture of appreciating purity and cleanliness in nature, and some of the most demanding health standards for foods and nutrition. Definitely the tap water in any Swedish or Swiss city would rival the quality of bottled spring water in most Western cities.

Forty years ago these countries did not have an imported bottled still water market. Yet today water brands such as Perrier and Evian from the French Alps are imported to both of these countries and sold as a premium brand water.

If you can convince the Swiss and Swedes to import water from France, then you definitely can convince internet users to pay for content and services that once used to be free. It will not be easy and it will take time, but Perrier and

Evian in Switzerland and Sweden proves that more significant marketing challenges have been overcome. Incidentally, the bottled water industry worldwide has grown to a 100 billion dollar business according to CNBC in May 2007 so this is no mean feat.

While we all will feel the pain in our hearts that once it all used to be free that is not a feasible way to handle valuable content. Now that we all are dependent on quality content on the internet, we have to start to pay for it. The key is to not price above the pain threshold.

Long Tail and cellphones

Since the book *The Long Tail* by Chris Anderson came out in 2006, many have commented on the various sides of the long tail in the internet space. Long tail means that for a given category of a service or content, say music for example, there is a small head (the high end of the graph) where we have the big global hits of music selling into the millions, but then as we follow into the "long tail" we find ever more bands with ever more obscure music, into those that are truly selling only in the dozens of songs in total in any given year, etc. The point is that in the long tail, there is much more value than in the short head. In addition, prior to the internet, it was most difficult to try to monetize the long tail. Who cares for jazz fusion hip-hop sung in French? There are some, but outside of France, most music stores could not afford to stock such obscure genres of music. Nevertheless, the Long Tail on the internet has made it possible to monetize such niche markets.

The next logical step is for the Long Tail to make its presence on cellphone based mobile internet. The digital services guru at UK magazine publishing giant, Emap, David Cushman, writes about how the Long Tail will apply in the mobile internet in this way:

> *The socialisation/democratisation of the web set new standards. We will insist those standards apply to mobile web. So while the fixed line internet was initially grown by content providers of the mass industrial age, the mobile web will explode as a direct result of users coming together to create and share their own content, services – and ultimately products. These communities of niche shared interest will dominate in a faster and more pervasive way than we saw with the original fixed-line internet. The long tail –its almost limitless potential for segmentation - will wag the mobile internet dog much faster and more vigorously than it did the fixed line internet.*
> - David Cushman, Digital Development Director, Emap UK

I totally agree. Because the mobile internet has its ability to generate payments that will drive content. Content owners, say the bands who cannot get their old vinyl records re-released on CD because their record label marketing research says there is not a large enough market - can now release their music directly to cellphones as MP3 files, and still make money. The long tail will be even more important on cellphones than on in the legacy fixed wireline internet.

Are not mutually exclusive

The fixed wireline and (mostly) free internet has its uses and users, and there are numerous services and areas where the fixed internet is superior to anything on a wireless device. The fixed and (mostly) free internet will continue to be a tremendous force in e-business, especially in B2B (Business to Business) areas, as well as generating information and entertainment content. There are very many areas where a large screen of a PC or digital TV is preferable to the small screen of the handheld device. There are numerous applications, which need the fastest possible speeds delivered by broadband internet and even faster fixed telecommunication technologies. There are also countless applications, services and content, which does not significantly benefit from mobility or from personal portable access, and those will continue to reside primarily on the fixed internet.

Good examples of these include massively multiplayer gaming; TV on the internet, what is often called IPTV (Internet Protocol TeleVision) and serious academic research.

Money drives mobile internet

The mobile internet is bound to grow faster because the money is there. The content providers will port versions of their best and most current content to the mobile internet because that is where the money is. I have given several examples in this book already, such as *Cyworld's* music income and *Kart Rider's* customization income in South Korea, and the remarkable success of the *Mice Love Rice* song distributed free in China but earning its money through Waiting Tones/Ringback Tones. The grand-daddy of the internet companies to turn to profits via cellphones is of course *Habbo Hotel* discussed in the gaming chapter.

In addition to the easy payments, the majority of access devices and users are going to be on the wireless internet. As the best and most current content migrates to the mobile internet, so too will an increasing amount of internet usage migrate from the free and fixed internet to the mobile internet.

E   INEVITABLE TREND TO CELLPHONES

Where will the best content reside. There are hundreds of millions of users on the fixed internet, yet within a few years there will be even more users on the mobile internet. On the fixed internet it is near-impossible to bill for small amounts, such as a page of content, while on the mobile internet, micropayment billing is built-in from the start. Where the fixed internet users demand free content, all cellular phone users know that every second of air time incurs a charge.

On one side we have less users, difficult billing, and an attitude of demanding content for free. On the other side we have more users, easy billing, and an attitude to pay for content. Where will the best internet content migrate. This is, a "no-brainer" - of course the best content migrates to the mobile internet.

That is not to say that the free internet model will disappear. Consider books. Today you can buy books but today you can also read books for free. If you do not want to pay for books or magazines, you can go to the public library and read them for free. However, the vast majority of all printed books and magazines are bought for and read as paid and owned volumes, not borrowed in libraries. Both models exist, but paid ownership tends to be the dominant one.

The big trend

One does not have to be a genius to see the basis for a megatrend. By the end of 2008 there will be more users accessing internet content (including WAP) via cellphones than PCs. The content providers and service providers prefer the mobile internet because it is naturally built to handle money. The money will migrate from the fixed internet to the mobile internet. The users prefer services that are mobile rather than those that are tied to fixed networks. The best and most valuable services, the largest amount of users, the most money -- and definitely the most profits -- will go to the mobile internet.

That model of user-generated content for the mobile internet by *SeeMeTV*, where the original content creator is paid a revenue-share, has since been copied on various other wireless internet models, from *MyNuMo* in the USA to *Cyworld* in South Korea to Vodafone's *Self Central* in New Zealand. In the near future all content owners will be paid for their content. That will not happen on the legacy fixed wireline internet, but it will happen on the mobile cellphone based internet.

And if you do not believe me, then would you believe the CEO of the biggest internet company, Google? Eric Schmidt the CEO of Google wrote in the **Financial Times** on 22 May, 2005, *"Mobile phones are cheaper than PCs, there are three times more of them, growing at twice the speed, and they increasingly have internet access. Mobile is going to be the next big internet phenomenon. It holds the key to greater access to everyone - with all the benefits that entails."*

Case Study 12 from Japan
Mobile Books

While it is relatively easy to accept that music or breaking news will soon migrate to cellphones, some of the more established media seem well insulated from a threat by the cellphone. None more so than classic printed books. Can you imagine attempting to read this book, squinting off the tiny screen of your cellphone? I was very skeptical of traditional books migrating to cellphones.

Even more, I was pretty sure, having authored five books that there was no viable opportunity to author books using the clumsy triple-tapping keypad of a cellphone. Even as I average nearly 20 SMS text messages sent per day, I cannot imagine the aching thumbs it would take to author my next book this way. Yet again, my favorite industry manages to dumbfound me.

In Japan in 2007, five of the ten best-selling books of 2007 were based on "mobile books" that have been written by the youth, on cellphones, for primarily cellphone based consumption. The most successful of the m-books are then published as printed books on paper and yes, five out of the top ten printed book bestsellers in Japan in 2007 were books that were originally released for cellphones, and mostly also written on phones.

The traditional book business is very inefficient as a delivery system and massively destructive pricing system as a book once read can easily be resold as used, for example via Amazon. With m-books there is no bottleneck, no overstock, under stock. Furthermore, mobile books cannot be resold by the person who bought the book.

All this means that m-books can be produced at far lower costs than traditional paper based bound volumes. The publisher and author can get a fair return on a book that costs much less to the end-user than traditional paper printed books. And the buying public gets original, exciting, new content, released direct to mobile.

Then think of the writer of the future. Mobile books are written by young authors, to be consumed on mobile. So they are much closer to SMS text messaging and blogging in style than they are to traditional writing. Older Japanese adults deplore these new mobile books, as their sentence structure is short and weak in grammar. The language used, the vocabulary, is not as rich as in older Japanese books. And the mobile books contain the cryptic shorthand of text messaging such as "C U L8", which means "see you later" and uses "emoticons" (the smiley faces many use in email, instant messaging and SMS) to convey emotional status of the writer etc.

A good example of a mobile novel is "Love Sky" the first novel by a female author named Mika. It is a story of sadness and desperation including rape, pregnancy and a fatal disease. The book in its mobile version was downloaded 20 million times in Japan. It was then released as a printed book, became a number 1 bestseller in Japan and has since been released also as a movie.

How big is the mobile books business? 82 million dollars worth of mobile books were sold to cellphones in Japan in 2006. There were 90 million cellphones in Japan. Averaging across the Japanese user base, cellphone books earned 90 cents per subscriber in 2006. If we multiply 90 cents across the 3.3 billion subscribers globally, there is a potential 3 billion dollar worldwide market for books on cellphones.

Meanwhile in Japan the local author community is debating whether cellphone novels will "kill the author", and a Japanese literary journal, *Bungaku-kai* even put that question on its cover of the January 2008 issue: *"Cellphones killing books?"*

Tomi T Ahonen

"Nobody is as clever as everybody."
Alan Moore CEO of SMLXL

XIV
Mobile Social Networking
Digital communities and web 2.0

Business Week in its special issue dedicated to customer community power on June 20, 2005, said that community power was the biggest change to society since the industrial revolution. That puts digital communities ahead in importance to such massively disruptive inventions as electricity, the automobile, the telephone, radio, television, credit cards, the computer, the internet and e-mail and yes, the cellphone as well. *Time* put the "You" of user-generated content onto the cover of the Person of the Year issue in 2006. User generated content, i.e. digital communities.

The *Economist* featured the same topic on its cover and special report on April 2, 2005 and warned in its editorial that *"Many firms do not yet seem aware of the revolutionary implications of newly empowered consumers."* They then concluded with this chilling warning: *"only those firms ready and able to serve these new (connected customers) will survive."* Not only is this the biggest change, but if you do not learn to understand community power, your company will not survive. I will not spend much time on the basics of social networking. This chapter will focus more on the impact of social networking to cellphones as the 7th Mass Media Channel.

A   WHAT ARE DIGITAL COMMUNITIES

A digital community is a group of people who share some interest at least in part using electronic communication methods. A group of fans of the British soccer team Manchester United who are exchanging comments about the team on a chat board, are a digital community. If the fans only meet up at a pub in Manchester, then they are a community, which is not digital. We have digital communities in multiplayer online gaming, in online dating, in virtual worlds (like *Second Life*), on collaborative websites like *Wikipedia*, etc. Most of the best-known digital communities in 2008 are still online, such as *MySpace, Facebook, Flickr, YouTube, Linked In, World of Warcraft, Second Life* and *eBay*. Note that many non-digital communities have digital dimensions. If a group of retired ladies who get together to play Bridge on Saturdays, and communicates via email and SMS text messaging to coordinate their games, then while their meeting is face-to-face (so they do not play Bridge online) they also are a digital community, as they manage their activity at least in part through digital means.

There is plenty of argument within this industry of what constitutes a "social networking" site or "digital community" and there are somewhat synonymous terms such as User-Generated Content, citizen journalism and Web 2.0/Mobile Web 2.0. This chapter is not intended to be a treatise on the fundamentals of digital communities. It is rather intended to explore how the Seventh Mass Media Channel is being adopted by digital communities. I ask the readers' indulgence in a very broad definition of what is a digital community, as the intention of this book is not to restrict and define what exists on the Seventh Mass Media, but rather to explore what might be possible in this new and dramatically evolving space.

I have written and spoken a lot about digital communities for several years now and lecture on the topic at Oxford University's short course on Mobile Social Networking. So in that context, considering the topic of this book, I want to start off this chapter saying that digital communities are to cellphones like commuters are to cars. There is a lot of overlap, but just like with cars there are other users of cars, such as professional drivers (taxi drivers for example) who also use cars. Equally there is more than one way of commuting, so cellphones are not the only way to engage in digital community behavior. Do not misunderstand me, there are many other ways to engage in social networking behavior that do not require cellphones. The most obvious method is using the internet. However, considering the near future, the relevant point is this: the majority of community behavior is going to migrate to cellphones. It is the inevitable direction for community activity.

Worth 5 billion dollars

So lets go to the money to begin with. The first social networking service to launch on cellphone was the mobile version of *Cyworld* in South Korea in 2003. In two years social networking on cellphones grew to over a billion dollars worldwide. By 2006 the value was over 3.4 billion, and passed 5.05 billion dollars by 2007 according to Informa.

Zero to five billion dollars in four years. This is the fastest-growing industry of all time.

To put it in context, social networks existed online even before the

Tomi T Ahonen

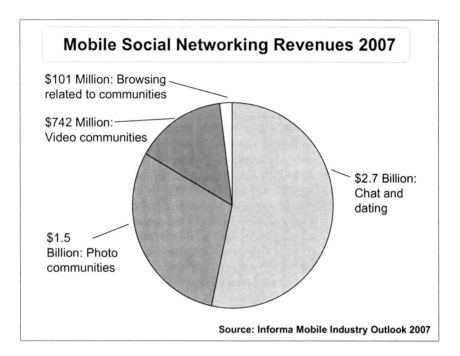

Mobile Social Networking Revenues 2007

$101 Million: Browsing related to communities

$742 Million: Video communities

$1.5 Billion: Photo communities

$2.7 Billion: Chat and dating

Source: Informa Mobile Industry Outlook 2007

worldwide web was launched. However, even if we count from the mass-market "birth" of the internet - when *Time* and *Newsweek* put the internet on their covers in 1994, then social networking has existed for at least 13 years online. *Ebay* with its online auctions, *Amazon* with its user-ratings, *MSN* with instant messaging all have digital community services and have been around for more than ten years.

Even though they are more than three times as old, all online social networks earned less than 3 billion dollars in 2007. Compare that with mobile social networking already worth over 5 billion dollars. Many of the Case Studies in this book, such as *Flirtomatic, MyNuMo* and *Cyworld* are mobile social networking. A particularly popular one in many markets is *Itsmy*, originally from Germany. I should point out that the reader should not add together this mobile community revenue with those in the previous chapters because there is overlap and double-counting. Some of the 5 billion in social networking revenue on cellphones is also in video sharing (remember *SeeMeTV*) or in multiplayer games for cellphones (like Disney's *Pirates*). Still, five billion in four years. Wow.

Massively Multiplayer Mobile

So lets start briefly with the gaming. I discussed these at considerable length in the gaming chapter, but it bears repeating that a multiplayer online game is naturally a social networking service. *World of Warcraft, Lineage 2, Everquest, CounterStrike* etc are all social networking services. When multiplayer gaming is brought to mobile, like *Pirates of the Caribbean, Elven Legends* or the Nokia N-Gage *Pocket Kingdom.*, then we have a robust mobile social networking service.

The game need not be exclusive to mobile. It can be partly online on the fixed internet, and partly on mobile, such as the Volvo round-the-world race, which can be played online for free. However, as the virtual sailing race mimics the real wind conditions of the real live race in progress simultaneously, a gamer cannot win the virtual Volvo race unless the gamer signs up to premium SMS based alerts. This is a way to turn a free game into a money-maker through the user of mobile. It is similar to *BotFighter* that I described also before.

Then the virtual world need not be that much a linear game, and can be more of a playground. Again, *Habbo Hotel* is the prototypical virtual world, where gaming is online, but money is made via cellphone premium SMS payments. *Habbo Hotel's* cellphone variation launched in 2007. The South Korean *Cyworld* is another similar concept also both on broadband internet and 3G cellphones, but developed far beyond *Habbo* with its music stores, blogging, video sharing etc.

Monetizing community on cellphones

The modern customer is also actively interested in using the new digital tools and methods to create and customize content. That would then be shared with given friends, or in some cases even sold.

We developed the **"Flower Diagram"** with Alan Moore in our book to help explore the business opportunities with digital communities and social networking. The Flower has four C's, in no particular order they are Connectivity, Commerce, Culture and Community. These do not "naturally" mix, we do not for example get our operas and theater (culture) through the phone (connectivity) and we do not go to the concert or Broadway play (culture) to discuss with our friends during the show (connectivity). Similarly we do not go to a supermarket or bank (commerce) to meet up with our colleagues after work (community) nor do we go to our church (community) to do our grocery shopping (commerce). However, digital communities can thrive in this "artificial" center and we have numerous case studies in this book.

New services are now appearing that allow consumers to co-create value and to acquire revenue-sharing benefits. The pioneer in this space was *SeeMeTV* as I discussed in its Case Study earlier. This *SeeMeTV* idea has since been adapted or copied in various ways. *MyNuMo* in the USA allows users to create their own games, ringing tones, pictures, puzzles, etc and to sell those, and get a revenue-share. *Self Central* on the Vodafone network in New Zealand is a virtual worlds and social networking site (imagine *Facebook* merging with

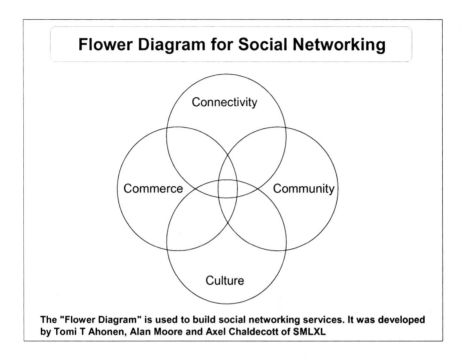

Flower Diagram for Social Networking

Connectivity

Commerce

Community

Culture

The "Flower Diagram" is used to build social networking services. It was developed by Tomi T Ahonen, Alan Moore and Axel Chaldecott of SMLXL

Second Life) with avatars, virtual rooms, etc. On *Self Central* the user-generated content creators earn a 20% revenue-share on the content they create.

Other major players moving into this space at high speed include Nokia, who were perhaps the first global player to make a move into mobile social networking with their *Lifeblog* in 2004. While *Lifeblog* was not actually a mobile *blogging* solution, the more recent Ovi initiative by Nokia is its natural progression to social networking on cellphones. T-Mobile has been another major player to embrace mobile social networking very early on, with CEO Rene Obermann stating their strategic goal is to mobilize web 2.0 communities. A good example of T-Mobile's interest is their *My Faves* user interface.

B   POWER TO THE PEOPLE

But so far social networking seems like a random other service category for the interactive media, internet and mobile. Why would **Business Week** say it is the biggest change since the industrial revolution? Why would the **Economist** say that only those businesses that understand digital communities will survive? Let me examine digital communities. It is all about power. Dramatic shifts in power.

Previously global power was centered on three entities. The biggest power was with the government, including anything from the police to the military to even the church in many cultures such as many Muslim countries. The counter-balancing power to government often is the news media. A third major power is business. A different type of power, still our employers often decide not only whether we get a job and any salary increases and promotions; but also what we must wear at work, what hours we must be at work, even what we may do with our email and internet access and our cellphone, etc.

Meet the smart mob

The last few years have seen a rapid erosion in those previously imperial sources of power and that new power is digital communities. Lets start with government. A vivid illustration of the clout of cellphone based communities was seen in the Philippines, when the Philippines Government of Joseph Estrada was peacefully overthrown by a "smart mob" of enormous size in 2001 after charges of corruption were brought against him. During the four days of the uprising, leading to Estrada's removal from office, SMS text messaging was used to coordinate protests and to mobilize citizens to march, to bring food, and to keep vigil. In the end the peaceful revolution succeeded. This was the first case ever of a peaceful mob overthrowing a government. It could not be done with email and

---

3.5% of US Cellphone users access social networks in 2007
Source: M:Metrics May 2007

IM instant messaging on the internet or via calls on landline phones. Howard Rheingold in his book *Smart Mobs* writes about the impact of cellphones:

> *The technologies that are beginning to make smart mobs possible are mobile communication devices and pervasive computing - inexpensive microprocessors embedded in everyday objects and environments. Already, governments have fallen, youth subcultures have blossomed from Asia to Scandinavia, new industries have been born and older industries launched furious counterattacks.*
> - Howard Rheingold, *Smart Mobs*, 2002

Government is not an isolated case. The same happened in media and business. This kind of digital consumer community revolt was what happened in the overthrow of Dan Rather as the most trusted news anchor on CBS News in the USA. Similarly the worlds' leading bicycle and motorcycle locks manufacturer, Kryptonite, went through its community crisis, when it attempted

---

Tomi T Ahonen

to hush-up a manufacturing defect, and in the ensuing online consumer revolt the company almost went bankrupt. I discussed Kryptonite as one of the Case Studies in my book *Communities Dominate Brands* with Alan Moore so I will not repeat that here. We have lots of more modern examples of community power.

Dell Hell

Since our book we've seen several other widely publicized instances. One of the worst examples is known in the blogosphere as *"Dell Hell"* - how Dell disastrously tried to shut down complaints and honest customer feedback at its user-generated help desk. The ensuing PR disaster helped eliminate about half of Dells' value in the stock market and it took two years for the Dell Hell entries to no longer be visible at the top of Google search results.

Sprint 1,000

Then in 2007 we witnessed the bewildering marketing blunder of the *"Sprint 1,000"* fiasco. In an all-time industry low even for the cellphone industry accused of arrogance and lack of customer care, Sprint Nextel in some delusional moment of customer service madness decided to fire the 1,000 customers who

---

14.3% (5.5M) South Koreans access *Mobile Cyworld* in 2007
Source: Korea Times 16 August 2007

"complained too much." For non-American readers it should be pointed out that Sprint Nextel had the worst customer service experiences, regularly dropping callers in the middle of complaint calls, and forcing customers to call back.

Sprint Nextel was so bad in the overall quality of its customer service that early in 2007 it finished dead-last among all American companies in customer service. Not just worst among telecoms operators, literally dead-last among all US companies. Thus it was not a case that these 1,000 callers were somehow "abusive" callers, who made "excessive" amounts of calls to the calling centers. Sprint Nextel PR people admitted publicly that the company had thousands of customers with *legitimate reasons* to call daily to complain for service problems that were not resolved for periods lasting *more than a month*. The web was soon buzzing with horror-stories of the worst of the examples and Sprint Nextel quietly invited some fired customers to return.

Nonetheless, the ensuing firestorm of criticism of this "innovation" by Sprint Nextel echoed in dozens of major newspapers and even international TV

---

news. It caused ridicule to Sprint Nextel all the way to the night-time talk shows. The long-term damage to Sprint Nextel's brand, loyalty and stock price was so immense that the stock price plummeted to under half its value while an exodus of Sprint Nextel's customers caused it to be the only one of four major carriers in America to lose customers in the second half of 2007. The overall damage in revenues was quoted in the billions of dollars. CEO Gary Forsee was forced to resign only one quarter later and the new management fired the incompetent Chief Marketing Officer Tim Kelly as well.

Community always wins

Still another example is the Live 8 rock concert in Britain in 2006. The concert had its tickets distributed by SMS lottery. Soon some tickets emerged on Ebay, which angered the organizers. Bob Geldof the rock-and-roller who was organizing the event, initiated a consumer revolt against Ebay, and forced them to stop all Live 8 concert ticket sales. Again, we see the power of a community that has decided to act together. Governments, the media and businesses have to accept the greater power of digital communities.

From Wikipedia to AQA

The power of communities is not only disruptive. Today we have numerous examples of content generated by volunteer citizens. These range from Wikipedia the free online encyclopedia written and edited by volunteers -, which was found to be nearly as accurate as Encyclopedia Britannica, to cellphone based information sources such as *AQA*, Any Question Answered, where real people respond to questions sent in by SMS text message. At one UK Pound (two Dollars) per question, *AQA* in Britain has already answered 8 million questions. This also helps illustrate the differences between cellphone based communities and their online sisters and cousins. The cellphone communities tend to be smaller in user numbers, but vastly more lucrative in revenues.

Make it fun

More than anything, social networking and digital communities should be fun. We are often hurried and stressed-out when we engage with our cellphone. An interruption at work, while we drive, at the grocery store, etc. So the services should try to emphasize the fun side of life. A good example was *Flirtomatic* that I discussed in the Case Study earlier in the book. *Flirtomatic* has had it as a basic focus for all of its service development, to focus on fun. They are not "only" a dating/flirting service, but they see *Flirtomatic* as an entertainment service. They want users to be delighted when using the service.

When *Flirtomatic* launched and many users did not have an experience

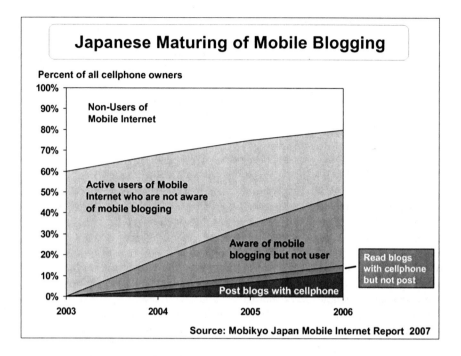

Japanese Maturing of Mobile Blogging

Percent of all cellphone owners

Non-Users of Mobile Internet

Active users of Mobile Internet who are not aware of mobile blogging

Aware of mobile blogging but not user

Read blogs with cellphone but not post

Post blogs with cellphone

Source: Mobikyo Japan Mobile Internet Report 2007

yet in flirting, *Flirtomatic* had a team of "professional flirters" to help get new users up to speed on the service, and to exchange with. This was very important in setting the right tone to the early users, so they in turn would the carry on the fun, tongue-in-cheek style of young adult flirting messages on the service. *Flirtomatic* also kept the service very clean, so their internal informal guide was that if that sort of comment, picture or word was inappropriate for the BBC to broadcast on TV, then it was inappropriate for *Flirtomatic*. The users should feel comfortable with it. *Flirtomatic* was not a pornographic site.

The user experience was soon showing clear differences between internet/broadband users and WAP/mobile internet users. The fixed internet users would tend to come into *Flirtomatic* often during the day - perhaps being bored at work. Nevertheless, mobile *Flirtomatic* users would come into the service in the evenings and late at night, often accessing *Flirtomatic* from a pub or restaurant, etc. A fun-loving companion was really only a short *Flirtomatic* contact away, in your pocket or purse.

C   INVITE CUSTOMER TO PARTICIPATE

Companies must learn to move from interruption to inviting participation. At the simplest level participation is a vote or rating, such as voting a player off *American Idol* via SMS text message or say giving a book five stars on Amazon. A much deeper level of involvement is possible. I discussed engagement marketing briefly in the Mobile Advertising chapter. In addition, a good example of how social networking can be used in adapting classic TV content is the case of *Pop Kids, which* I had as a case study earlier in this book.

Survival of the fastest

Digital communities are also fluid and can shift rapidly. A good example on the mass audience side is the shift from *MySpace* to *Facebook, which* occurred in the time period of 2006-2007. Communities also evolve at enormous speeds. A good example comes from the professional expert community on the fixed Internet, *Ecademy, which* features "clubs" of experts in various fields. From early on *Ecademy* members were invited to submit digital photos to their personal biography pages. Then around 2004 one of the *Ecademy* members suggested it would help personalize the service if for every discussion stream, the system would automatically display the image of the *Ecademy* member who had posted that comment. It would seem more real, when you saw the face of who was posting a comment. The idea was trialed and deployed in a week. The community loved the innovation and the sudden appearance of the face images acted as a catalyst for those who had not yet posted their image to do so.

But *Ecademy* also stumbled. Around Christmas of 2004 *Ecademy* announced that its members would no longer be able to post comments unless they took a minimum subscription to the service and paid an annual fee. This caused a huge outrage among many members who had been loyal and active on *Ecademy* for many years. Among the *Ecademy* mobile applications club there were many members who felt angry that they could no longer participate in the discussions. So they went out to seek a new site that would promise to be free forever, and neutral. A few months later *Forum Oxford* - a mobile industry leaders' discussion forum, free and forever free - was born. The early membership of *Forum Oxford* in late 2005 was a near mirror image of *Ecademy's* Mobile Applications Club from late 2004.

Many of the members remained on both, such as I did for more than a year after that point. However, the best minds and most active members did depart *Ecademy* never to return. The discussions on *Forum Oxford* on any one day are more than on *Ecademy's* mobile applications club on any week. Communities learn fast and move fast.

Are far more nimble

Because they exist solely in a virtual space, and on digital platforms, communities can evolve at far faster speeds than any real business entity can ever hope to match. The contrast would be like comparing the acceleration ability of a bicycle to a jet fighter. For the first few seconds the bicycle might seem like it might stay in the contest of accelerating, but the jet can keep on accelerating long past the absolute top speed of the fastest conceivable bicycle. No business, brand, good or service can "outwit" or "defeat" a community. There can be no victory in a battle against a community, the only way to win is to join the community. Or more precisely to participate and engage each community that is relevant to the brand.

A good example is internet darling Google: Google's social networking site Orkut includes two communities with over 1,000 subscribers: *"What Should Google Do?"* and *"What Should Orkut Do?"* Google seeks the opinion of its own community, its users to find ways how to grow and evolve. These are all examples of engaging customers.

Social networking users on mobile tend to be younger and often have less time to focus on a given social networking acivity. So the interaction and engagement needs to be even more tailored to their tastes. A great example was with *MoBlog UK*, an early mobile blogging service provider in the UK, which ran a nationwide contest for the best anti-Valentine's Day cards, via cameraphones and MMS messages, from its youth members in 2005. Adult concepts of the romance of Valentine's Day include hearts, chocolates, roses, etc. Nevertheless, the pictures submitted by *MoBlog UK's* users were truly in the spirit of anti-Valentine's Day, with anger and hostility and humor, such as the forbidden entry traffic sign superimposed over a red heart, and so forth. This is the attitude and ethos of younger users on mobile social networks.

D   CITIZEN JOURNALISM

A closely related phenomenon is that of user-generated content, and perhaps its poster child is citizen journalism, invented by Mr Oh and his **Ohmy News** in South Korea, which is one of the case studies in my previous book **Digital Korea**. I will not spend more time on **Ohmy News** except to summarize that this citizen journalist daily web newspaper is generated by a pool of 74,000 citizen journalists. It has become one of South Korea's most respected and trusted news sources. Just because the content is generated by citizens does not make it bad. **Ohmy News** has very highly trained editors who work very hard to turn citizen content into real news worthy of printing, going through normal journalistic processes of checking stories, sources, etc.

Meanwhile the 2007 International Citizen Reporters' Forum held in Seoul South Korea reported that already 41 citizen journalism newspapers similar to **Ohmy News** had launched in 15 countries on five continents. There is a trend under way and a citizen-generated newspaper is headed your way soon. The CEO and founder of **Ohmy News**, Oh Yeon-ho wrote about the nature of citizen journalism contrasting it to blogging in 2006 with these words:

> *Writing a news story requires a good deal of time and consideration. It is much more difficult, for example, than leaving a comment or posting a blog entry. Though we are an open platform accessible to everyone, not everyone can write a news story. Only those citizen reporters who are passionately committed to social change and reporting make our project possible. The main reason that citizen journalism has not grown and spread more rapidly is the difficult task of finding and organizing these passionate citizen reporters in waiting.*
>
> Oh Yeon-ho, CEO and Founder *Ohmy News* 2006

Somewhere between the total amateur and the semi-professional citizen journalist, is the accidental paparazzi. Examples include British youth magazine *Heat* reporting already 80 cameraphone snaps sent to them every week to the car racing magazine *F1 Racing* now featuring a citizen paparazzi picture in every issue. Another example is of course CNN's i-Reporter, mentioned before.

The cameraphone is now the way to collect memories and events. Perhaps the best tidbit was about the Pope's funeral, where many used camera-

---

Citizen Journalism Around the World

40 Citizen Journalism news sources had launched by 2007 in 15 countries on 5 continents by June 2007

North America	16 sites	Canada, USA
Asia	10 sites	Indonesia, Israel, Japan, Nepal, South Korea
Europe	11 sites	Estonia, France, Poland, Russia, Ukraine, UK
Latin America	2 sites	Brazil
Africa	1 site	South Africa

**Source: Ohmy News International
Citizen Reporters' Forum 2007**

---

phones to snap an image of their beloved Pope. The *New York Times* quoted Gianluca Nicoletti of Italy's *La Stampa* newspaper as saying, *"In the past, pilgrims would take away a relic, like a piece of cloth on the saint's body. Here, there's been the transposition to a level of unreality. They're bringing home a digital relic."*

The 7/7 London bombings

The 7/7 bombings of the London Tube by terrorists in the Summer of 2005, were the first major news event to have the majority of the video content shown on the air to be provided by amateur journalists. In an event that was shorter in duration, and much more condensed in geographical area coverage - than the Tsunami half a year earlier - yet the London event had over 300 video clips sent to the BBC alone (in addition to over 1000 still images). Helen Boaden, Director of the BBC News said, *"No one knows where this is going to take us. The gap between the professional and non-professional news gatherers is getting narrower."* Simon Bucks, Associate Editor of Sky News echoes these themes by saying, *"This is probably the first big story in Britain where we have seen this effect, where camera phones allow eyewitnesses a method of recording news and getting it broadcast."*

With the rapid spread of cameraphones worldwide, such citizen journalism becomes a much more widely spread resource than even the world's largest news gathering organizations, like CNN or BBC can hope to maintain. Thus increasingly we will see the early footage of unanticipated breaking news stories captured by amateour journalists.

Trust word of mouth

The very underlying premise in this shift in the balance of power from the brands to the communities, is that we trust community opinions more than messages of corporations. In fact, we will take a total stranger's opinion, on a community we trust, as more valid than the press release statement of a known executive of a corporation we deal with. The word-of-mouth can lead to rapid success of a new service and the Alpha User is a critical concept when considering cellphone based digital communities, as I discussed in the earlier chapter on mobile advertising.

E   ACTIVATE WITH DIGITAL CHANNELS

We can activate, cultivate and motivate such communities through games, interactivity and feedback systems using new tools like SMS text messaging, IM

Instant messaging, blogging and MMS picture messaging. Receiving feedback through the most efficient digital communication channels is vast, rich and rapid.

But remember that you can no longer control a digital community. If you try to fight them, your effect is almost meaningless, but the community remains and may even become more powerful because of it. Remember the example of *Ecademy*. Even if you do a lot of things right, if you suddenly do something wrong, you jeopardize the whole experience. You cannot beat them, you can only join them. As Randolf Kluver, Associate Professor at the Singapore Internet Research Centre says, *"To apply media laws on bloggers is like firing a howitzer at a swarm of mosquitoes. You will change the configuration for about half a minute, then it will be like you never fired it at all."*

Community and the cellphone

Again, just like in the previous chapter about the evolution of the internet, the community behavior will migrate to cellphones. A good example is *Twitter*, the mobile blogging service that is rapidly gaining popularity in late 2007. There are many similarities to blogging with *Twitter*, yet *Twitter* brings more of a personal conversational experience to community discussion. More like a small group at a party or restaurant, two people might be engaged in conversation, and others to be listening, paying attention. Then suddenly another person might join into the discussion and share thoughts. *Twitter* is bringing the social networking phenomenon even more to a personal and real-time experience. This makes perfect sense. We have seen in the Generation-C chapter that the cellphone is the communication tool of preference.

In areas of digital community behavior, we see a clear migration to cellphones. From blogging - already a third of all Koreans use cellphones for mobile blogging - to dating to chat to smart mobs to TV-interactivity, in all walks of life, the migration of community activism is going to cellphones. I do not mean that communities will stop using the web, such as on Ebay or giving ratings on Amazon or joining friends finders services. However, the preference and most intense activity will migrate to the cellphones. If you are interested in community behavior, you will need to observe that transition to cellphones.

Alan Moore and I put it this way in our book ***Communities Dominate Brands***, in 2005: *"Community power is inevitable and companies that ignore communities will wither and disappear, to be taken over by the new players who understand the relevance of this new customer power."*

Case Study 13 from the USA
MyNuMo

Following on the innovations of *SeeMeTV*, where the original creator of videos were paid one penny per view of their content on the Three/Hutchison services, *MyNuMo* launched a similar service in the USA, but offering both a much wider opportunity to sell content and providing a much larger revenue sharing portion to the content creator.

MyNuMo launched in 2006 and offered its users the chance to create almost anything in a digital space that could be consumed on a cellphone. These included user-generated ringing tones and pictures and screen savers, to more advanced content such as videos and games.

The content revenue-sharing was set to always be very strongly motivating the content owner to deliver excellence. Typically for content worth a dollar, *MyNuMo* would pay 40 cents of a revenue-share to the original creator. Also the original content creator is not charged for uploading content, which helps content creators to revise and improve their content and keep it fresh and up-to-date.

MyNuMo has been the able to rapidly capitalize on various popular content and phenomena, as content can be delivered on extremely short notice.

MyNuMo also offers many games that can be turned around and deployed in a day, to start to capitalize on popular phenomena, whether it is Paris Hilton in a scandal or a Senator caught in a lewd act in a public mens room etc. After the iPhone launched, *MyNuMo* has also become a major provider of content for the iPhone, in particular new games for the device.

The beauty of *MyNuMo* is its business model, which allows creative talent to easily create cellphone content, and then to be paid for it. This is a clear sign of the way the industry will be evolving.

Many users come from miscellaneous internet creative content providers in anything from horoscopes to daily jokes to cartoons, music, etc.

Similar concepts of rewarding members for user-generated content have been then adopted for example by Vodafone with its service *Self Central* in New Zealand, which also features a rich array of user-generated content, where original creators are also gaining a revenue-share.

"Cameraphones are the death of us all. There are no more secrets."
David Spade

XV
Eight C's of Cellphones
Capabilities from communication to cool

The cellphone started off as a communication device. For its first 20 years that was all it did like its 100-year-old sibling, the fixed landline telephone. However, over the last ten years, the cellphone has suddenly taken on ever more capabilities. In so doing the cellphone has rapidly cannibalized industries and technologies and is currently threatening even more.

A   CELLPHONES AND EIGHT C'S

While the phone has gone from being only a communication device to also a consumption device, such as allowing us to consume music or videogaming on the phone; to also a creative device, with the integration of the camera; and now mobile commerce, advertising etc., the cellphone is also getting to be remarkably complex. I will walk through the changes in what I like to call the Eight C's of Cellphones.

First C - Communication (voice and messaging)

The oldest need of cellphones is calling. Or more accurately communication. This arrived as a legacy of the fixed landline telecoms business: voice calls. That is why phones have numbered dial pads, and we all have phone numbers. Because the early phone systems started to assign fixed landline owners phone numbers, and then later introduced the rotary dial with 10 digits to let us make the call connections ourselves, without the need to talk to an operator to connect our calls. We had wireless phones used in some government, police and military uses, but for consumer use we had to wait for cellular technology to give us mobility in our phone calls.

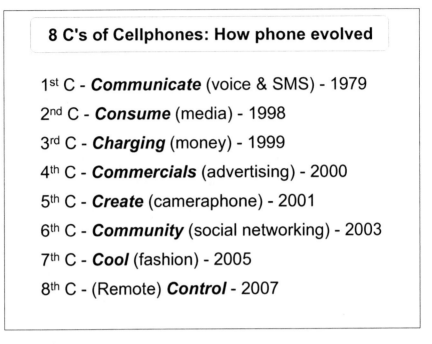

8 C's of Cellphones: How phone evolved

1st C - *Communicate* (voice & SMS) - 1979

2nd C - *Consume* (media) - 1998

3rd C - *Charging* (money) - 1999

4th C - *Commercials* (advertising) - 2000

5th C - *Create* (cameraphone) - 2001

6th C - *Community* (social networking) - 2003

7th C - *Cool* (fashion) - 2005

8th C - (Remote) *Control* - 2007

Invented in America, the first commercial launch of cellular telephony was in Japan by NTT Nippon Telephone and Telegraph, the Japanese incumbent in 1979. So from day 1, cellphones have served a communication need. Moreover, since then cellphones took over from all other forms of communication as the predominant communication channel. Today more than twice as many people make calls on cellphones than on fixed landline calls around the world, the total traffic and the total revenues on voice calls from cellphones are dramatically larger than those on fixed landline phones.

Late in 1993, we saw the advent of the first person-to-person SMS text message in Finland. Today SMS has become the most widely used data application on the planet, with some 2.5 billion people sending messages, which is about 74% of all cellphone subscribers. The world average is 2.6 SMS text messages sent per day per cellphone subscriber. So yes, communication is the First C of Cellphones.

Second C - Consumption (downloadable content)

In 1998 in Finland, Radiolinja (now Elisa) introduced a radical innovation for the cellphone. They invented the downloadable ringing tone. So ten years ago the first expansion of the capabilities of the cellphone began and phones offered the chance to consume content. The next year, 1999, Japanese NTT DoCoMo introduced the prototypical content portal service for cellphones, i-Mode and launched what is commonly called the mobile internet. Today all cellphones and all networks offer the chances to consume content from the very basic SMS based news alerts to consuming WAP and web pages to downloading full track MP3 files to MMS multi-Channel messages to watching live TV and beyond.

Now, the interesting comparison is with the internet of course. While the consumption ability was being invented for the cellphone in obscure corners of the world in Finland and Japan, four years earlier the internet had broken into the mainstream in America being on the covers of *Newsweek* and *Time* in 1994. In addition, the internet offered a lot of content consumption opportunities back then, and massive amounts of content today. The Discovery Channel said in 2006 that the equivalent amount of data, as exists in all of the books in the Library of Congress, are moved on the internet globally every 16 minutes. Truly enormous volumes of information and entertainment there on the internet to be consumed. So what of the cellphone consumption.

How is the internet content industry doing? Actually any new media channel will discover that the first content is of adult oriented nature. The first playing cards featured naked ladies, the first moving picture reels were peep shows, the first videocassette rental money was made in porn as were the first DVD sales. Yes, adult content drives any new media and internet was no exception. The adult industry discovered the internet first. A difficult industry sector to measure, web based adult content industry was worth 2.5 billion dollars worldwide according to the Internet Filter Review in 2006.

Most major studies report that adult pages and adult content (and adult topics in search) continue to be the top content on the web, or else the study says in its footnotes that adult content was excluded from the measurements. For example Hitwise reported in April 2007 that 13% of all web traffic related to adult entertainment topics. For comparison Hitwise said search was only 7% of all internet traffic. So it is quite normal for the adult entertainment industry to discover any new media first and to make business out of it.

The internet is not only porn, obviously. In 2006 there were many other viable content industries on the web. The second largest content category was gambling at about 2 B dollars, and then videogaming at about 1.9 B dollars. The other content categories then such as music sales (think iTunes) or access to the premium pages of the *Wall Street Journal* and other such branded content sites etc, are in the single billions in size. The total content industry for the 14-year-old internet is about 25 billion dollars according to the *Guardian* in 2007, led by porn and gambling. In percentage terms, adult content powers 10% of the total internet content industry and gambling adds another 8%. So that is our context.

Now consider the younger media channel, Mobile as 7th of the Mass Media. The content industry on cellphones has already grown past internet content in total size by 2004 and was worth 31 billion dollars according to the same article in the *Guardian*. Informa reported that cellphone content grew strongly again in 2007 to reach a total of 45 billion dollars by year end.

Yes. Younger in age, yet already much larger than internet content by revenues and growing much faster. Now lets consider the maturity of cellphone content. Yes, adult entertainment is there on cellphones, of course, at about 1.7 billion dollars according to Informa in 2007. Thus adult entertainment is only 4% of the "mobile internet." Gambling is there as well at about 1 billion dollars globally (2% of the total). However, adult entertainment and gambling are no longer the two largest content categories on cellphones. Informa reported that six content groups are larger than adult on mobile as a mass media channel, led by music at 8.8 billion dollars. There also is infotainment, images, gaming, video and web browsing all ahead of adult and gambling as paid content categories on cellphones.

Content on mobile is younger than web content, larger in dollar terms, growing faster and is more mature as a media channel. Not bad for a 10-year-old.

UK consumer cellphone voice traffic declined 25% in 2007
Source: JD Power Annual Survey 2007

And also remember that Hollywood earns under 30 billion dollars in box office income annually. The music industry earns less than 30 billion dollars of worldwide music sales. Videogaming software industry is also under 30 billion dollars in aggregate size globally. Nevertheless, younger than any of them, this 10-year old content media channel, mobile, already delivers more paid content than the total size of any of those giant media industries worldwide.

Would you want to be an executive at Paramount in movies or at Warner in music or at an EA in gaming? Now such giants are being born for the mobile content industry, and most of those companies are totally under the radar as mobile content appeared so suddenly and so much seems frivolous like the *Crazy Frog* ringing tone in 2005.

Bear in mind that even though the iPod had been around since 2001 with most major popular music available on it, suddenly out of nowhere, in 2005 that one annoying ringing tone, *Crazy Frog* alone outsold all of iTunes worldwide in 2005 according to numbers by Apple and Jamba. Yes, the cellphone has arrived, it is now a fully valid media channel and has discovered its wings in the Second C: Content.

Third C: Commercials (advertising).

The first mobile ads were used in Finland in 2000 to sponsor free news headline

---

services using SMS text messaging. Mobile advertising or perhaps more accurately called "mobile marketing" became a mass-market offering in Japan when the country's largest mobile operator/carrier NTT DoCoMo got together with the country's largest advertising agency, Dentsu and formed D2 the world's first major advertising company specializing on mobile in 2001.

Soon both of its national rivals had launched similar ventures, KDDI joined with Japan's second largest ad agency Hakuhodo and their venture is called Mediba. Meanwhile Softbank the third largest wireless carrier offers mobile advertising under the J-Mobile subsidiary. Similar ventures have appeared in several other advanced Asian markets, such as AirCross in South Korea, the mobile advertising arm of the largest wireless carrier SK Telecom.

In some countries mobile advertising has taken off quite well such as in Spain in Europe where three out of four cellphone owners already receive ads. However, in most countries mobile advertising/marketing seems to be almost an afterthought, a minor component of the interactive part of a larger ad campaign.

UK consumer cellphone SMS traffic increased 44% in 2007
Source: JD Power Annual Survey 2007

When advertising is designed for the unique benefits of the cellphone and use the philosophies of "engagement marketing", then the reverse happens. Consumers sign up to ads, are willing to consume ads, and in particularly successful campaigns, will actually want more ads onto their phones. In Japan 54% of all cellphone owners receive ads (opting in to ad campaigns) according to Wireless Watch Japan in September 2006. While that is a stunning statistic, the more bewildering one is that by 2006 already 44% of Japanese cellphone owners actually *click* on ads they have received onto their phones (Goo Research July 2006).

A brilliant example of how far the Japanese market has evolved in this space is in the book *Mobile Advertising* by Chetan Sharma, Joe Herzog and Victor Melfi. They tell of a Northwest Airlines cellphone ad campaign:

> *(The cellphone ad campaign...) enticed consumers to engage in an interactive "Guess the name of the city" quiz written in the style of Japanese senryu poems. The answers are all cities in the United States and Asia that Northwest Airlines flies to, North America being the biggest market for Japanese travelers. Prizes include e-coupons that count towards discounted fares and WorldPerks Bonus Miles. A further twist to the campaign allows consumers submit their own senryu poem about travel to the United States on Northwest Airlines. The best of*

---

these appear on the site, and people can vote on their favorites, bringing customers back to the NWA site time and time again.
Chetan Sharma, Joe Herzog and Victor Melfi, ***Mobile Advertising***, 2008

This is cellphone advertising in Japan. If more than 4 out of 10 cellphone users are willing to click on ads they have received onto their phones, it means they like the ads they receive. The ads contain value (coupons, discounts, free offers, etc). The ads are funny and entertaining. Or they have valuable information. At times the ads have exclusive benefits. This is what the ad agencies in the rest of the world need to learn. How to make mobile advertising so appealing that users are compelled to click on them, to consume them. Not spam on SMS text messaging but true engagement advertising.

So yes, cellphones are emerging as a channel to deliver commercials. One of the trailblazers in this space is Admob, already proclaiming itself to be the biggest provider of advertisements on cellphones worldwide. Two years from launch, operating in a dozen countries including the USA and UK, Admob was delivering 2 billion wireless advertisements to cellphones every month, at the end of 2007. I discussed mobile advertising in its own chapter earlier in the book. Google better watch out. Its time to wake up and smell the cellphone. Moreover, yes, Commercials are emerging as the third C of cellphones.

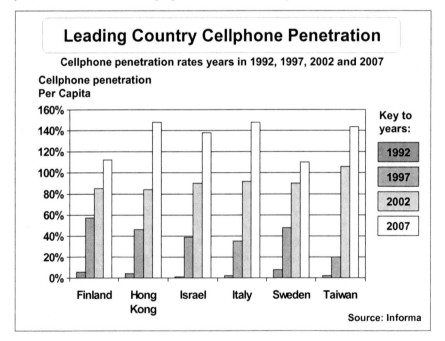

Leading Country Cellphone Penetration

Cellphone penetration rates years in 1992, 1997, 2002 and 2007

Source: Informa

Tomi T Ahonen

Fourth C: Charging (mobile payments).

There had been pilot projects to allow consumers to make payments with cellphones for individual services as far back as 1997 for the two Coca Cola vending machines in Finland, or in 2000 in Norway to pay for parking etc. However, the first mass consumer payment systems where cellphones could be used in multiple locations nationwide, were introduced in short succession in the Philippines by their wireless giant carriers Smart and Globe.

Today various cellphone based payment systems are in most countries. I listed many in the Society chapter, but they range from paying your congestion charge in London by cellphone (20% already do) to paying for your public transportation in Finland (57% of single tickets to Helsinki's trams are paid by cellphone). In Slovenia you can pay by cellphone in McDonalds. In addition, the most advanced systems are in Japan and South Korea. In Japan the use of the keitai (the cellphone) as the "mobile wallet" is so advanced that they are already constructing apartment buildings where the locks operate by cellphone.

In South Korea more than half of the population pay by credit cards and banking accounts already embedded onto the cellphone. In many countries from South Africa to the Philippines you can get your whole salary paid onto your cellphone banking account. In Kenya the limit on the maximum single transaction on cellphone based payment is a million US dollars. Moreover, also

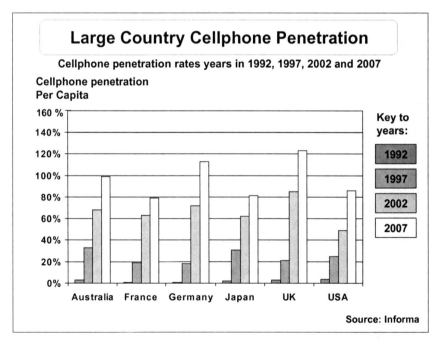

in Kenya, of all banking accounts in use, one in five is a cellphone banking account. Yes, coming soon to a pocket near you, your taxes, your salary, your spare cash, your credit (and your keys, access passes, loyalty cards, etc) will be embedded onto your phone. The Cellphone discovered its fourth C: Charging.

Fifth C - Creation (cameraphones)

Then in 2001 a weird combination arrived from the challenger carrier in Japan, J-Phone (since Vodafone KK now Softbank): the cameraphone. Not strictly the first integration of camera and cellphone but certainly the first mass-market offering of what is now known as the cameraphone. It took off like a rocket. In the next 18 months over 40% of J-Phone's customers had snapped up these new gadgets. Before you could say Nokia Samsung Motorola SonyEricsson LG, all phone makers added the camera feature to the phones.

Today 100% of phones sold in Japan and South Korea are cameraphones. More than half of all phones sold worldwide are cameraphones. In addition, even after removing the old phones due to the 18 month replacement cycles, there were about 1.6 billion cameraphones in use by the end of 2007, meaning there are more cameraphones (with color screens) than all internet users worldwide, and four times as many cameraphones as laptop computers.

This helps explain why 30% of American users of Flickr send pictures straight from cameraphones to *Flickr*. It also explains why 90% of South Koreans do the same to their equivalent service, *Cyworld*. Moreover, why Japan in 2006 became the first country where PC sales dropped by 18% - while cellphone sales keep setting new records. I should mention that yes, Japan has one of the highest penetrations of broadband, highest speed broadband, and lowest cost broadband in the world, roughly on par with South Korea. As the Japanese Ministry for Communications reported in 2006, not only does Japan have more people accessing the web via cellphones, cellphone based internet users also access the internet more often than PC based internet users.

The famed author and mobile expert Tony Fish coined the phrase that the cellphone is *"available at the moment of creative inspiration"*. What use is our wonderful 10 megapixel digital Nikon camera if it is back home in its camera case, when we are on the road and a wonderful view is upon us and we want to snap a picture. Nevertheless, the trusty cameraphone is there with us, always. Literally always, as I have said, Morgan Stanley reported in 2007 that 91% of cellphone owners will keep the phone within arm's reach twenty four hours a day. If not physically in bed with them at night, then at the bedside table. Its that personal. In addition, as the phone is with us, its camera is always-on the ready. At the Pope's funeral more people chronicled their visit with the beloved Pope using cameraphones than digital cameras or camcorders. The 7/7 London bombings, the Boxing Day Tsunami, the abuse of the monks in Myanmar (ex-Burma).

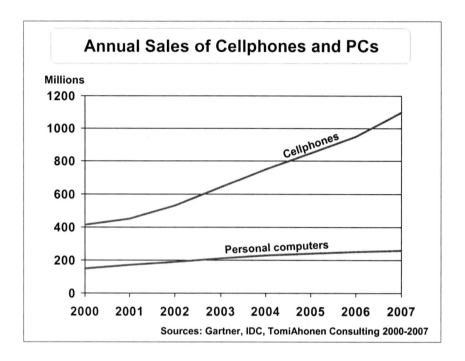

Annual Sales of Cellphones and PCs

Sources: Gartner, IDC, TomiAhonen Consulting 2000-2007

Where there is news breaking, today there also are lots of cameraphones. So yes, seven years ago the cellphone added its fifth C: Creation.

Sixth C - Community (social networking)

Then there is this crazy phenomenon around *YouTube, MySpace, Flickr, Facebook, Second Life, Habbo Hotel, World of Warcraft, Wikipedia* and blogging. It is what many call social networking. Or others call Web 2.0. What Alan Moore and I called "digital communities" in our book *Communities Dominate Brands* in March 2005. What *Business Week* in its cover story in June 2005 said was so meaningful that it is the biggest change in mankind's history since the industrial revolution. So relevant that *Time* put the concept on the cover of the *Person of the Year* issue in 2006.

So with social networking I am talking about user generated content. Digital communities are nothing new. Electronic communities had been around in academia, military and government in the mainframe computing environment from the 1970s and even on PCs there were modem connection based clubs and chat boards on "BBS" (Bulleting Board System) services from the 1980s. These tended to be limited to any given internet service provider and still in the early 1990s they tended to be "walled garden" systems of closed user groups, such as

Compuserve, Genie, Prodigy and *AOL*. These eventually connected to each other via the internet protocol in the middle of the 1990s.

For contrast, while many smaller trials and niche markets for communities did exist on mobile - I was part of one of the world's first trials of cellphone based chat on Elisa's network in Finland in 1998, for example. For practical commercial purposes the first mass-market consumer communities for mobile were launched in South Korea by SK Telecom when *Cyworld* released its wireless version of *Cyworld* in 2003. So communities have existed on the web for more than 14 years but on cellphones only for five years.

Soon various online communities started to appear on cellphone networks around the world. One of the innovators was *MeTV* in Singapore, launched by the wireless carrier/mobile operator MobileOne (M1). A similar service, *SeeMeTV* was soon launched by Three/Hutchison in the UK, Italy, Austria, Australia, etc. Other rivals appeared such as *LookAtMe* by O2 in the UK. *MeTV, SeeMeTV* and *LookAtMe* are video sharing services of user-generated video, similar to *YouTube* on the internet. However, the big innovation was rewarding the creator of the video with a revenue-share every time someone

---

The Nokia N93 had 31 keys or buttons in 2007
Source: Nokia

---

viewed the video. So if I created the video and you went to watch it, I was paid a penny. A hundred people watched my video and I earned a dollar. Thousand people, ten dollars into my pocket. And so forth. Not the *YouTube* free model, but rather *rewarding* the creator for the content. This is why the service is so popular. I discussed *SeeMeTV* in a case study already in the book.

Other commercial social networking successes on cellphones range from *Flirtomatic* the dating/flirting cellphone service in the UK, to *BotFighter* the LBS robot fighting multiplayer videogame in Sweden to *MyNuMo* the user-generated content distribution service in the USA to Cyworld in South Korea. *Flirtomatic, MyNuMo* and *Cyworld* are cases in this book.

So how do they compare? The social networking/community content online on the PC based internet is worth under 3 billion dollars in total worldwide revenues in 2007, with by far the biggest chunk coming from the subscribers to MMOGs (Massively Multiplayer Online Games) such as *World of Warcraft, Lineage, Counterstrike, Everquest* etc. Also some money is earned by the *Second Life* type environments and the online dating services like *Match.com* and professional communities like *Linked In* and *Ecademy* etc.

For contrast, social networking revenues earned on cellphones were measured to be worth over 5 billion dollars in 2007 (Informa 2007), with already

---

Tomi T Ahonen

over 100 million active paying users around the world. The industry grew 46% year-on-year   From zero to five billion dollars in four years? Yes that is definitely the world record for fastest growth of a new billion dollar industry, ever. Social networking on cellphones, wireless communities, mobile web 2.0. However, you want to call it, this is the biggest business opportunity of this decade. I looked at cellphone community services in its own chapter of the book. Nevertheless, yes, the cellphone has discovered its sixth C: Community.

Seventh C: Control (as in Remote Control).

And where will this all lead? The communication device in our pocket already has expanded to offer six converged functionalities and is rapidly becoming master of them all. What next? I'll tell you what next. In our research for my fifth book, *Digital Korea*, co-authored with Jim O'Reilly in 2007, we found that South Korea was already deeply on the path to make the cellphone the central remote control for all of our household gadgets, our home, our car, even the home robots that South Koreans have started to buy now.

The Apple iPhone had 1 key or button in 2007
Source: Apple

In South Korea today the cellphone is becoming the "universal remote control" for just about everything. There are remote control systems sold commercially to have your cellphone operate your home heating and air conditioning etc. Cellphone operated remote control for the locks on your car. Combined with the payment functions "the mobile wallet" the cellphone takes on the functions of our keys to our home and the passkeys to our offices, etc.

It is not limited to Korea. I have mentioned apartment buildings in Japan with cellphone operated locks. There are parking garages that use cellphone operation of the gate in Finland, which means there is no need for a parking garage gate operator. Also in Finland there are remote control modules to have your sauna turned on, a valuable feature on a particularly cold night of the Finnish winter, to be able to have your sauna roaring hot and ready for you when you get home. Of course, controlled by cellphone. So we can see the cellphone starting to adopt its seventh function: (remote) control.

Eighth C - Cool (fashion)

The latest and last of the Eight C's of Cellphone functionality is what was submitted by Michelle Huet a member of the mobile industry expert community

---

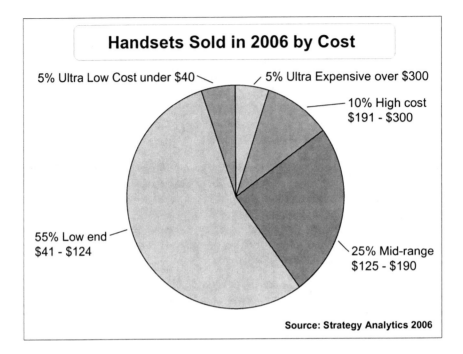

Handsets Sold in 2006 by Cost

5% Ultra Low Cost under $40

5% Ultra Expensive over $300

10% High cost $191 - $300

55% Low end $41 - $124

25% Mid-range $125 - $190

Source: Strategy Analytics 2006

Forum Oxford, and she called it "cool" for fashion. There were early steps by Nokia to move into the fashion industry with the launch of the Vertu line of jewelry style luxury cellphones in 2002 (the lowest cost platinum Vertu phone was priced at 21,000 dollars).

I would count the mass-market launch of a fashion brand onto a cellphone, being the first Benetton branded phone on the NTT DoCoMo network in 2006. Motorola did its collaboration with Dolce & Gabbana. The Apple iPhone was a fashion statement in 2007. Since then we've seen numerous fashion brands rushing into the space from cellphones by Prada (LG) and Armani (Samsung) to watchmakers, T-shirt makers and blue jeans brands all incorporating telecoms functionality such as SMS text messaging interfaces. Thus the cellphone is now also a part of our "bling" and a fashion accessory.

The replacement cycle for young employed adults in advanced fashion-aware markets such as Hong Kong, Japan and South Korea, is now six months, having harmonized to the Spring Collections and Fall Collections cycle of the fashion industry. The phone makers incorporate their latest phones to the catwalks of the fashion industry, as Nokia started doing five years ago. Now in Japan for example the three wireless carriers/mobile operators, all have fashion launches of their Spring Collection and Fall Collection of new phone models. All synchronized to the colors of the season. Ladies in Japan do color-coordinate their phones with their shoes and handbags. Undeniably, the cellphone is now gaining its eight C, Cool. It is becoming a fashion statement. Look at most owners of iPhones, and see how proudly they display their favorite gadget.

So there they are, the Eight C's of Cellphones. Communication, Consumption, Commercials, Charging, Creation, Community, (remote) Control and Cool (fashion). In the past ten years the cellphone has extended its skills set and functionality from one to eight.

B   MOST COMPLEX

This all has come at a price. The technology of the cellphone is most demanding; it is the most complex piece of consumer electronics today. The requirements on the CPU, the built-in memory, the storage ability, the display, the camera all set constraints to the size, weight, cost, and perhaps most distinctly to battery life.

Packed full of radio gear

The number of radio units on a typical modern phone is bewildering - Nokia's top end N82 in December 2007 had a quad-band GSM radio for 2G calls and traffic; the 3G/3.5G WCDMA and HSDPA radio for high speed data traffic; the FM radio receiver; the Bluetooth transmitter; the WiFi transmitter; and a GPS (Global Positioning System) receiver. Each has its own antenna inbuilt somewhere into the phone structure and needs to be considered how the phone is used, its angle of use, the position of the users' hand(s) etc. All this in a device smaller and lighter than an iPhone. Each radio component adds complexity, drains the battery and CPU. In addition, consider that for example the payment enabled phones in Japan using the Felica chip, incorporate yet another near-field radio technology into the same phone. South Korean TV-tuner phones add the digital DMB TV receiver as well (as do Japanese "1Seg" TV phones and European DVB-H phones). Yet another radio unit to incorporate.

The 2G and 3G radio units need to provide "seamless cross-over" so if you are on a call on one system and as you move, you pass the coverage range of that radio base station, but come into the reach of another, and this happens to be on the other technology, the user should not drop his call. The complexity is considerable. If the phone is called "optimistic" it thinks it can achieve connection with the network, and shows "bars" on the display for good coverage, but the call will not go through frustrating the caller. If the phone is called "pessimistic" it would have acceptable radio connection, but the phone refuses to connect, thinking the connection is too weak and the phone makes unnecessary attempts to re-connect, draining the battery.

All this for an industry, which ships over 1.2 billion new phones every year, and, which has over 500 different phone models on offer at any one point in time, and typically 2,000 different phone models active in any one national market. As the replacement cycle is 18 months for the global market and down to 6 months for the most demanding market segments in the most advanced markets, the innovation requirements are also remarkably competitive. The near term handset feature expectations include inbuilt WiMax transmission abilities; projection screen technologies and 3D (Three Dimensional) image projection just to name three innovations already in the pipeline.

18 months of design

It takes typically 18 months from drawing board to shipping a new cellphone model. The design tends to be frozen 9 months in. The big makers all have several models under simultaneous development, so they can release new phones every few weeks. They release new mainstream phone models on "platforms", which are developed on longer cycles. This all needs to be accurately mapped to fickle consumer demands. Should the next phone form factor want candybar or clamshell or slider or twister or perhaps transformer? The Apple iPhone large screen touch-screen phone may have been all the rage in the newest look of phones in 2007 spawning countless copy-cats; it is unlikely to remain the hottest new phone form-factor in 2009.

To then try to forecast the right dimensions and form factor; the right screen size and camera resolution; with the correct mix of radio gear, their respective antennae and all related software and applications. These all drain the CPU and memory. The end-user may want to load all kinds of stored data to the phone, depending on the above. For example if the phone is to have a GPS receiver, the user is going to need maps stored on the phone, adding to the need to have data storage ability on the phone. Or if the phone is equipped with the digital TV tuner like in South Korea, then the user may want TiVo type of "pausing live TV" functionality, particularly useful if a phone call interrupts watching TV. Now the phone needs an in-built hard disk drive.

To this then add the right display characteristics, not just screen size but screen form-factor and resolution. Many clamshell phones have two screens so display management becomes an issue. The screen drains the battery, so if the clamshell is opened to reveal the larger screen, it makes sense to turn off the alternate screen. However, what all content should be displayed on the smaller screen when the phone is closed. The complexity just with screens is enormous.

And that all will have impacts and is often limited by the operating system of the phone. Again, at the inception phase of the phone, the handset maker has to select an operating system, whether Symbian or Microsoft Windows for Mobile, or any one of the proprietary operating systems from those of Nokia, Samsung, SonyEricsson, Motorola etc; down to the ones at RIM Blackberry, Google Android and Apple iPhone's OS/X. To then forecast how will that operating system evolve and at, which point will it need to be frozen for this given phone model to be readied for network testing.

And then there are about 300 significant wireless carriers/mobile operators around the world, who will each individually test and accept a given cellphone model to their market. Each national cellular network lives not only on one of a wide range of radio frequencies, but also by its own national regulatory environment - such as the approved maximum heights of radio masts, and maximum radio power transmission levels. Cellular networks can include transmission equipment from many network providers, some equipment new, others upgraded, and in cases of the developing world, at times transmission equipment, which is second hand. The same cellphone that passes all tests beautifully in one country, may fail miserably in the neighboring country. Moreover, if the handset maker wants to sell in that country, they need to make a variant of the phone that corresponds to the requirements of that country.

I am not kidding when I say this is the most complex industry. It is not like rocket science. It is far more complex than rocket science.

C   INTO THE VALLEY OF DEATH

The market is very demanding and fiercely competitive, littered with the corpses of former global giants of home electronics, engineering and telecoms. Each had seen cellphones as a massive growth opportunity and invested heavily into it, and then pulled out due to it being too demanding.

Epitaphs of past masters

Philips, once the world's largest consumer electronics company and a major European cellphone maker has quit the cellphone business. Siemens, the world's largest engineering company sold its cellphone unit to BenQ in 2005. Sony, currently the world's largest consumer electronics giant and Ericsson, the world's largest telecoms equipment manufacturer found the cellphone market too challenging to go it alone in 2001 and set up a joint venture for cellphones under SonyEricsson. Panasonic, Sharp, NEC, Sanyo and other familiar Japanese electronics brands mostly pulled out of international cellphone markets as too competitive and now concentrate only on the domestic Japanese market.

Motorola the once largest handset maker slipped to number two in 2000 and now has fallen further in 2007 to number three in size behind Nokia and Samsung and some rumors in early 2008 suggested Motorola might even get out of the handset business it invented. It is a cut-throat market making phones with global giants dueling for market share. Behind the big five of Nokia, Samsung, Motorola, SonyEricsson and LG are about two dozen smaller mostly Asian manufacturers like HTC, Pantech, ZTE, Ningbo Bird, BenQ and Huawei.

Into this market we see the occasional newcomer appear like Canadian RIM with the Blackberry, and UK based Sendo. There is continuous interest by major IT companies to make moves into the cellphone space whether by Apple with the iPhone or Dell's rumored smartphone. Other major players come into a given area of the industry such as Microsoft and Google entering the operating system sector of the cellphone business.

Supercomputer in your pocket

And as a final indicator of just how enormously powerful our pocket friend has become, let me recount an analysis I did for the Canadian Wireless Telecoms Association in 2005. I was invited to speak at the 20th Anniversary of Cellphones in Canada, and asked to make predictions of what the next 20 years would bring. Talk about a hopeless forecasting task...

What I did, was made a thorough analysis of the previous 20 years, and made some projections based on how far the phone had evolved in the previous two decades. I of course added that my guess was as good as anyone else's and that nobody could foresee such disruptive and counter-intuitive inventions as we've seen with for example person-to-person SMS text messaging, and ringtones. In my analysis, I observed that a top-end 3G smartphone in 2005, was equivalent in CPU processing power, inbuilt memory capacity, data storage ability, communication speed, etc, as a low-end laptop computer of five years earlier. This was similar in performance to a top-end desktop computer from ten years ago. That in turn was equivalent to a mini computer from 15 years ago, and of the top end supercomputer, a Cray XMP only 20 years ago.

Yes, the top end smartphone in our pocket today, is equivalent, in computing power, by all major measures, to the world's most powerful supercomputer only 20 years before. NASA went to the moon in 1969 using computers far less powerful than that smartphone in our pocket. The Space Shuttle was designed using computers far less capable than our cellphone today.

Where will it go?

I have shown how the cellphone has added new functionalities through the Eight C's. Will it end here? I do not think so. Probably the phone will still find new uses. As new phones now are adding again new features, such as digital TV tuners and GPS mapping technologies, no doubt the phone will become ever more able. I like the guidance by the man they call the godfather of mobile phone user design in Finland, and who was the father of the Series 60 user interface for Nokia, Christian Lindholm the author and now Director at Fjord, who says about mobile phone design, *"Everything can always be simplified and made more delightful to use."* Then he usually adds, *"Everything that can be mobile will be mobile."*

Tomi T Ahonen

Case Study 14 from Japan
Camera Jiten
The Magical Cameraphone Dictionary

A service I often use as an example of the truly magical, is called *Kamera-Jiten*, developed by Enfour Group in Japan. It is the "Cameraphone Dictionary". I like to think of it as the "magical magnifying glass, which translates".

This is how *Kamera Jiten* works. You take your cameraphone with the *Kamera Jiten* feature installed and enabled, and point the cameraphone at a regular printed page of a magazine, newspaper or book written in English. Turn on the *Kamera-Jiten* service. It snaps a picture of the page, performs an OCR (Optical Character Recognition) conversion (from an image into text), then connects with the network, sends the text to their servers, then does an automated online translation from English to Japanese, and sends the Japanese text back to your phone written now in Japanese characters.

When your cameraphone aims at text written in English, it will display, in near-real time the Japanese text is on your phone screen!

This is magical. It is like using a magnifying glass over a page with small text and the magnifying glass makes the text larger to read. Except that in this case the technologies enabled by smartphones, cameraphones and fast networks, allow the intelligent cameraphone dictionary to look at a printed page in one language, and display it on the cameraphone's screen in another language. They started with English-to-Japanese conversion and now are adding many more languages, as is quite to be expected.

This service to my mind, is a perfect example of early magic in mobile, going far beyond copying something from TV or the web onto the 7th Mass Media Channel.the Three/Hutchison services. It is a need we all have had at some point, and one we could not imagine any technical solution could even possibly exist.

But the modern cellphone is a cameraphone. The basic digital camera on any megapixel cameraphone is a good enough scanner to read most pages of printed text. Suddenly the pocket translator becomes possible. Magic!

"Men who lack a past are unreliable guides to the future."
Henry Kissinger

XVI
Disruptive Concepts
Convergence, MVNOs and the iPhone

I want to add three shorter essays about a couple of concepts that are very relevant to cellphones as a media channel. I will briefly cover these here. These will be digital convergence, the business model of the MVNO wireless telecoms carrier (mobile operator), and the impact of the Apple iPhone.

A   CONVERGENCE

I was employed by Elisa Corporation (Helsinki Telephone, Radiolinja and Finnet International) in the mid 1990s when one of my first projects was to deploy a fixed-mobile converged solution. Our project turned out to be the first commercially launched fixed-mobile service in the world in 1996. I am not going to waste the readers' time with Fixed-Mobile Convergence (FMC) as this is increasingly an outdated concept by now, and is mostly only a defensive (some could say desperation) move by those telecoms carriers/operators who own fixed telecoms networks assets. The more practical convergence topic in fixed and mobile is "fixed-mobile substitution" and the migration from fixed to mobile.

When I joined Nokia in 1998 my first task was deploying "Indirect Access" technologies, one part of, which was to enable internet access to cellphones. Again, I was in the middle of the bleeding edge of digital convergence and I wrote Nokia's first White Paper, which discussed how to do the internet on mobile phones. Each of my five books has discussed convergence and my fifth book, ***Digital Korea***, with Jim O'Reilly, was a case study about the country where digital convergence on all of its fronts had advanced the furthest by 2007. For readers interested in this digital convergence that book is the one to read. I will only briefly outline the basic concepts here.

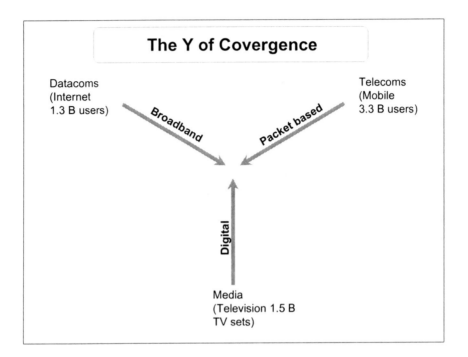

The Y of Covergence

Datacoms
(Internet
1.3 B users)

Telecoms
(Mobile
3.3 B users)

Broadband

Packet based

Digital

Media
(Television 1.5 B
TV sets)

Y of Convergence

The Y of Convergence was valid for about 2004-2007 time frame. Since then and based on advanced experiences in South Korea, I have moved beyond that and now see an expanded convergence of five industries. Nevertheless, many reading this book who have not lived in the most advanced countries may need to start with the basics, so let me first cover the Y of Convergence, the first three industries and technologies to merge. This is widely accepted as reality today.

Like the letter "Y" there are three elements of technology - and their related industries - that form the major trends of digital convergence today in 2008. The three axis with no order of preference are datacoms, telecoms and broadcast media. Each has several subgroups, but also each of the three axis has one dominant technology. With datacoms it is the internet - with about 1.3 billion users at the end of 2007; with telecoms it is cellphones with about 3.3 billion users; and with broadcast it is television with about 1.4 billion TV sets. I will use those three dominant technologies as the proxies for the convergence.

Datacoms / the internet

The datacoms axis of the Y of Convergence is that leg, which was always digital from the start and since the early 1990s has been IP (Internet Protocol) based. Its evolution is going to broadband. While some wireless networking technologies (so-called 802.11x standards) were being developed in the 1990s, it was not until the advent of the WiFi standard that datacoms and the internet started to become seriously wireless. Worldwide the leading countries where internet/datacoms innovation is taking place are South Korea, Hong Kong, Denmark, Netherlands and Sweden. The USA and Canada are both well ahead of the mainstream but no longer the leading industrialized countries on this axis.

Telecoms / cellphones

The cellular telecoms axis is for all practical purposes digital and inherently wireless. The cellular industry is now migrating to "packet based" networks and technologies and adopting IP based systems. As the internet, cellular is going to broadband. The leading countries where cellphone innovation is taking place today are Japan, South Korea, Italy, Austria and the UK.

Broadcast / TV

TV has always been providing broadband content (as defined by the internet and cellular industries) and is increasing its bandwidth now to "high definition". However, TV is still migrating to digital and introducing IP based services. The digital technologies allow theoretically interactivity, although in most cases actual interactivity is rather done via the cellphone as in the *American Idol* voting etc. One should remember that over-the-air broadcast is wireless as such as is satellite broadcasting, but there are cable TV systems that are currently still mostly wireline based. The leading countries in TV innovation worldwide are the USA, Japan, Canada, the UK and Finland.

Each has to learn, each has to offer

Note that of the three industries, in each case one has a natural domain of competence, the internet is IP based and digital, cellular is wireless and digital, and TV is broadband. Each wants to learn from a rival: internet wants to go wireless and broadband; cellular wants to go IP based and broadband; TV wants to go IP based, digital and wireless. Each side has something to offer and something to learn. This is a healthy opportunity both for collaboration and innovation.

Center of convergence

At the center of the three axis of the Y of Convergence is the end-state, the focal point for all converging technologies. As the center of the convergence is

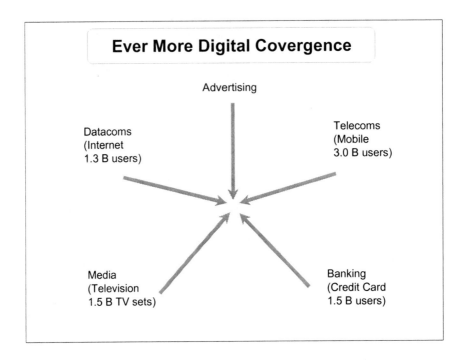

inherently packet based and on the IP (Internet Protocol) standards, as it is all wireless and broadband; the center is also a new battleground for the dominant players in each of the three converging elements.

From three to five industries converging

So what is digital convergence beyond the Y. In my workshops I like to call the evolution of convergence as the "Daimler-Chrysler" diagram, as we go from a three-pointed star, like Mercedes Benz to the five-pointed star like that of Chrysler. So beyond internet, telecoms and broadcast media converging, I now observe two other giant industries are strongly joining the party. These are the advertising industry, and the finance industry, i.e. credit cards, banks, insurance etc. Now we have five major global industries on course to crash into each other. Some learn to partner along the way and build a future together. Others will fall prey of the cannibalization by others and perish. It will be exciting but it will also be challenging. Let the carnage begin.

Banking and credit cards

I have already discussed the cannibalizing nature of cellphones the credit card

---

and banking industry. As I explained in the beginning of the book, half of all Koreans use cellphones to make payments, and 20% of Kenyan bank accounts are on cellphones and that in the Philippines you can get your whole paycheck paid to your cellphone and in Estonia if you want to park your car, the only way to pay for parking is with the cellphone. Clearly the phone is emerging as a new rival to the credit card and banking services.

So consider the scale. There are about 1.5 billion people with at least one credit card in their wallet, worldwide. In addition, twice as many cellphone subscriptions. Yes, a rude wake-up call to the finance industries. Worse yet, in most countries local banking regulations prevent kids under age 18 from having credit cards, but these kids all have cellphones. In addition, with a post-paid (monthly billing contract) account, kids actually do have, effectively, short-term credit on their phones. A McBurger bought today and paid by cellphone, will not show up on the phone bill until next month. Kids often discover their first credit not on Visa or Mastercard, but on their cellphone account.

SK Telecom in South Korea was the first carrier to issue its cellphones with Visa credit card functionality in 2002. Now numerous carriers do that from Telenor in Norway with Visa to Smart in the Philippines with Mastercard.

Money goes mobile

The customer proposition on having money merge with their cellphone is compelling. First, we are more dependent on our phone than our wallet. Think how many times per day you dig out your wallet, but how many times per day you look at your cellphone. Did I get a call, do I have a message, what time is it, etc. Remember we report lost wallets in 26 hours, but a lost phone in 68 minutes.

Cash is always a limited resource. We are constrained by what we happen to have in our pocket or wallet. Our wealth is much more than the cash we have on hand (in most cases, obviously). So any credit or debit payment system allows us access to all our funds rather than cash on hand

Credit cards and debit cards are much better, but they do not have a screen. They are not interactive. Moreover, they are not connected. We have to have a credit card/debit card *reader* to have access to your money - either a cash register in a store to handle the payment or else we need to go to a cash machine/ATM (Automated Teller Machine).

The cellphone is far superior. We can have the payment authorized on our device, *without a reader*. Send an SMS text message to authorize the payment from your phone for example. The cellphone has the screen on, which we can do a wide range of better services than are possible on the plastic of a credit card. We can for example show the currency exchange rate of an international purchase. So if this is Yen or Euros, what is it in Dollars. A credit card cannot show us that, but the screen on our cellphone can.

The phone is permanently connected to the network. We can achieve real time balances, alerts when our card has been activated, etc. If we run out of money, we can borrow money from our family and friends and have that money credited directly from their cellphone account to our account, like they do in Spain. Or we can contact a quick loan service via the phone and get an immediate small bank loan within a few minutes, as they do in Sweden or Finland. All this far trumps the plastic card, as a credit card or debit card solution. The cellphone can do absolutely everything the plastic card can do, but much much more that the card cannot do.

And thats before we think of the full mobile wallet applications. In the mobile banking chapter of my previous book, ***Digital Korea***, I show real examples of these, so let me just briefly summarize. We can have our loyalty card on the phone and collect frequent flier miles, loyalty points, etc. We can have our office identity card and pass embedded on the phone, so our phone becomes our passkey to the office. We can have our home locks operated by cellphone - apartment buildings in Japan and South Korea already exist, which can be operated by cellphone.

Finally the cellphone is more secure than any card. It can have all the protection we can put on a card, such as requesting a PIN code. It has the separate SIM card - a secure and unique identity module such as on modern credit cards. Nevertheless, the cellphone can have much added protection from phone passwords to fingerprint scanners, eye retina scanners, voiceprint verification etc. In addition, most of all, a cellphone can be de-activated remotely and its functionality can be transferred in real time to another device. So if you lose your phone or it is stolen, it is much faster to get you back in touch and control of your finances than waiting for the credit card company to rush you a new plastic replacement card.

Advertising

I also want to mention advertising briefly here. I already had a whole chapter on mAd, mobile advertising or cellphone based advertising so we do not need to rehash that here. Suffice it to say that the advertising industry is headed to a cellphone near you. Another 450 Billion dollar industry crashing our party...

What we now start to see in this five-pointed convergence is services that merge advertising with internet with telecoms with media with banking. For example Blyk the case study in the mobile advertising chapter was a good example of this kind of innovation.

There is much more to convergence, and this book is not meant to be on that topic. However, the cellphone is centrally involved with all convergence. You can use the Y of Convergence - or the newer concept of the 5-pointed star - as the underlying theory to understand how convergence may affect your business or life. Nevertheless, bear in mind that the cellphone is emerging as the

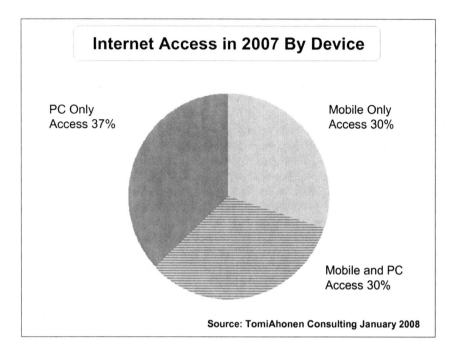

Internet Access in 2007 By Device

PC Only
Access 37%

Mobile Only
Access 30%

Mobile and PC
Access 30%

Source: TomiAhonen Consulting January 2008

essential element in this convergence, both in identifying the users explicitly, and in handling the payments and money transfers for the converged services.

Will there be one internet?

Many argue that the convergence of the industries will mean that there will emerge a single entity at the end. I do not think so. I think that for the foreseeable future, say the next 5-10 years at least, we will have distinct separate internet, telecoms, television, banking and advertising industries. Yes, there will be ever more cross-over, overlap and cannibalization, but they will not merge into one. There will be convergence, but not the end of them all as distinct industries. Remembering the metaphor of the 30 second tasks and 30 minute tasks that I talked about early in the book, we will have particular needs for our cellphone (as a mass media and otherwise) and we will also have particular needs for our laptops and computers, and the "legacy" internet, the sixth mass media.

I think author Kim Dushinski puts it very well in her upcoming book *The Mobile Marketing Handbook* when she writes:

> *You will undoubtedly hear that there is "one web" and that people want the "same experience on their mobile device as they want on their*

computer." I totally disagree. On my computer I have a 17 inch wide monitor, a full keyboard and enough computing power to handle whatever the Internet dishes up. My phone has a less than 2 inch monitor, my QWERTY keyboard requires me to use my thumbs to type and minimal computing power; plus I am using it somewhere besides my comfortable, quiet office. Why would I want the same thing served to me regardless of, which device I use? Neither do your customers, despite what you will be told by many people in the mobile industry. This argument of customers wanting the same experience on mobile as they do with the desktop often comes from the companies who have built the technology to provide just that. It is in their best interest that businesses use their technology. Make no mistake about it; it is in your best interest to provide what your customers want. Keep that in mind as you forge ahead into the mobile web.

Kim Dushinski, *The Mobile Marketing Handbook*, 2009

Do not believe those who suggest there "should be only one internet", whether that currently on the PCs, transformed to the cellphones, or the one on cellphones, expanded to PCs. Think of radio and TV. Of the broadcast radio content, which existed prior to TV, all was launched onto TV. Some of it worked better on TV and is no longer on radio (soap operas for example). Others continue on both such as sports. After that, TV invented forms that cannot work on radio, such as music videos and reality TV. Moreover, also after that, radio invented new forms to capture its own niches, such as drive-time talk shows and traffic congestion updates, which do not work on (mainstream broadcast) TV.

This pattern will be replicated as the mobile internet matures. All existing internet content (or essentially all of it) will attempt the transfer to mobile. Most will succeed. Some will move totally to mobile, it is too early to tell what those will be. Some will thrive on both. Some new content forms will be invented purely for mobile that cannot survive on the PC based internet - SMS text messaging and ringing tones are early examples of these. In addition, after the mobile internet has established itself, the legacy internet will discover its niches and serve opportunities we currently cannot even see.

B   MVNO

What is an MVNO? An MVNO, Mobile Virtual Network Operator is a low-margin/high volume telecoms reseller business. An MVNO negotiates a wholesale telecoms traffic contract with an existing wireless carrier (T-Mobile, Sprint, Vodafone etc) and then finds a target audience to sell the services. The MVNO will not build or operate a cellular network, they only resell the network capacity of their host network. To end-users, MVNOs can seem identical to

TVs, Internet and Cellphones in 2 Worlds

Comparison of major technology adoption rates in the Industrialized world and the Developing world in 2006

Industrialized World		Developing World	
1.1 B	Population	5.3 B	Population
384 M	TV sets is 33% per capita	816 M	TV sets is 15% per capita
656 M	Internet users is 56% per capita	309 M	Internet users is 6% per capita
1.2 B	Cellphone users is 102% per capita	977 M	Cellphone users is 18% per capita

Source: ITU Digital Life Report 2006

existing carriers. MVNOs often provide full services from cellphones to SIM cards, with service portfolios including phone numbers, voice minute tariffs, SMS text messages, internet browsing, etc. Some MVNOs offer custom services and even branded handsets. Best-known MVNOs include Virgin in the UK, USA, Canada, Australia and Singapore (since failed); MTV in Sweden, Germany, Belgium; Disney in the USA (since failed) and Japan.

How big?

The MVNO business is a new opportunity that only emerged in 2000 in a few very advanced wireless markets with very liberal rules on telecoms competition in Scandinavia, parts of Asia and the UK. Soon the MVNO model spread and today most of Europe, parts of Eastern Europe, about half of Asia, Australia, USA and Canada are open to MVNOs. *Total Telecom* measured the worldwide MVNO revenues to be over 18 billion dollars in 2005. This number is likely to be double by 2010 into the 35-40 billion dollar range.

Denmark, Hong Kong, the UK and Finland are the oldest and most mature MVNO markets. In Denmark MVNOs had taken almost 25% of the total market of cellphone users by 2004. The largest MVNO in Denmark, Telmore captured nearly 20% of all cellular wireless subscribers.

The best known MVNO is Virgin, which achieved successful MVNO launches in the UK, Australia, USA and Canada, as well as a failed MVNO attempt in Singapore. Virgin's UK operation is often used as a benchmark with lessons to the industry. I will cover Virgin in more detail in the case study at the end of this chapter. However, for now it can be noted that Virgin UK achieved a 6% market share in the British mobile phone market by the summer of 2007, where the next largest MVNO, Tesco had achieved 2%.

There are actually significantly better national performers in other countries than Virgin in the UK. I have mentioned Telmore in Denmark, which achieved about 20% national penetration rate as an MVNO. In Finland Saunalahti took more than 10% before it was merged with the incumbent Elisa. In Belgium MTV has 13% of the domestic market. .

MVNOs local

MVNO's tend to be locally strong brands and companies. The largest MVNOs in each of the four most mature MVNO markets are all locally strong, but not internationally strong brands, with differing backgrounds. Examples include

---

10% of US households had abandoned fixed landline in 2007
Source: CTIA 2007

Tesco's UK (supermarket), Carphone Warehouse UK (handset retailer), Stockmann's Finland (department store) and Narvesen in Norway (kiosk chain). Sometimes MVNOs are used by major telecoms players in one country to operate in a neighboring country like Tele2, which is a network operator/carrier in Sweden, operates as MVNO in neighboring Norway. Often successful MVNOs are new entrant telcos like Trident and China Motion in Hong Kong.

The most visible MVNOs tend to be the big national brands like supermarket chains such as Aldi in Germany, Carrefour the French supermarket chain as an MVNO in Italy, or Seven Eleven in the USA and Malaysia for example, etc. Other major national brands are also very visible from radio stations like NRJ in France, TV stations like MTV in Sweden, hamburger chains like Hesburger in Finland and coffee shop chains like Tschibo in Germany. Even a bank, Privatbank in the Ukraine, has launched as MVNO.

Within any one national market there is only a limited opportunity for a few major national brands to succeed as national MVNOs, due to the competitive nature of the business. Easymobile, related to the various Easy businesses best known for the Easyjet discount airline failed in the UK, because rival Virgin and other MVNOs had taken so much of the British market. Amp'd, ESPN and Disney MVNO's all failed in the USA while others like Virgin thrived.

Language MVNOs

So lets look at some niche MVNOs. An obvious category is the language or cultural subgroup MVNO. Some of the earliest MVNOs in this space was an MVNO on the E-Plus network serving the Turkish populations in Germany. The idea is that apart from your normal calls and messages, the service offers calling center support and your phone bill in your native language as well as low cost calls to that country, in this case from Germany to Turkey. Soon after that in America Viva and Movida offered cellphone telecoms services for the Spanish speaking segments. Now there are many such language and culture oriented MVNOs in most mature MVNO markets

A variant on this model is the Eurokeitai MVNO in France. Eurokeitai is targeting the Japanese expatriate business executive community living in France. As any language MVNO it of course offers phone menus in Japanese characters, calling center and billing info in Japanese and calls to Japan at low costs. As this service targets business users it soon acquired a very large proportion of Japanese expats living in France and as the phone calls from these

---

54% of Finnish households had abandoned landline in 2007
Source: Eurobarometer April 2007

---

high salary foreign postings of Japanese corporate giants like Toyota, Canon, Sony, Honda, etc place lots of business calls back home to Japan, the service was able to become profitable at only about 1,000 subscribers.

Disney MVNO

A most obvious strong candiate for MVNO success is Disney. From the perennial popularity young children favorites such as Mickey Mouse to the continuing stable of Disney movie hits such as Pirates of the Caribbean, Disney is a brand the youth love, and one that their parents trust. As Disney was among the first Western brands to discover cellphones as a new mass media, being on the launch brand portfolio of NTT DoCoMo's i-Mode service in Japan in 1999, certainly Disney has deep knowledge of what cellphones can be to the youth.

Disney waited for a play outside of Japan for many years and finally launched its MVNO in the USA in 2006. There was a lot of speculation of rapid expansion of the MVNO opportunities into other Western markets, but in 2007 Disney suddenly shut down its USA operation after heavy losses. As Disney also owns the ESPN brand, which had closed earlier in 2007, many felt that Disney had indicated an end to its adventures into cellphones.

It then came as quite a shock to the industry to learn only weeks after Disney MVNO in the USA closed that Disney would be the first MVNO to launch in Japan on the Softbank network in 2008. After its MVNO had failed in the laggard cellphone market of the USA, Disney boldly jumped into the most advanced cellphone market of Japan.

Analysts have been speculating what went wrong with the Disney MVNO operation in the USA (as well as that of ESPN). There seems to have been some arrogance in thinking about cellular telecoms on an "old fashioned" model, with a legacy of USA centric and thus obsolescent mindsets, rather than more fresh MVNO thinking from European and Asian insights such as that of Virgin USA, which also targets youth and perhaps Helio, which is backed by South Korean cellphone carrier giant SK Telecom, but, which has yet to turn a profit in the USA.

Spy Phone?

One of the issues with Disney's USA MVNO failure seems to be the child-tracking feature of the Disney phones. Disney had enabled a location information based service to let parents track where their kids were. Children soon learned that Disney phones were "toxic" i.e. they were used by some parents to snoop on the kids. So children would soon not want the Disney phones. Worse yet, the

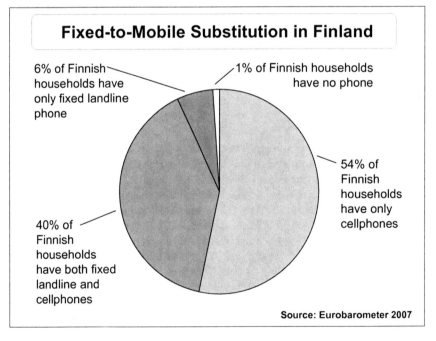

Fixed-to-Mobile Substitution in Finland

6% of Finnish households have only fixed landline phone

1% of Finnish households have no phone

54% of Finnish households have only cellphones

40% of Finnish households have both fixed landline and cellphones

Source: Eurobarometer 2007

child tracking feature was the worst kind of false sense of security. The parents felt that they knew where their kids were, or more precisely that parents could feel comfortable that their kids were not where they were not supposed to be.

But the children soon learned to cheat the system. So Johnny would go visit Billy supposedly to do homework. Then Johnny left his Disney cellphone at Billy's house, and then the boys would go to Mike's house to a party. The parents would be fooled into thinking Johnny was doing his homework at Billy's place when in reality, the boys were at a party. Of course, the boys would leave the phone turned on, but in silent mode. Then if the parents said why did not you answer the phone, the kid would say they had it on silent "because they were doing homework." A perfect circle of deception, very soon making a mockery of the good-intentioned idea of a child-tracker feature.

Community is MVNO

Another opportunity for MVNO is very specialized service areas. Videogaming is one. A good example comes from Hong Kong and Taiwan, where a videogame, *Super Stable*, offers gamers the chance to play the game using their cellphones. I discussed *Super Stable* as the Case Study in the Gaming chapter.

Another opportunity lies in fan clubs. I mentioned Twins Mobile from Hong Kong in the music chapter. Twins are an MVNO. Several rock/pop artists have moved into the MVNO space including Kiss and P Diddy (Puff Daddy).

Gayphone in Denmark

An other obvious subgroup of the society is the gay population. Danish MVNO *Gayphone* has targeted the gay community in Denmark and offers various alternate lifestyle services and gay bar finders, etc, as part of its phone service.

Blyk the advertising MVNO

I discussed *Blyk* in the Advertising chapter earlier and in its own case study. Suffice it to say that Blyk is only the first of a new category of MVNOs that aim their primary offering to the advertising brands (who pay) and then deliver free services to the end-users, in this case the 16-24-year-old segment in Britain. *Blyk* is rapidly expanding to several European countries during 2008.

No automatic license to print money

While Virgin succeeded well in the UK, and Australia, and is growing in the USA and Canada, Virgin MVNO also launched, but failed in Singapore. An MVNO is not an automatic guarantee to make money. Many major brands have launched MVNOs and then gone out of business, such as the ***Financial Times***

MVNO, which for a while was quite popular among younger investment bankers in the City of London, and the biggest commercial TV broadcaster in Finland, MainosTV3.

While some quit the MVNO game with less visibility, such as the Shell MVNO in Hong Kong or EasyPhone the MVNO of the parent company of EasyJet the low cost airline, 2007 saw the ends of three very visible major brand MVNOs in the USA. ESPN the cable TV sports broadcaster, Amp'd the youth MVNO and Disney's USA MVNO operation.

Thresholds

So what are the numbers? The actual markets differ, but profitable MVNOs have been set up in Europe with customer numbers at the levels of 25,000 residential customers (on pre-paid/pay-as-you-go basis) or 5,000 enterprise/corporate customers (post-paid/contract basis). Analysts have suggested that break-even points for MVNO operations can be as low as 5,000-10,000 subscribers if their monthly phone spending is strong enough and obviously under exceptional cases, like *Eurokeitai*, the break-even point can be even lower.

The costs to set up an MVNO can run from as low as 30,000 dollars to over a million dollars depending on the country, its telecoms market, and the scope of the MVNO operation. Monthly costs of operation depend much on the services to be offered and the need to have paid staff, but can be as little as 10,000 dollars. From the point of view of a major national TV advertising campaign for example, the costs of an MVNO are often seen as a very viable - and engaging - customer marketing proposition.

The MVNO's will typically launch on price levels about 5%-10% below the major brand prices in their markets and they are in effect primarily marketing organizations, not telecoms providers.

I must stress that it is not an automatic license to print money. Plenty of promising MVNOs have found no commercial opportunity in MVNO and in the worst cases, such as Amp'd, ESPN and Disney in the USA, it can be a very costly misadventure indeed. As always, a solid business case should be built before any such venture. In the final analysis success of MVNO's depends on understanding telecoms economics, in particular the profits in so-called "termination revenues" and interconnect.

Every brand should consider MVNOs. Nevertheless, MVNOs are a short-term opportunity, very viable over the next few years but not necessarily one for the very long term. It is a way to get into the pockets of customers, using the most pervasive, most personal and most connected media of them all.

Where markets open for MVNOs, a natural opportunity also often emerges for the MVNE (Mobile Virtual Network Enabler). An MVNE buys wholesale bulk telecoms traffic from one of the network carriers/operators and then sets up a distributor wholesale organization, recruiting usually smaller brands to set up niche MVNO operations. The MVNE typically has strong telecoms infrastructure and facilities such as telecoms switching equipment, a billing system, SIM card management, a calling center etc. Some of the MVNEs that have set up include Saunalahti in Finland, Spinbox in Sweden, MEC in the Netherlands, Transatel in the Benelux area and TelSpace in the USA.

C   BEFORE iPHONE, AFTER IPHONE

There have been many iconic cellphones, from the Motorola Razr to Nokia's Communicator, but so far there has been one transformational phone. It is the Apple iPhone. I blogged about the iPhone before its launch, and some mistakenly attributed my blog to claim that the iPhone was the "Jesus Phone" (which I never said, and, which also was repeatedly acknowledged by many in the blogosphere). Yet the Jesusphone moniker remained and I can be said to be the (unwitting, unwilling) "father" of that notion. I never claimed it to be in any way a religious phone. My reference was that of a chronological significance like the Western Calendar marks time BC and AD (Before Christ and Anno Domini, after the death of Jesus Christ). I blogged about a demarcation of time for cellphones as being bi and ai, before iPhone and after iPhone. Let me briefly explain.

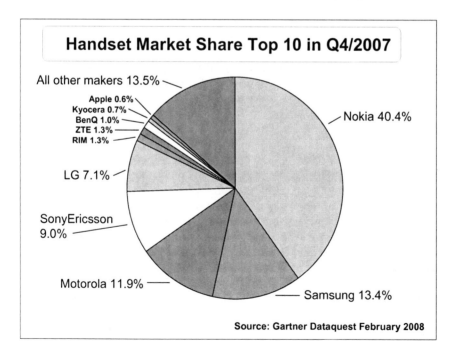

Apple, just like the Macintosh

Before the original Apple Macintosh computer, all personal computers were very complex to use. PC users attended courses not only to use the various software applications such as WordPerfect and Lotus 1-2-3 but also to learn to simply *use* a computer. The operating system with most computers was based on Microsoft's DOS (Disk Operating System) and various activities with the computer required typing in cryptic codes. Users could not just point at what they wanted with a mouse.

That all changed with the Apple Macintosh. Today's Windows operating system by Microsoft is their response to the Mac operating system. The Apple Mac brought us the icon-based menu structure, by, which we point at the program icons on the screen, using a mouse. Moreover, perhaps even more importantly, for all that is the current PC based internet, the Apple Mac introduced the mainstream PC user world to something called "Hypertext". You probably are not aware that you use Hypertext several times every day, it is that once underlined link on a web page that gets you to another web page. That strange internet hop, is powered by what is called a Hypertext link and can be embedded into any document or other file. Hypertext forms the distinctive feature of what made the internet a mass-market proposition and the HTML standard is HyperText Markup Language, which necessitates Hypertext ability. This was first brought to mass-market customers on the Macintosh.

There have been many very important personal computers, such as the Apple 2, the original IBM PC, the first Compaq portable PC and the first Toshiba 1000 laptop. However, only the Macintosh truly transformed the PC industry, making the PC so easy to use that users did not need to attend courses anymore.

iPod and Newton

Apple has a knack of looking at an existing technology, and re-inventing it to become far more user-friendly. The Apple iPod revolutionized how portable music is experienced. In addition, those who follow closely the PDA technologies tend to attribute a similar role to the Apple Newton PDA. While the Newton ended up not being a market success, it did also radically alter the whole world of PDAs. Now the iPhone has done it again for Apple, changing forever how user-friendly a cellphone can be. I have started to talk about two eras in cellphones, the bi era (before iPhone) and the ai era (after iPhone).

Before the iPhone as the cellphone was gathering ever more abilities, it needed more controls. The phones were also getting ever smaller. So we had the trend of cellphones getting smaller and smaller, with displays growing bigger and bigger, all the while the phone was being crammed with more and more buttons, icons, and ever tinier text fonts.

I counted that my first cellphone (a Nokia 2110 in 1995) has 15 buttons including the on/off switch. 6 years later my first GPRS phone had climbed up to 18 buttons. Nevertheless, now as the phones take on ever more functionality, today my Nokia N93 has 31 buttons! Here too, the iPhone comes at a critical time for our industry. We cannot keep on adding buttons to the tiny device, something has to be done, and much of that has to be in intelligent design such as the amazing user interface on the iPhone.

Handsets BI and AI

So what all changes with the advent of the iPhone. Lets start with the obvious. From June 2007 all handset makers finally had their first tests of Apple's iPhone. Then Nokia, Motorola, Samsung, SonyEricsson, LG, and the dozens of second and third tier manufacturers saw what they were up against. Not the outwardly form factor - yes, the iPhone is cool and slick and sexy - but the more important internal software. How did they make it so user-friendly? This is Apple's strong suit. More so than even stunning outwardly design, is the internal software on user interface.

So from 2007 on all reviewers around the world started to compare the user interface of all new high-end phones with that of the iPhone. A clear watershed moment in the industry. For the first time a major handset device, which was designed from the start to be both a multipurpose smartphone and yet easy to use.

The media industry BI and AI

The major media moguls also woke up to cellphones in June 2007. Why? Not that the 50 or 60-year-old board members at TimeWarner and Disney and Viacom etc would actually "use" an iPhone to surf the web or download MP3 files, but rather because the top strategist at the media giants started to be exposed to the Apple marketing blitz around the iPhone in June 2007. Most of the media giants around the rest of the world had already jumped onto the cellphone as media bandwagon by 2007, but the American media giants ignored the cellphone. Up until June 2007. Now they look at the iPhone and they believe. Now all major media players have a cellphone strategy.

Advertising BI and AI

And while on the subject of media, then advertising. New York's Madison Avenue woke up to cellphones as a mainstream advertising channel. "Look at this wonderful iPhone ! Look at that big screen. Look at all the internet content and music and gaming and web browsing and video clips." Then came the inevitable "eureka" moment, *"We need to be there. That iPhone is a magnificent advertising media channel."*

Silicon valley BI and AI

The biggest single change I think that will emerge as a direct result of the iPhone will be a new gold rush, a Klondyke, for the IT industry. The iPhone jump-started the interest in the cellphone for the West Coast. When iconic Apple Computer drops "Computer" from its corporate name that says something. Soon there were rumors of a cellphone by Google (which turned into a cellphone operating system Android by year-end). Rumors of Dell getting into cellphones. Microsoft bought Danger. All of the majors in the IT industry were on the warpath, heading for the 7th Mass Media device.

Ironically lost in the shuffle is the fact that Nokia had stopped calling its top-end smartphones, the N-Series, mobile phones (or cellphones). The N-Series - the phone series most competitive with the iPhone at launch - has been called *Multimedia Computers* by Nokia since 2005. However, this is something that happened in the dark ages, BI. When the history of cellphones will be written, the "true coming" of the first honest pocket computer will be attributed to the iPhone. It will be an exciting time, AI.

In sum

So we have seen several of the early media concepts for the cellphone. I have discussed what kind of customers will be consuming media on the cellphone, and how the business will be made. In this chapter I have touched upon convergence, which will bring four other giant industries, IT, Media, Finance and Advertising to the convergence with the cellphone. I have also briefly high-lighted some examples of the MVNO business model, a feasible way for some brands to become more deeply immersed in the opportunity. Moreover, finally I have shown how the iPhone has accelerated the interest in mobile as the 7th mass media channel, in particular among the various other industries based in the USA.

I'd like to end on the idea of where is the personal computer and the internet headed. Early in this book I quoted Nokia's famed former CEO Jorma Ollila when he suggested the internet in every pocket. This is what the *Economist* wrote inn its 25th Anniversary of the PC special issue on 29 July in 2006: *"There is no question the PC has democratised computing and unleashed innovations; but it is the mobile phone that now seems most likely to carry the dream of the "personal computer" to its conclusion."*

Case Study 15 from the UK
Virgin Mobile MVNO

Virgin Mobile is probably the best-known MVNO, which has launched in the UK, USA, Australia, Canada and Singapore. An MVNO is a Mobile Virtual Network Operator, which negotiates a wholesale telecoms traffic contract with one of the incumbent network operators, and then offers its own branded services to its customers. The end-user does not often perceive any significant difference between an MVNO and the incumbents. MVNOs offer phone numbers, voice minutes, text messages and more advanced services. They often even provide phones.

Virgin UK was a profitable telecoms operation, running on the T-Mobile network, with about 8% of the UK subscriber base, and consistently the highest customer satisfaction ratings in the UK.

A remarkable performance measure for Virgin In the UK, has been its performance in the annual user satisfaction survey of telecoms carriers/operators In the UK, market. Bearing in mind that the host network for Virgin Uk is T-Mobile UK, so technically, from the radio network, the handsets, SIM cards, voice quality and SMS delivery etc, the T-Mobile UK and Virgin Mobile UK services have been identical.

With identical services technically, one would assume that in the annual satisfaction survey T-Mobile and Virgin would finish with near-identical scores. Yet they never did. When Virgin Mobile finished on the top as the network with the best customer satisfaction, T-Mobile finished second-to-last among the carriers/operators surveyed.

The point to take home from this all, is that the cellular telecoms industry is shifting away from being an engineering industry, to a customer-service industry. It is the customer expectation - and marketing -, which decide, which carriers and other players in the market will succeed. Virgin In the UK, has consistently been best at its marketing (now suffering somewhat from the integration with its new parent NTL). By its marketing, T-Mobile was always seen as the worst among the UK mobile operators (carriers). The future success of any player in the industry will increasingly be determined by the customer service, not by technical excellence.

Virgin UK were sold to the UK cable TV operator NTL, which rebranded its triple-play offering as Virgin after the merger. Virgin Australia was sold to one of the incumbent telcos, Optus. And while Virgin is often quoted as the most successful MVNO, even they didn't always get it right; Virgin Singapore was unable to succeed in that market and closed down less than a year from launch.

*"If I wanted to become a tramp, I would seek advice from the most
successful tramp I could find. If I wanted to become a failure,
I would seek advice from men who had never succeeded."*
Joseph Marshall Wade

XVII
Why America Lags in Cellular
The blind leading the blind?

I am often asked why is it that the USA and Canada lag the rest of the
Industrialized World in mobile telecoms. It was Motorola, after all that invented
the cellphone and so much of closely related industries from microchips with
Intel to software with Microsoft being based in the USA.

Not so many years ago the American industry in cellular telecoms was
robust and expanded far beyond North America. Nevertheless, those days are
past. Motorola, once the largest handset maker in the world, has fallen to third
behind the Finns (Nokia) and South Koreans (Samsung). Lucent, which at its
peak was the largest telecoms infrastructure vendor, is now owned by the French
(Alcatel). American telecoms carriers tended to have ownerships in countless
wireless carriers around the world. Today not only have most of those assets
been sold, but the foreigners are making inroads to the American carriers.
Verizon is 40% owned by the British (Vodafone) and AT&T has a minority
ownership by the Japanese (NTT DoCoMo). T-Mobile is wholly owned by the
Germans (Deutsche Telecom).

Most Latin American cellular carriers were once owned by Americans.
Today the biggest owners of Latin American carriers are the Spanish
(Telefonica) and the Italians (TIM). When the North American industry
innovates, with such products as the Blackberry and the iPhone, they do well
domestically, but cannot repeat their success overseas.

Many American colleagues get quite frustrated when they hear
European or Asian experts make statements that the North Americans do not lead
the industry anymore. Some even feel hostile and quite defensive about it and are
quick to point out recent statistics and innovations on the North American
continent. Yet it is true, sadly. Not only has North America fallen behind the
most advanced mobile telecoms markets like Finland, Sweden, Japan and South

Korea; Canada and the USA have fallen behind *most other* Industrialized countries, and even worse, Eastern European countries are now catching up, such as the Czech Republic, Poland and Russia! Even Latin America is catching up and by some measures ahead of the North Americans, led by Chile.

A   WHAT WENT WRONG?

Why is it that the foreigners seem to be doing so much better than the Americans at this game both on American shores and overseas? Lets take a look at the past decade or so in mobile telecoms and a dozen of the significant changes in this industry and observe where the innovation happened, at what level is the innovation worldwide, and when did that concept appear in North America. We will see a clear pattern.

1) Networks

Lets start with the big picture. The cellular telecoms industry has gone through

---

US launched 1G in 1984, 2G in 1994 and 3G in 2002

---

two complete technical evolution cycles and has entered its third, in only 29 years. By complete cycle, I mean that the technology of one cycle is incompatible with the next and requires a complete re-investment of the full network infrastructure as well as total replacement of all end-user equipment, i.e. cellular handsets. These three cycles are now conveniently called first, second and third generation of mobile telecommunications.

For the first generation of cellular telecoms systems, the analog cellphones like AMPS in America and NMT in many parts of Europe, America was not the first country to launch, it was NTT in Japan in 1979. America took five years to get its first network commercially launched and Canada two years beyond that. Many countries got into cellular before the USA, including the four Nordic countries, Denmark, Finland, Norway and Sweden in 1981.

For the launch of the second generation, digital systems like CDMA, GSM and TDMA, America was again not the first. It was Finland, when Radiolinja (Elisa) launched on GSM in 1991. Again, the USA lagged, joining three years later. By then over a dozen other countries had launched second generation cellular systems including Canada. In many of the countries where 2G was launched that was also the starting point of national competition in mobile telecoms. The advent of competition dramatically expedited each given country's

---

Tomi T Ahonen

local telecoms environment. This was the case in Finland so competitive mobile telecoms started in Finland. Japan's first digital service was commercially launched two years later, in 1993.

On the second generation systems there were several significant innovations. Person-to-Person SMS text messaging was introduced in 1993... in Finland. Smartphones were launched in 1996, in Finland. Downloadable content (ringing tones) were introduced in 1998... in Finland. The wireless internet was introduced, in Japan. In addition, in 2001 cameraphones appeared... in Japan. Incidentally, the old first generation networks are being decommissioned and dismantled. The first country to shut off their first generation cellular network... was Finland. For all the biggest innovations for the industry that now form separate clusters of industries - and chapters in this book for example - at no time was that innovation launched commercially first in North America.

Then we had the third generation or 3G, such as WCDMA also known as UMTS, and CDMA 1x EV-DO. 3G was commercially launched in 2001. Moreover, that was again NTT DoCoMo in Japan. This time there was indeed an American 3G carrier that launched only one year after the Japanese, but that carrier, Monet, went bankrupt. The second US based carrier to launch 3G,

---

Japan launched 1G in 1979, 2G in 1993 and 3G in 2001

Verizon, did it two years after the Japanese in 2003. While no country has yet started to decommission 2G networks, Japan has became the first country in the world, where new 2G phones were no longer being sold, as of December 2007.

For every generation of cellular networks, the first country to launch has been either European or Asian. The USA and Canada have lagged every one of these major steps.

2) Subscribers

A significant measure most often used by the telecoms industry, as the measure of a nation's relative maturity in cellular telecoms compared to other countries, is the national cellphone subscriber penetration rate. For this purpose I am excluding the tiny countries of less than one million population such as Monaco, Luxembourg etc. In 1990 the world's leading country by cellphone penetration was Sweden. By 1995 it was Finland. By 2000 it was Italy. By 2005 it was Taiwan and today it is Hong Kong. The last time the USA was in the top 5 by penetration rate was over 15 years ago and dropped out of the top 10 twelve years ago. It has been a rough ride downhill ever since. Today the USA and Canada are *not even in the top 50* highest cellular penetration countries of the

---

world. The average penetration rate for Western Europe was 110% at the end of 2007. The USA was at about 85% and Canada at about 65%. By this measure the USA lags leading countries by about four years, Canada lags by five years.

3) Evolution of the cellphone handsets

A decade ago a cellphone was a single-purpose device (communication). As I wrote in the Early Eight chapter, over the past ten years we have added seven other functionalities, which are in order and country of first launch: 2) consumption (i.e. media device) Finland 1998; 3) charging (payment device) Philippines 1999; 4) commercials (advertising) Finland 2000; 5) creation (cameraphone) Japan 2001; 6) community i.e. social networking (mobile blogging etc) South Korea 2003; 7) cool (i.e. fashion) Benetton phones in Japan in 2005; and now 8) remote control in South Korea in 2007. None of these innovations came from the USA or Canada.

4) Advanced handsets

The three most celebrated innovative feature-phones in America have been the RIM Blackberry as email phone, the Motorola Rokr (briefly) as musicphone, and the Apple iPhone as the media phone. Yet the Blackberry was not the first cellphone/smartphone with email in 2001, Nokia's Communicator was five years earlier in 1996. Motorola's Rokr was not the first musicphone in 2005, Samsung and LG had MP3 playing musicphones two years earlier in 2003. In addition, the Apple iPhone was not the first touch screen smartphone with large screen and one button operation in 2007, LG had won an award for industrial design as a touch-screen smartphone with a large screen and one button operation, a year prior to the announcement of the iPhone, in 2006. We know that design-winning LG phone in the West where it is marketed as the LG Prada. To illustrate just how different the perception of the iPhone was, comparing the USA to Japan - while the American industry celebrated the iPhone as a radical new phone that would change the industry, in Japan they stopped selling any phones older than 3G in December 2007, so the original Apple iPhone released only six months earlier in the USA and not even yet launched in Japan, was quite literally *obsolete* for the Japanese market.

5) Costs of handsets

The American industry was also bewildered by the "enormous" cost of the Apple iPhone, when it initially was introduced in two models, costing 599 and 499 dollars. After it was announced in January, and before the hype reached fever pitch in June 2007, many USA based pundits speculated whether the iPhone had been priced to be too expensive, wondering if there was a mass-market for

25 Advanced Mobile Countries

1	Japan	95%	
2	South Korea	91%	TomiAhonen Consulting tracks the maturity of the mobile telecoms market.
3	Italy	86%	
4	Austria	84%	
5	UK	82%	
6	Taiwan	81%	The leadership rating is based on global lead on four criteria: networks, handsets, subscribers and services.
7	Finland	79%	
8	Israel	78%	
9	Ireland	76%	
10	Sweden	75%	
11	Singapore	74%	The theoretical maximum rating is 100%. Approximiately 10 percentage points equals one year of leadership
12	Spain	73%	
13	Denmark	72%	
14	Australia	71%	
15	Germany	70%	
16 tie	Norway	69%	
16 tie	Hong Kong	69%	Japan has held the lead since 2003
18	Portugal	68%	
19	Netherlands	67%	
20	Switzerland	66%	Next countries just below the Top 25 are Belgium, Estonia and Hungary
21	France	65%	
22	Czech Rep.	64%	
23	U.A.E.	63%	
24 tie	USA	62%	
24 tie	Greece	62%	Source: TomiAhonen Consulting February 2008

phones costing 600 dollars. What the American industry had not even noticed, was that Nokia's top model at the time, the N93 had a retail price in its unsubsidized form of 1,200 dollars. (The N93 was a 3G smartphone with an exceptional camera featuring Carl Zeiss optics, built-in flash and both optical and digital zoom; a top-line video recording and playing function including DVD quality video recording and TV-out connection; a second camera for videocalls; built-in FM radio; 2D barcode reader; a removable memory card slot; etc plus essentially every Nokia variant of what Apple had loaded in, such as WiFi, musicplayer, media player, internet browser, etc, except for the touch screen and motion sensors). Phones costing in the range of 1,200 dollars were commonplace in most markets from Scandinavia, Japan and South Korea, to the UK, Italy, Singapore, Hong Kong etc. The markets beyond North America are more willing to purchase extremely high-end superphones.

6) From voice to SMS

Ten years ago the primary service on cellphones was voice; and many American top telecoms experts in wireless still today will repeat this faulty mantra *"but in the end, we must remember that the cellphone is primarily a voice communication device"*. This is *totally wrong*. All advanced mobile telecoms countries have already come to the conclusion that the cellphone users today think that SMS text messaging is the primary service, the "killer application" for

---

US cellphone penetration rate was 85% per capita in 2007

---

cellphones. Voice is an optional extra. The story is repeated in country after country and not just the high text messaging countries like Singapore or the Philippines. The UK and Ireland reported this already. However, for North American executives, even many who work for the American wireless carriers, the concept of the total population preferring SMS to voice is anathema.

So where did we observe SMS addiction first? In Finland in 1999 with Professor Timo Kopomaa's study *Tietoyhteiskunnan Synty* (*The City in Your Pocket*). Yet it was not until 2007 that half of the US population used SMS text messaging. The European usage of SMS was 85% in 2007 . For the whole world it is 74%. The shift in preference from voice to texting has not even happened in America yet. This has drastic impacts to anyone who wants to deploy any kind of media services to cellphones, as I describe in this book. The average consumer in the developing world is far more familiar with data services on cellphones than American consumers are. The whole world uses SMS. Moreover, the step from SMS to downloading a game or accessing a web site via a cellphone is a lot smaller, than convincing a voice user to start to surf the web on the phone.

7) Advanced data services

The cellphone expanded past being only a communication device in 1998 and

---

Tomi T Ahonen

offered content consumption when Radiolinja in Finland launched ringing tones. Thus the phone became a media device and Value-Add Services were launched commercially. This book has been the story of that growth, so I will not repeat it all. Just in short succession the launch countries. Ringtones i.e. music: Finland 1998. Gaming: Japan 1999. Payments: Philippines 1999. News: Japan 1999. Advertising: Finland 2000. Mobile TV: Finland 2001. Full track music downloads: South Korea 2003. Social networking on mobile: South Korea 2003. Advergames: India 2005. In addition, where is the lead in the advanced data services? The world's largest provider of mobile data services by revenues and profits, is NTT DoCoMo's iMode in Japan. The world's largest supplier of solutions in mobile data services is Buongiorno out of Italy.

8) Beyond enterprise customers

Ten years ago the majority of cellphone subscriptions were with enterprise/corporate customers. Not today, enterprise/corporate accounts consist of only 20% of all subscriptions in the Western world, even less in the

---

Hong Kong cellphone penetration rate was 139% in 2007

---

developing world and four out of five cellphone subscriptions are with residential customers. Again, this was first observed in Finland ten years ago and the rest of the Industrialized World followed over the next years, with USA and Canada dead last on this metric, as the USA found this trend only four years ago. Still today many USA based wireless experts speak passionately about enterprise solutions being the "main driver" of cellphone penetrations. The Blackberry is a prime example of this kind of outdated thinking.

9) Prepaid

Ten years ago almost all cellphone subscriptions around the world were postpaid i.e. based on monthly contracts. Today the majority of all subscriptions worldwide are prepaid (pay-as-you-go/voucher) based. This invention comes from Portugal and Italy just over ten years ago and still today most American accounts are postpaid/contract accounts. In the vast majority of the developed world, and essentially all of the developing world, most cellphone accounts are prepaid/pay-as-you-go/voucher type. Another huge change that vastly expands cellphone ownership past the middle class to the less wealthy. A change that has occurred in the world but not yet in America. Can poor people afford to have cellphones? In many parts of the planet they already do.

10) Telecoms prices

Some American telecoms experts like to point out to the high usage of minutes on American networks, and then the calculated costs of the per-minute cost. Superficially it does seem like the American industry at least leads the rest of the world by user-friendly tariffs. This is mirage. The harsh reality is that North American telecoms is still stuck in the model of heavily subsidized cellphones, which are tied to usually 24 month contracts. The customer is promised a "free phone" but has to sign to monthly fees that average 50 dollars. European average cellphone monthly fees are about half that rate. In leading countries like Hong Kong and Finland, prices are a tiny fraction of what Americans pay. In Hong Kong the cost of an average voice minute from any cellphone to any network in Hong Kong was 0.25 US cents (four minutes for one US cent). In Finland, the monthly cost of the bargain contracts was 0.67 Euros or about 1 US dollar per month. On the actual monthly spend level, customers in the USA and Canada pay among most expensive cellphone rates, and in exchange they get the worst quality networks, worst quality phones, and worst rated customer service from their carriers. This is not a good bargain for American consumers.

58% of US cellphone users send SMS text messages

---

11) Network quality

Today North American carriers have by far the worst cellular network coverage of any developed country. Even Russia, a country significantly larger than the USA or Canada, has far better cellular networks. A good example is cellphone coverage underground. In Helsinki Finland the subway train was built 150 feet underground into solid granite - this is the hardest rock, bedrock, and totally impregnable by cellphone radio signals (and was intended to provide Helsinki residents nuclear fallout shelter in case of Soviet nuclear attack) - yet as you descend deep into the bedrock on those long escalators, you have perfect cellular coverage on all three networks. All the way to the subway platform. Moreover, the perfect network coverage continues onboard the subway train as it speeds through the subway tunnels deep underground. In America it is not uncommon to lose cellular coverage if your parking garage is below street level.

Another concrete example is dead zones. In South Korea if you happen to find a location in Seoul the capital, in any building, any skyscraper, any shopping mall, any underground parking garage, anywhere that your cellphone drops its call and you lose the network - you just call your carrier the moment you regain network coverage moments later and report this gap in the cellular

---

coverage. The carriers take it as a matter of honor to have that fault fixed by tomorrow. By tomorrow! How many times have American customers complained about the network coverage of a given area time and again, years on end, to no avail. Its a total different mindset to coverage.

12) Obsolete business model

Perhaps the biggest cause for why North America lags, in my mind, is the business model. The North American market operates on an obsolete concept known in the industry as the "receiving party pays" business principle (which more accurately means that in America both the calling party and the receiving party pay part of the cost of the call). This may seem "fair" and "reasonable." After all, if a fixed landline caller calls another fixed landline phone, there is no part of the phone call going through the cellular network. If a cellphone caller calls anyone else, on a cellphone or landline, then the caller should be charged. In addition, quite logically, if the cellphone caller decides to accept a call onto the cellphone, is it not fair that that cellphone owner then also covers the cost of receiving calls that go through the cellular network?

> # 99% of South Korean cellphone users send SMS texts

At the start of the industry all cellular networks operated on that principle. It is yet another relic of an outdated principle unfortunately still hindering the American industry. I do consider this "receiving party pays" principle the single biggest reason why American carriers suffer so much, grow at such anemic rates, and why the whole North American wireless telecoms industry is in such malaise. It is an outmoded idea to charge for both outgoing calls and inbound calls (and messages). The American industry has tried to get around it with short-term remedies such as giving huge buckets of free minutes, but charging inbound calls against the minutes allowance. This business model has delayed the maturing of the American telecoms consumers as well as the American cellular telecoms market.

The more modern business model is called the "calling party pays" model by, which the full cost of the cellphone call is born by the caller alone. Note that in the big economic picture the total costs remain the same, but the balance shifts. Those people who tend to make many more calls than receiving calls on cellphones end up paying more for their phone bill. Equally, those people who tend to receive many more calls than making calls on cellphones, will end up paying less for their total cellphone bill. There is also often a shifting of balance in the payments from fixed landline telcos to the cellular carriers/operators. With the newer model of calling party pays, the receiving party has no reason to keep the phone turned off, or indeed no reason why not to carry the phone at all times, even keep it on at night.

(I also need to point out that there is one major exception to this rule, and that is international roaming. With international roaming even under the calling party pays rule, the receiving party - who is the internationally roaming party - pays the international part of the total call).

All countries that have switched to calling party pays have discovered dramatically better economics, because *the total amount of calls grows*. This is due to the concept I call "Reachability", which I discussed in my third book, *3G Marketing*, the core element of addictiveness to cellphones. Think about it. If your carrier charges you for inbound calls - and some telemarketer calls you on your cellphone, you'd become angry at the call. You are paying for it. So you would prefer to keep your phone turned off. Moreover, you would not want to answer any calls of numbers you do not recognize.

Now reverse the equation. What if you were never charged for inbound calls. Now, suddenly, you have no reason whatsoever to fear accepting a call. You'd carry the phone more often and of course keep the phone always turned on. This increases the total amount of telecoms traffic. Of course, the overall economics stays the same, what was charged against the receiving party, is now charged to the caller. So initially, at this change, the cost of placing calls on cellphones does go up, while the cost of receiving calls disappears. For the end-users there is a short-term price shock. Nevertheless, as this change has been seen in more than a hundred countries already, it is very short-term and soon forgotten. Almost all other countries in the world have adopted this model, but still today, USA and Canada and a few remaining legacy countries like China do not offer calling party pays.

There are many other reasons as well, but I think these twelve are the most relevant reasons why the USA lags the rest of the Industrialized world in the mobile telecoms industry, and in cellphones and their services.

B   THESE FIVE ARE NOT THE REASONS WHY

I also hear many mostly American telecoms analysts suggest several reasons, some that sound like excuses, why North America has lagged. I want to cover these also briefly, and show why these commonly cited reasons are all flawed.

Geography is not the reason.

Many say that it is much easier to launch a cellular network in a relatively small country like the Netherlands or Belgium or Britain or Hong Kong, Taiwan and Singapore, than the USA and Canada. This seems very reasonable. All of Europe

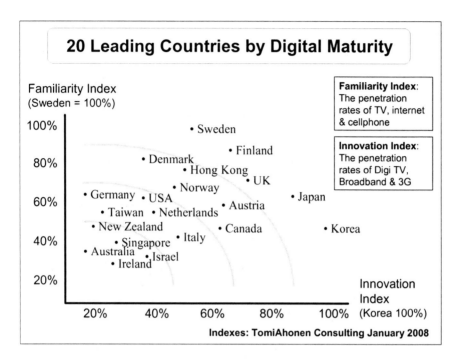

20 Leading Countries by Digital Maturity

Familiarity Index
(Sweden = 100%)

Familiarity Index:
The penetration
rates of TV, internet
& cellphone

Innovation Index:
The penetration
rates of Digi TV,
Broadband & 3G

Indexes: TomiAhonen Consulting January 2008

is about the size of the USA. Or take Britain, the UK is about the size of the state of Colorado, the USA is 40 times larger than the UK. Certainly it is easier to build a network for mobile calls to cover a small nation than a vast one.

That sounds reasonable. In addition, this argument works well for Canada as well. However, the very quick proof of the logical failure is evidence of other large countries, which have launched cellular networks *after* the USA, and have better networks, services and cellphone penetration rates. Australia and China are very similar in size to the USA and Canada, yet China and Australia have far better networks and services - bear in mind China is a developing nation - and Australia has higher penetration levels than the USA and Canada. Moreover, the ultimate proof? Russia - another developing nation - the world's largest country, has better networks, services and yes, now even higher penetration rates than both the USA and Canada. Therefore, size cannot be the reason.

Number of network technologies is not the reason

Many telecoms experts compare North America to Europe, and notice that most of Europe was on one standard, GSM, while the USA had four prevailing standards, three digital standards TDMA, CDMA, GSM and the analog standard

AMPS. Surely this must be the reason? Actually it is not. First, this argument fails on mis-analyzing Europe. Yes, on the 2G level, Europe has one standard, GSM, but while GSM was rapidly taking over during the 1990s, Europe had its analog systems as well. Not just one, NMT, but Europe actually had six separate and incompatible analog systems. So Europe had *seven* incompatible cellular systems to America's four. The Americans should have led by this reasoning. In addition, the ultimate proof comes from Israel, where at one point in 2003, five incompatible digital standards were commercially in use, by three network operators. Yet Israel's penetration rates, service use, network quality and competitiveness were all far superior to that of the USA. Number of networks is not the reason.

Some have also said that the American hodge-podge of licenses and cellular coverage areas prevented national carriers from emerging. So still today, the big four carriers in the USA only cover about 85% of all cellular subscribers and numerous tiny local carriers have licenses to operate in a given state . This is actually similar to how Europe still is today, except that in Europe there is no Europe-wide license. None of the big European carriers, Vodafone, Orange, Telefonica/O2, T-Mobile etc have a total European footprint. So they have learned to work in partnerships, with affiliates in the region. The complexity of acquiring spectrum within a geographic area and thus a network footprint - and customers continent-wide- is actually far easier in the USA than it is in Europe.

Long term contracts are not the reason

Then I have heard some argue that the long-term contracts in America are the reason the continent lags. They cite examples from Italy and Spain and Portugal with high prepaid customer proportions and point out European customers are not tied to long-term contracts. Yes, this is true in many markets, but it does not explain many countries with high proportions of contract customers such as Japan and Finland; even the UK has more prepaid customers. Many countries have a majority of the total customer base on postpaid contracts, with 18 month and 24 month contracts. Therefore long term contracts cannot be the reason.

Low landline penetration rates were not the reason

Another argument I hear from telecoms experts who tend to come from the side of fixed landline telecoms, is to claim the cellphone penetrations shot past fixed landline penetrations in countries where the landline penetration was very low to begin with, such as in Eastern Europe, Asia and the developing world. This sounds very reasonable. It is expensive to build fixed landline networks as you have to dig up the streets and pull cabling into existing buildings etc. Very costly and time-consuming. So in countries where the fixed landline penetration level was low, such as in Eastern Europe, this logic is very compelling. The logic of the argument fails, when one observes that the first country where cellphone penetrations exceeded fixed landlines was Finland, one of the world's most advanced *fixed* telecoms markets. Even though Finland had "complete" fixed landline household penetration, yet in 1998 the cellphone penetration rate grew past landline penetrations, and the fixed landline subscription rates started to fall.

Soon Sweden, Denmark and the rest of the advanced European countries followed Finland's lead. If the phenomenon was only observed in countries of low fixed landline penetration, then this argument might hold water. Nevertheless, as the pattern is also seen in countries where fixed landline penetration levels were at or even *above* those of the USA and Canada, then no, this cannot be the reason.

Architecture of tall buildings is not the reason

Perhaps the most quaint argument I hear is that the American architecture is a relevant factor in bad cellular services. The argument goes like this: since American cities like New York and Chicago have tall skyscrapers built very close to each other, they create very difficult radio environments and cellular signals will have difficulty penetrating the buildings and providing the coverage. Moreover, this challenge has prevented the American industry from keeping up with the other countries.

This argument falls first on America alone. If that was true, then why do cities of almost no skyscrapers like Los Angeles have poor coverage. If this was true, then the Queens and Brooklyn Boroughs of New York should have excellent networks, coverage and services, and only Manhattan be a problem. However, again, this falls on international comparisons. The world's cities most like New York and Chicago, in terms of skyscrapers, are Hong Kong and Tokyo. Both have lots of very tall skyscrapers and especially in Hong Kong, at vastly more compacted space than even those on Manhattan. Yet both Tokyo and Hong Kong have excellent cellular coverage - including inside all tall buildings, all the way to the tops of the skyscrapers - and excellent services and high cellphone penetration rates. Therefore architecture of skyscrapers cannot be the reason.

Numbers do not lie

I think I have made my point. On every one of the biggest changes to the cellular telecoms industry, the innovative country was not the USA or Canada. With all the examples I listed, the USA and Canada have been among the last to discover that change, often 5, even 10 years after the change was first observed. In several cases, the change that has already taken place in most of the rest of the world, has not even arrived on American shores.

The malaise of American the mobile telecoms industry is unfortunate on two levels. First of all, Motorola invented the cellphone and thus America had once held a "head-start" to the industry. Nevertheless, recently there has also been a dramatic shift in the industry. All telecoms experts worldwide, acknowledge that the mobile telecoms industry is shifting from being an engineering led and technology focused industry, to becoming a marketing led and customer focused business. If one might suggest that the Germans, Japanese, Swedes and Finns excel at engineering; certainly nobody doubts that Americans excel at marketing. If the industries around the cellphone were engineering and technology obsessed in the previous decade, but are now maturing into more prudent business with marketing and customer focus, then certainly American giant corporations should have been able to capitalize on this trend and use their natural competitive strengths to (re)capture their lead. Today they do not lead, but it is certainly possible that the North American based companies might still revive the industry and regain a lead.

Car guru from the Soviet Union?

Where can we go to learn? Let me use a simple America-focused analogy to illustrate. Imagine being a car executive 40 years ago - before the first oil crisis, when the big four American car makers, GM, Ford, Chrysler and American Motors were among the largest car makers of the world.

If you wanted to learn the latest car engineering, marketing and business know-how, you would not seek the guidance of the executives of car factories in the Soviet Union (where they still made cars based on German Opel designs from World War 2). That is not where you could learn about modern methods of just-in-time manufacturing and advanced customer segmentation and incorporating electronics into car design.

Just like the Soviet Union car manufacturing was years behind the Developed World, so too today is the American cellphone and mobile telecoms industry. Yes, certainly Microsoft and Intel and Google and Apple are global leaders in the internet and PC industries, but in cellphones and the cellular telecoms industry, American companies are no longer the leaders. The global leadership is centered around an axis of Japan and South Korea, with another around Finland and Sweden, with pockets of leadership in several other leading countries from the UK and Italy to Singapore and Hong Kong.

Finally, I do want to stress the point that I really do wish the American "sleeping giant" of cellular telecoms would wake up. The advent of the iPhone has helped, but there is a lot that needs to be done. This book is my contribution in trying to spread the best insights from several of those more advanced markets. In addition, for readers in the rest of the world, please be warned: America will wake up, and will return to fight for a leading role on the 7th of the Mass Media.

Tomi T Ahonen

Case Study 16 from Finland
Everyman's Idol

The *Pop Idol/American Idol* format show, developed by Fremantle and 19 Management, is the most popular reality TV show in the world. An analysis of the show by SMLXL, discussed in their White Paper entitled *Pop Idol*, revealed that the 67 Pop Idol contests that had already been completed by the summer of 2006, had achieved a total of 3.2 billion viewings worldwide. The more amazing number is that these viewings had generated 1.9 billion viewer votes, mostly as SMS text votes. These 1.9 billion televotes have produced the owners of the show a windfall income of 600 million dollars by the summer of 2006. This amount was split of course between the broadcasters and telecoms carriers (operators).

So the *Idol* format itself has been a powerful engine for expanding TV-interactivity via SMS text messaging and cellphone participation. In January 2006, the Finnish variant, *Finnish Idol*, created by ad agency Taivas Ego for Elisa and MainosTV3, introduced a novel enhancement to the show, called the *Peoples' Idols*, or *Everyman's Idols* (*"Jokamiehen Idols"*). Or perhaps in line with citizen journalism, this was the Citizens Idols. User-generated *Pop Idol* contestants.

It worked so that as viewers in Finland watched the *Finnish Idols* broadcast show on their TV sets, those viewers who thought they really should have been included in the contest, could now just take their cellphone, call a number, hear the music of a familiar song on a cellphone karaoke service, and start to sing. These entries would form the *Everyman's Idols* parallel contest, running simultaneously as the *Finnish Idols* show on TV.

Nobody could guess the success. While *Finnish Idols* broke its own viewing and voting records on TV, the *Everyman's* Idols variant generated more votes. Only 1,682 Finns were brave enough to pick up their phones and sing, to enter the contest. After that, 150,000

Finns went in to listen to them and to vote. This out of a total population of 5 million in Finland. And then they voted. Boy did they vote. The *Everyman's Idols* variant generated 1.95 Million votes. More votes than the TV show with the "proper" *Finnish Idols*.

That is why "*Everyman's Idol*" is such a radical departure. Up to now, if there was a TV show on the air, there was no way for average viewers to go and join that show. We could comment on it. We could send clips to it and hope they showed them. We could go and make our own videos and show them elsewhere. But if the TV channel broadcasts some show, we cannot just decide to join it. The selection of game show contestants has always been up to the producers of the show.

Not anymore. That is where *Everyman's Idol* is such a radical change. Now anyone can join their favorite TV show, simply by picking up their phone. Expect the *Everyman's Idols* innovation to spread far into the broadcast world.

"Truth travels slowly, but it will reach even you in time."
Benjamin Disraeli

XVIII
Conclusion
The ubiquitous media

The digital videogaming industry says they are going wireless. The music industry is going to digital downloads and increasingly directly to cellphones. The biggest internet players say the next internet is on cellphones. The messaging world is shifting from fixed internet desktop PCs to wireless, laptops, PDAs and cellphones. TV is already converging content with broadband internet, and starting to go to the "fourth screen" i.e. cellphone. Advertising says the future is cellphones. Credit cards heading to cellphones. Blogging is growing rapidly, but where is its future? To *mobile* blogging of course as we can already see in South Korea where more people moblog than use a PC for blogging.

No movement the other way

But nobody says with a straight face that any of the major trends will shift away from the cellphone. Cameraphone users are not about to shift back from cellphones to stand-alone digital cameras. Busy execs are not suddenly abandoning Blackberries. SMS users are not in some transition to e-Mail, no they show a clear preference to SMS, considering e-Mail is for the older generations, like perhaps their boss at work like they now say in Korea.

The cellphone is the only device we all carry, everywhere. We do take the cellphone to bed with us. We take it to the bathroom with us. We stop wearing wristwatches just relying on the clock and alarm on the cellphone. Chinese people bury dead people with depictions of cellphones, so that the departed can take their most valued gadget with them to the next life. If we leave home without the phone, we turn around to get the phone. It is that important.

The cellphone is cannibalizing all other digital technologies. The internet finds it difficult to bill for services? No problem, the cellphone can handle fixed internet billing, like the innovative *Habbo Hotel* already does. TV

Mobile is *Not the Crippled* Internet

The mobile internet is not the somehow "deprived" or "deficient" or "lesser" internet. It is the more capable and powerful internet.

PC INTERNET	MOBILE INTERNET
smaller internet	bigger internet
dumb pipe	smart internet
cumbersome web	efficient web
poor internet	money internet
occasional internet	ubiquitous internet
legacy internet	next internet

stations and radio broadcasters are turning to SMS text messaging to connect to audiences. What is best about this gadget that 50% of the human population already carries every day? The replacement cycle at 18 months on average.

I do not mean we will give up our plasma screen TVs. I do not mean wedding photographers start to snap with cameraphones. In addition, while I did discuss cellphone-written youth novels in Japan that end up printed as bestsellers books, you can bet your bottom dollar that I will not author my next book triple-tapping the tiny keypad of my N-series. However, for my nephews and nieces there is nothing bizarre about writing books using their phones, in particular if they were paid to do so, like a *"real author like our Uncle Tomi"*. So yes, for mainstream digital convergence and in particular for Generation C, the natural end-state is the cellphone. It will crush any and all pretenders.

The money, follow the money

I want to return to something I wrote back in 2002 in my second book, *M-Profits* about this fledgling content industry for cellphones:

> Now I offer this vision of the future: "Within a few years, all content creators will be paid for their content." That is quite a bold statement

when we think about the billions of internet pages at millions of websites, most of, which are available for free. Today most content providers are struggling with the dilemma of tiny value. Most websites have a loyal collection of users who clearly appreciate the content - loyal visitors and browsing customers who keep coming back - yet nobody seems to be willing to pay for the access to the content.
Tomi Ahonen in *M-Profits*, 2002

I am totally convinced this vision will happen. It is only timing, which has been delayed a bit. This model has started to appear on the mobile internet. The ability to charge for small value content will radically alter the internet. Mobile as 7th of the Mass Media is far superior to the internet as the 6th.

The cellular phone is not inherently good, nor is it inherently bad. The cellphone is a new way to communicate, which includes functionalities beyond the traditional fixed wireline telephone. Cellphones have been used by criminals and by the police; kids use them to cheat in exams or to tease others in school. With this book I do not mean to suggest the phone is only a "good" technology. As a technology it is neutral; it is how we use it that will bring benefits or harms.

You ain't seen nothin' yet

Finally I'd like to remind readers that the cellphone and its related services and the emerging wireless industry is still very young. The cellphone was introduced in Japan 29 years ago and became a mass-market media device only some ten years ago. As the seventh mass media channel the cellphone is only a decade old. All of the innovation and invention in this space is still very recent.

The world's biggest internet company in terms of revenues and profits is not Google or Amazon or Ebay, it is the *internet arm* of Japanese wireless carrier NTT DoCoMo. The fixed internet did provide dramatic cannibalization of various industries such as airline bookings, book sales, advertising etc. However, those pale in comparison to cannibalization to be seen on mobile.

No technology ever, not electricity, not the personal computer, not the internet, has had such a fast cannibalization of existing industries as we are seeing now with Mobile as the 7th of the Mass Media. Yet this industry is still in its infancy. Do not try to just copy the existing, but seek to create the exceptional. Create magic. The Googles and Amazons and Ebays of the next decade will be based on mobile. Join in now to learn about this new medium and be among the big winners. Don't wait.

It is clear that we will see more change in this space in the next ten years, than what has happened in the past ten years. With that, I would like to remind readers of what Charles Darwin wrote about who will be winners in times of change, in his book, ***Origin of the Species***, *"It is not the strongest that will survive, nor is it the most intelligent; but the one most adaptive to change."*

Postscript... So what next? You've read the book. What is your next move? I hope I have awakened an appetite to this opportunity. Now you should follow the thought leaders. My company, TomiAhonen Consulting is of course helping explore this area and I run workshops, seminars and even custom courses for major telecoms, media, advertising and IT companies interested in this area.

There are many top experts echoing the same story and expanding our knowledge of it. SMLXL, run by Alan Moore released the first White Paper on this topic. Dot Mobi was one of the first industry bodies to publicize the seven media. Nokia runs the story with a twist, around the topic of the *"fourth screen"*, which obviously was the subtitle of the chapter in this book dedicated to the 7th of the Mass Media. Many leading bloggers in this space from Howard Rheingold at Smart Mobs, Russell Buckley at Mob Happy, Oliver Starr at Mobile Crunch and Ajit Jaokar at Open Gardens have discussed it. Tony Fish at AMF Ventures is an early proponent as is David Cushman at Emap and Colin Crawford at IDG.

If you want to see companies "doing it" while not necessarily preaching the 7th Mass Media story, some of the best that are worth watching include Blyk, Flirtomatic, Admob, MyNuMo, Itsmy, Ohmy News, and among the big company plays into this space, pay attention to SeeMeTV with Three/Hutchison; Ovi and Adserve by Nokia, T-Mobile's activities around digital communities and social networking, such as their My Faves user interface. Several global carrier group giants are active, such as Vodafone, Orange, MTS and Telenor. Companies that are perennial innovators into the 7th Mass Media space start with MTV and include Fremantle (i.e. Pop Idol/American Idol), Endemol (i.e. Big Brother) and CNN with its i-Report. Cyworld by SK Telecom is perhaps the most advanced concept. NTT DoCoMo would merit a chapter all by itself, and the other big Japanese and South Korean carriers, KDDI, Softbank, KTF and LG Telecom all warrant attention. Google fully "gets it" For the ad industry D2, AirCross, Ogilvy, R/GA and MoviDream are well tuned in. Among handset makers Apple will be an innovator and Samsung, LG and SonyEricsson as well.

Then there are the creators, technology platforms and providers, which include Fjord obviously behind many of the innovations mentioned in this book: Nokia's Lifeblog, Yahoo Go, T-Mobile MyFaves, Flirtomatic, etc. Many other world class innovators include Artificial Life, Digital Chocolate, Cybird, Enfour, Nexgen, Ex Machina, Taivas Ego, Satama Interactive, Buongiorno, Comverse etc. Xtract is the obvious thought leader into the social context of the 7th of the Mass Media and warrants exceptional attention to anything they might release.

As to me, I'll blog about all of these topics at 7thMassMedia.com. You'll see me at conferences and quoted in the press. If your company needs a rapid crash course, I'll bring my seminar or workshop, but if you just want a two day course about it at modest cost, my course at Oxford University runs in July and December. If you do like the book, I'd ask you to tell your friends about it and lend them this book. I'd also urge you to please also write your evaluation of this book at Amazon so others can find this book as well.

"Humor is just another defense against the universe."
Mel Brooks

CelluLatin
Humorous Interlude

Several famous profound and insightful thoughts have been expressed in Latin. Now, with the change in society happening with mobile phones, perhaps updates are needed to reflect our changed habits. Please note that I know no Latin, the following joke phrases are total gibberish.

Ad nausium - Until seasickness
mAd nausium - Mobile advertising makes me sick

Amicus certus in re incerta cernitur. - A friend in need is a friend indeed.
Amicus certus in re incalla sellitur - A friend in true need will be calling on a cellular phone

Audentes fortuna iuvat. - Fortune favors the brave.
Ahonentes fortuna duvet - Ahonen prefers to lay in bed

Caveat emptor. - Let the buyer beware.
Sellular emptor - The phone battery is empty

Cogito, ergo sum. - I think, therefore I am
Cogito, ergo SMS - I think... I still have time to send an SMS

Dictum, factum. - Said and done.
Dictum, voistum - Said and left on voice mail

E pluribus onum - One out of many
e-mailibus onum - I get too many e-mails

Errare humanum est, ignoscere divinum. - To err is human, to forgive divine.
Errare humongous est, ignoramus digitum - To make really enormous errors requires a computer

Margaritas ante porcos iacere. - Throw pearls before the swines.
Manageras ante porcos locare - You can control your pigs with location-based services

Ne furtum facias. - Thou shalt not steal.
Novus fonus facias - Thine mobile phone has a new face plate

O tempora! O mores! - O times! O customs!
O tempora! O mobiles! - Oh times! Oh the mobile phones!

Primus inter pares. - First among equals.
Primus iponus Paris - First iPhones were smuggled to Paris

Quem di diligunt adolescens moritur. - He whom the gods love dies young.
Qu empti prepaidunt adolescens telefoniur - He who is young, has no credit left on the prepaid account

Quia natura mutari non potest idcirco verae amicitiae sempiternae sunt. - Since nature cannot change, true friendships are eternal.
Quia kamera mutari non potest idcirco verae imagiae fotoshopernae sunt - Since the camera does not lie, eternal pictures need some fotoshop

Quod scripsi, scripsi. - What I have written, I have written.
Quod snakesi, scorsi - He Snakes, he scores!

Saepe creat molles aspera spina rosas. - Often the prickly thorn produces tender roses
Saepe creat mobiles aspera spina ringsas - Often it is the ugly phone that produces beautiful ringing tones

Tempora mutantur, nos et mutantur in illis. - Times change and we change with the times
Tempora mutantur, nos et mutantur in billis - Times change and our new nasty habits show up on the phone bill

Timeo Danaos et dona ferentes. - I fear the Greeks even when they're bringing gifts
Timeo Tomio et dona jokentes - I worry about Tomi's sense of humour

Variatio delectat - There's nothing like change
Videoteleo delectat - There's nothing like video telephones

Vestis virum reddit. - The clothes make the man
Vappis virum rubbis - The WAP makes the crap

The above for entertainment purposes only. Does not reflect the opinions of any of the employers, present nor past, nor current customers and colleagues of the author, nor any of the technologies, nor any of the companies or public personalities mentioned. No Latins were hurt or killed in the making of this Joke. Original humour by Tomi T Ahonen/HatRat, 2002-2008.

"Ole valmis. Aina valmiina." (Be prepared)
The Boy Scouts' Motto in Finnish (and English)

To the Reader
This is my sixth book...

I am the luckiest man in the world. My (step)father, Jan W Brans tought me to love books. My high school English teacher, Renee Brinker taught me to love language. My college debate coach Barry McCauliff taught me to enjoy performing on stage. Now I am paid to write books and speak in public, every day, all around the world. I love my job.

So as I travel the world I meet up with you, my readers and fans. People who picked up one of my books recommended by a boss, or found it in a library or on a shelf of obscure telecoms tech books, or perhaps discovered my books through my blog or perhaps saw me on stage somewhere. Some people will come up to me often a bit embarrassed with one of my books hidden in their briefcase, waiting until all others have gone, then asking would I mind autographing the book. I always say yes. These are among my best moments, I truly do love it. If you ever have the chance to meet up with me, bring this book, I promise I will sign it for you

And I love hearing the stories, what brought my readers to telecoms or this converging media/tech space; what their company does, how they found me and what they think of my writings and thoughts. I hear the most heart-warming stories, of people like a Senior Vice President of one of the global ten largest wireless carrier groups, who was prepping for a job interview by reading my book and then showing he knew the industry, he was hired to his current job. Or another, a Strategy Director for another of the global ten biggest carrier groups, who said he had read all of my books, and written his current strategy based on them, and now his group was performing so well to that strategy that he had received a promotion. These were not former colleagues of mine; they were total strangers to me, who found my books, and their lives had changed because of my writing. I cannot explain how much this makes me happy as an author and "expert".

And it need not be big giant corporations where it happens. I met up with a nice gentleman at one conference who came up to me clutching one of my books, and said in broken English that he had launched an idea out of the book into his country, and it was the market leader. It had made his career. I was delighted to sign that book. I met a lady who traveled across an ocean to hear me speak after reading one of my books and said she got her current job based on implementing some of my writings. There was the CEO of a company of a handful people, who read my book, and contacted me and asked if a couple of the ideas in that book might work in his company in his country. I said yes I thought they would work, and his company used those ideas to become profitable within a few months and has now grown to far larger size and has already expanded abroad.

These are the kinds of stories I love to hear. What is your business, how did you find this industry and what kind of innovations you work on today. I love these stories partly because they help validate some of my early ideas, so there is undoubtedly an "ego trip" element to them for me.

But more than that, there is the youthful thrill of discovery and delight, of curiosity satisfied. How can *you* make money on the Seventh of the Mass Media. Almost all of the stories in this book, and my presentations, come from friends who launched something in their country. I don't mean the big global innovative companies like NTT DoCoMo of Japan, SK Telecom of South Korea and Three of the UK with their case studies (which are among my reference customers). I mean the small start-ups and surprising innovators. For example of the Case Studies in this book, I've met up with Mark Curtis of Flirtomatic from before his company launched, discussing its growth regularly. The Finnair mobile check-in, I met up with Heikki Karimo, then with Finnair, now with IBM Finland, who developed it and discussed the innovation almost from the day it launched. Blyk, I first met co-founder Antti Öhrling back when I still worked for Nokia in 2000 and greatly admired the man when he ran Finnish creative ad agency Contra. Now with my co-author Alan Moore serving on Blyk's board, I have been very closely involved and well abreast of, while not actually consulting for, Blyk. And William Volk, the CEO of MyNuMo in the USA, is another friend from years earlier when he was with Bonus Mobile and he was one of the early people to join Forum Oxford where he and I regularly exchange comments on the daily happenings of the industry.

There are the other kind of contacts, where I initially learn of a cool new service from a friend or colleage "Tomi have you heard of Hotelli Kultakala?" (what turned into Habbo Hotel) and the like. Then I write about them and very often we then end up meeting with that company later. Like we did with Sulake, the owners of Habbo. Or after I wrote about Shazam in glowing terms, I met up with their management at a conference. Then there is the former project manager of Sony Music in South Korea, with the Ricky Martin innovation, which launched MP3 music to cellphones. That man is today a CEO of a major Korean company not involved in music. But we met up quite by accident when I was in Seoul promoting my previous book *Digital Korea*. Leafing through the book, he discovered his service described and was thrilled. In a similar way when presenting at a conference in Tokyo I met up with the nice people at Enfour Group who developed Kamera Jiten in Japan, another case study in this book..

I was once giving a keynote to a telecoms CEO audience at an exclusive event, and ended my presentation with a story I called the best example of marketing in mobile. Unbeknownst to me, in the audience sat the CEO of that very company, and suddenly several people started smiling broadly and turned to look at that CEO who nodded his head. I met up with him afterwards and he was glowing as the famous author and consultant had singled his company innovation as one of such leadership.

But the point is that I truly love what I am blessed to be allowed to do. I love my job, I am the luckiest man on the planet. I truly do love speaking and writing about our industry. And I love meeting up with you, my readers, my fans. And you will honestly make my day, if you bring up one of my books and tell me a bit about what you do in our business. I will be most delighted to autograph this book for you.

Thank you to all of my readers for reading my books. As long as you find them useful, I will write more of them for you.

Tomi T Ahonen (the "HatRat")
Hong Kong

"The pen is mightier than the sword, and considerably easier to write with."
Marty Feldman

Abbreviations

1Seg	One Segment, the Japanese digital TV for cellphones	4G	Fourth Generation mobile telephony, also known as "Systems Beyond IMT 2000" currently being standardized with first commercial 4G standard-compliant networks expected to be launched 2012.
2D	Two Dimensional		
2G	Second Generation (current digital) mobile telephony. These include GSM, CDMA, TDMA, IDEN etc		
2.5G	"Two point Five G" enhancements to the second generation mobile telephony that are not 3G. These include GPRS, EDGE and CDMA2000 1x	6 M's	Mobile service creation tool consisting of Movement, Moment, Me, Multi-User, Money and Machines
3D	Three Dimensional	7 Mass Media (also 7th Mass Media) seven mass media in order of their launch: print, recordings, cinema, radio, TV, internet and mobile
3G	Third Generation ("next generation") mobile telephony. Also known by the technical standard IMT 2000. Mainly "true" 3G consist of WCDMA (UMTS), CDMA2000 EV-DO, and TD-SCDMA		
		B2B	Business to Business
		BBS	Bulletin Board System
		Blog	weB log
3GSM	Third Generation and GSM (Global System for Mobile)	CDMA	Code Division Multiple Access (a 2G cellular telecoms standard)
3.5G	"Three point Five G" enhancements to the third generation of mobile telephony beyond 3G but that are not 4G. For example HSDPA	CRM	Customer Relationship Management
		CTIA	Cellular Telecoms & Internet Association
		CWTA	Canadian Wireless Telecoms Association
		DMB	Digital Media Broadcasting

DRM	Digital Rights Management		Enabler
DVB-H	Digital Video Broadcasting - Handheld	MVNO	Mobile Virtual Network Operator
EBU	European Broadcasting Union	OCR	Optical Character Recognition
FMC	Fixed-Mobile Convergence		
Gen-C	Generation-C (Community)	PC	Personal Computer
GPS	Global Positioning Satellite	PDA	Personal Digital Assistant
GSM	Groupe Special Mobile, Global System for Mobile communications	PR	Public Relations
		PSP	PlayStation Portable
		PVR	Personal Video Recorder
HTML	Hypertext Markup Language	QR	Quick Response
ID	IDentity	RF	Radio Frequency
IFPI	International Federation of Phonographic Industry	RFID	Radio Frequency IDentification
IM	Instant Messaging	RSS	Really Simple Syndication
IP	Internet Protocol, also Intellectual Property	SIM	Subscriber Identity Module
		SMS	Short Message Service
IPTV	Internet Protocol TeleVision	UI	User Interface
ISP	Internet Service Provider	URL	Uniform Resource Locator
IT	Information Technology	VCR	Videocassetter Recorder
ITU	International Telecommunications Union	VHS	Video Home System
		VOD	Video On Demand
LBS	Location-Based Service	VoIP	Voice over Internet Protocol
MDA	Mobile Data Association	WAP	Wireless Application Protocol
MIDI	Musical Instrument Digital Interface	WCDMA	Wideband Code Division Multiple Access (a 3G cellular technology)
MMOG	Massively Multiplayer Online Game	WiFi	Wireless Fidelity
MMS	Multimedia Messaging Service	WiMax	Worldwide Interoperability for Microwave Access
MP3	MPEG-2 Layer 3 (Motion Picture Experts Group)	W-LAN	Wireless Local Area Network
MSN	MicroSoft Network		
MTV	Music TV	WWW	WorldWide Web
MVNE	Mobile Virtual Network		

"Build a man a fire and he'll be warm for a night.
Set him on fire and he'll burn the rest of his life."
Terry Pratchett

Bibliography

Agha, Rod Ghani. **The Wireless Dawn: Think Wireless to Outthink Your Competition**, Authorhouse, 2007, 155 pp

Ahonen Tomi. **m-Profits: Making Money from 3G**, Wiley, 2002, 360 pp

Ahonen Tomi, Timo Kasper Timo, Sara Melkko. **3G Marketing: Communities and Strategic Partnerships**, Wiley, 2004, 333 pp

Ahonen Tomi, Alan Moore. **Communities Dominate Brands: Business and Marketing Challenges for the 21st Century**. Futuretext, 2005, 274 pp

Ahonen Tomi, Jim O'Reilly. **Digital Korea: Convergence of Internet, Cell phones, Gaming, TV, Virtual Reality, Electronic Cash, Telematics, Robotics, E-Government and the Intelligent Home.** . Futuretext, 2007, 284 pp

Anderson Chris. **The Long Tail.** Random House, 2006, 256 pp

Ballard Barbara. **Designing the Mobile User Interface**. Wiley 2007, 260 pp

Beck John, Wade Mitchell. **Got Game**, Harvard Business School Press, 2004, 208 pp

Benkler Yochai. **Wealth of Networks**, Yale University Press, 2006. 528 pp

Calvo Agustin. **Open Your Eyes and Wake Up Your Business**, Calvo 2006, 30 pp

Curtis Mark. **Distraction**, Futuretext 2005, 222 pp

Donaton Scott. **Madison & Vine**. McGraw-Hill, 2004, 240 pp

Frengle Nick. **i-Mode, A Primer**, M&T Books, 2002, 485 pp

Gillin Paul. **The New Influencers**. Quill Driver Books, 2007. 258 pp

Golding Paul. **Next Generation Wireless Applications**, Wiley, 2004, 588 pp

Hayes Tom, **Jump Point**. McGraw-Hill, 2008, 240 pp

Jaokar Ajit, Fish Tony. **Mobile Web 2.0**, Futuretext, 2006, 176 pp

Jaokar Ajit, Fish Tony. **Open Gardens: Innovator's Guide to the Mobile Industry**, Futuretext, 2004, 176 pp

Jenkins Henry. **Convergence Culture**. NYU Press 2006, 336 pp

Kopomaa, Timo. **City in your Pocket, the birth of the information society**, Gaudeamus, 2000, 143 pp

Lindholm Christian, Keinonen Turkka. **Mobile Usability**. McGraw-Hill, 2003, 301pp

Moll, Cameron. **Mobile Web Design**. Lulu 2008. 108 pp

Radhakrishnan Rakesh. **Identity and Security**. Futuretext, 2007, 418 pp

Rheingold Howard. **Smart Mobs: The next social revolution**, Basic, 2002, 288 pp

Rigby Ben. **Mobilizing Generation 2.0.** Jossey-Bass, 2008. 288 pp

Scoble Robert. **Naked Conversations: How blogs are changing the way businesses talk with customers.** Hungry Minds, 2006, 251 pp

Sharma Chetan, Joe Herzog, Victor Melfi. **Mobile Advertising: Supercharge your Brand in the Exploding Wireless Market**, Wiley, 404 pp

Steinbock Dan. **The Mobile Revolution**, Kogan Page 2005, 304 pp

Weiss Tom. **Mobile Strategies**, Futuretext, 2006, 186 pp

Willmott Michael, William Nelson. **Complicated Lives Sophisticated Consumers; Intricate lifestyles simple solutions**, Wiley, 2003, 260 pp

"Most of us don't know exactly what we want, but we're pretty sure we don't have it"
Alfred E Neuman (Mad Magazine)

Good Websites and Blogs

160 Characters (SMS Text Messaging Association)
http://www.160characters.org

7th Mass Media blog (Tomi T Ahonen)
http://www.7thmassmedia.com

All About Symbian
http://www.allaboutsymbian.com

AORTA Always On Real Time Access (Chetan Sharma)
http://www.chetansharma.com/blog

Carnival of the Mobilists (every week different host)
http://www.mobili.st

Gigaom (Om Malik)
http://gigaom.com

Colin's Corner (Colin Crawford)
http://www.colincrawford.typepad.com

Communities Dominate Blogsite (Tomi T Ahonen and Alan Moore)
http://www.communitiesdominate.com

Faster Future (David Cushman)
http://www.fasterfuture.blogspot.com

Fjord (company website)
http://www.fjord.co.uk

Forum Oxford (registration required but free site)
http://www.forumoxford.com

M Search Groove (Peggy Ann Salz)
http://www.msearchgroove.com

M-Trends (Rudy de Waele)
http://www.m-trends.org

Mob Happy (Russell Buckley and Carlo Longino)
http://www.mobhappy.com

Mobile Crunch (Oliver Starr)
http://mobilecrunch.com

Mobile Data Association
http://www.themda.org

Mobile Monday Global Site
http://www.mobilemonday.net

Moconews (James Pearce)
http://www.moconews.net

Open Gardens (Ajit Jaokar)
http://www.opengardensblog.futuretext.com

Scobleizer (Robert Scoble)
http://scobleizer.com

SMLXL (company website)
http://www.smlxtralarge.com

Smart Mobs (Howard Rheingold)
http://www.smartmobs.com

Technokitten (Helen Keegan)
http://technokitten.blogspot.com

Textually (Emily Turrettini)
http://www.textually.org

Tomi T Ahonen (company website)
http://www.tomiahonen.com

Wireless Watch Japan (Daniel Scuka and Lars Cosh-Ishii)
http://wirelesswatch.jp

Wireless Wanders (Paul Golding)
http://blog.wirelesswanders.com

Xellular Identity (Xen Mendelsohn)
http://www.xellular.net

Xtract (company website)
http://www.xtract.com

ZD Net
http://www.zdnet.com

Index

About the Author

Tomi T Ahonen is a six-time best-selling author, consultant and motivational speaker based in Hong Kong. He is a guest lecturer at Oxford University's short courses on next generation mobile, new media and digital convergence. Widely respected, his books and theories are referenced already in 35 books by other authors. Tomi is the father of several significant theories and concepts for the industry including the *Six M's* (originally *Five M's*) the mobile industry service development tool used by all leading companies in the industry; the *Hockey Sticks* mobile industry revenues and costs equation; the *Connected Age* paradigm; *Generation C* for Community, and the *7 Mass Media* taxonomy, all of, which have been referenced in published books by other experts.

. Tomi is known as an evangelist for new technologies who has discussed over 1,000 of his "Pearls" in the public domain. Tomi has delivered keynotes at over 200 conferences on six continents and has been quoted in over 250 press articles in leading press such as *Wall Street Journal, Economist, Business Week, Financial Times*, etc. and is often seen on TV. His columns have appeared in *New Media Knowledge, Mobile Handset Analyst, Asia-Pacific Connect World, European Communications, IEE Communications Engineer, Telecommunications, Mobile Communications, Total Telecom*, etc. Serving as co-editor of the *Forum Oxford Journal*, Tomi sits the Editorial Board of the *Journal of Telecommunications Management* and on the Advisory Board of Mobile Monday. A founding member of Wireless Watch, Carnival of Mobilists and Engagement Alliance, Tomi co-chairs Forum Oxford. His blog at CommunitiesDominate.com is rated one of the most influential and is syndicated widely including at CNBC and the *New York Times*.

Tomi's consulting client list reads like the who's who of high tech, including BT, Ericsson, Hewlett-Packard, Intel, Motorola, Nokia, NTT DoCoMo, Orange, Siemens, SK Telecom, T-Mobile, Telenor, TeliaSonera, Vodafone. Tomi has consulted many non-technology customers including Aller, Bank of Finland, BBC, DHL, Economist, Emap, HSBC, MTV, Ogilvy, Royal Bank of Scotland, United Nations Security Council. Tomi serves on the Boards of several start-ups, and advises industry bodies such as the Singapore Infocomm Development Agency, Canadian Wireless Telecoms Association, Irish Marketing Association and Communications Industry Association of Japan.

Tomi set up his own telecoms and media consultancy in 2001. Before that he was employed by Nokia as Global Head of 3G Consulting where Tomi oversaw Nokia's end-user 3G Research Centre. Previously at Nokia he was Nokia's first Segmentation Manager and started with internet gateways. Prior to that he worked with Elisa and the Finnet Group where his accomplishments include the world's first fixed-mobile service bundle, the world's largest multi-operator billing system; and setting the world record for taking market share from the incumbent. Prior to that Tomi was Head of Marketing for New York's first internet service provider, OCSNY. He started his career on Wall Street.

Tomi holds an International Finance MBA (with hons) from St John's University NY and a bachelor's in International Marketing from Clarion University (with hons). His previous books are **Digital Korea** with Jim O'Reilly, **Communities Dominate Brands** with Alan Moore, **3G Marketing** with Timo Kasper and Sara Melkko, **m-Profits**, and **Services for UMTS** with Joe Barrett. Tomi is working on his seventh book around topics relating to mobile social networking. For more see www.tomiahonen.com

Other books by Tomi T Ahonen:

Digital Korea:
Convergence of Broadband Internet, 3G Cellphones, Multi-player Gaming, Digital TV, Virtual Reality, Electronic Cash, Telematics, Robotics, E-Government and the Intelligent Home
by Tomi T Ahonen & Jim O'Reilly
foreword by Dr Hyun-oh Yoo President and CEO SK Communications
284 pages hardcover, futuretext 2007, second printing 2008
ISBN 978-0-9556069-0-8

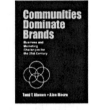

"A lot of what we in the UK, think of as futurology is actually already happening in Korea."
Peter Miles, CEO, **SubTV**, UK
"The book is an excellent summary of what has been going on for the past few years in Korea"
Book Review **Korea IT Times** August 2007 issue, South Korea

Communities Dominate Brands:
Business & Marketing Challenges for the 21st Century
by Tomi T Ahonen & Alan Moore
foreword by Stephen C Jones Chief Marketing Officer Coca Cola
280 pages, hardcover, futuretext, 2005, second printing 2005
first paperback edition futuretext 2008
ISBN   0-9544327-3-8   **NOW IN PAPERBACK !**

"Invaluable in how power will reside far more with ordinary people than with companies."
Rory Sutherland, Vice Chairman, **OgilvyOne** UK
"An excellent, reassuring book! In 5 years time it will a classic - the new bible for new marketeers."
Dr Axel Alber, Marketing Director, **Masterfoods** Europe

M-Profits
Making Money from 3G Services
By Tomi T Ahonen (360 pages, hardcover, John Wiley & Sons, 2002)
Foreword by Teppo Turkki Strategy Director Elisa Corporation
ISBN 0-470-84775-1

3G Marketing
Communities and Strategic Partnerships
By Tomi T Ahonen, Timo Kasper and Sara Melkko
(333 pages, hardcover, John Wiley & Sons, 2004)
Forewords by Mike Short VP O2 and Chairman MDA; and Jouko Ahvenainen Chairman Xtract Ltd
ISBN 0-470 -85100-7
second printing 2004 also translated into Chinese

Services for UMTS
Creating Killer Applications in 3G
Edited by Tomi T Ahonen and Joe Barrett
(373 pages, hardcover, John Wiley & Sons, 2002)
Forword by Alan Hadden Chairman GSM Suppliers Association
ISBN 0471 485500
also translated into Chinese

Excerpt from Tomi T Ahonen previous book
Digital Korea with Jim O'Reilly
(published by futuretext)
2007 first hardcover edition
ISBN 978-0-9556069-0-8

Chapter 1 - Introduction
The future exists in South Korea

What is the future like? We know that current trends suggest the internet will be available practically everywhere. We know that internet access is becoming increasingly broadband. We know broadband speeds are climbing. In addition, we know internet users are increasingly accessing the web wirelessly. We know cellphones reach ever more of the population. We know cellphones are going 3G high speed. We know that media is going digital, from music to movies and digital TV. We see convergence of media, web and communications, from such innovations as IPTV to services such as Skype and Vonage. But where will it all lead?

What will the world be like in the near future, when everybody has internet access, at high-speed broadband? When everybody has not only a cellphone, but also even teenagers have cameraphones on high-speed 3G high networks? How will our daily life be different when our home is digital and connected, when all government services are provided digitally when digital TV is in our car and on our phone? When virtual worlds are formed, digital communities emerge, our money is digital, and our online lives take on a meaning of their own? What happens to our work, our families, our lives?

This is a book about that future. It is not science fiction. That future is already now visible in only one country, South Korea. The country with the highest penetrations of wireless broadband internet, 3G mobile cellphones, portable digital TV, online virtual gaming and so forth. To see the future, you need to understand South Korea, or like we say, Digital Korea. Let us take you on a tour.

World leader

90% of South Korean homes have broadband internet access. The world average is about 20%. 63% of South Koreans make payments using their cellphones, the world average is under 5%. 43% of South Koreans maintain a blogsite or personal profile online like Americans might have on MySpace or the British on Bebo - the industrialized world average is about 10%. Over half of South Koreans have migrated their cellphone account to 3G (the world average is 5%).

100% of South Korean internet access has migrated to broadband (the world, about 30%). 25% of South Koreans have played the same multiplayer videogame (*Kart Rider*, a case study later in this book). 40% of South Koreans already have a digital representation of themselves, a so-called avatar such as Western people who use Second Life or Habbo Hotel. By every measure, South Korea leads the world in digital adoption and innovation. In a very literal sense, South Koreans are living in the near future of the digitally converging technologies from the viewpoint of the rest of the world.

This is a book to show to Western readers how incredible that future is, what is now commonplace in this melting pot of digital innovation. Moreover, to show glimpses of where South Koreans see their future going. In ten years, every South Korean household will have a robot. Yes, in ten years. Does that make you pause? Read on...

Seoul as digital nirvana

For most South Koreans today, their very lifestyle already revolves around services that require high-speed digital access. The networks are state-of-the-art wireless networks and handsets: both international standards of 3G networks have been launched (CDMA 2000 1x EVDO like in America and WCDMA or UMTS like in Europe). Faster 3.5G networks on HSDPA are already in commercial use. WiFi and WiBro (a variant of what is called WiMax in the West) is commercially available, as is DMB digital TV broadcasts to cellphones, cars, laptop PCs and other movable devices.

WiFi is offered on the world's most extensive broadband wireless network and can be accessed from 25,000 cyber cafés located around the country. On broadband not only have all South Korean internet access lines been migrated from narrow-band (dial-up) to broadband, South Korea leads the world in broadband adoption as well as broadband speeds offered. Where most industrialized countries offered broadband speeds in the 2 Mbit/s to 10 Mbit/s range at the end of 2006, in South Korea the standard offering is between 50 Mbit/s and 100 Mbit/s and South Korea is already rolling out the first pilot connections of Gigabit broadband (1,000 Mbit/s). And to add insult to injury, South Koreans pay for their broadband at the lowest rates in the world.

In a very literal sense, to be South Korean means to be connected.

South Korea has usually been it the shadow of the economic "miracles" of its bigger Japanese neighbor, from home electronics, the camera and wristwatch industries, to automobiles and robotics. But with the dawn of the "Connected Age" the new wirelessly connected society, which has moved beyond the "Networked Age" of the 1990s, the South Korean government, industry and academia all decided to pool resources and make a leap ahead of its Eastern neighbor across the sea.

A key ingredient is the Korean phrase "bballi bballi", which means to "hurry hurry". South Koreans work very hard for long hours, and this work ethic, together with the pooling of all resources have enabled a massive jump in the digital infrastructures. These in turn have helped propel the whole country and all other forms of society and economic life to gain from the lead in digitalization.

Ubiquitous is the word

The word you hear currently from all South Korean executives, officials and experts in the digitally converging industries is "ubiquitous". Ubiquitous computing, ubiquitous internet, ubiquitous gaming, ubiquitous coverage etc. Ubiquitous means "ever-present" or omnipresent; that something is everywhere, accessible at any location. Oxygen is ubiquitous on our planet but water is not (consider the Sahara desert for example). South Koreans are now on the verge of the world's first society where digital services are literally ubiquitous.

We take a survey of Digital Korea

Jim lives in the UK, and Tomi lives in Hong Kong. Both of us have regular business contacts with South Korea and have visited South Korea countless times. We research and discuss South Korean digital innovations regularly in our daily work both of us within the converging IT/telecoms/media industries. This book was intended to be a guidebook and overview of how advanced the society of Digital Korea is overall. What kind of synergies and serendipities start to happen when several closely related industries achieve the global cutting edge - or indeed the bleeding edge - of technological advances.

When broadband internet leadership is merged with multiplayer videogaming leadership and 3G mobile telecoms leadership and digital TV leadership, then tremendous advances from one will influence the other and so forth.

We start by studying the South Korean consumer, and examine how far Generation-C (the Community Generation) already exists in South Korea. We discuss several phenomena around youth and ubiquitous digital services. From cheating in school by using cellphones to spending hours inside multiplayer games to sending 100 text messages per day, we dig deep into the life of what being young, connected and Korean means today.

Then we start to examine various service areas. We look at the role of virtual realities such as recently very much in the press in the Western World as Second Life has reached 2 million users. Contrast that with virtual worlds in South Korea such as Cyworld and Kart Rider both with over 20 million users exploring virtual world entertainment and life; even employment. We then examine digital living and the intelligent home. For all the success of Western massively multiplayer online games and environments from Everquest to CounterStrike and World of Warcraft, with its 7 million gamers worldwide, the South Korean game Lineage is the world leader with over 14 million registered gamers inside the massively multiplayer gaming environment.

We discuss the rapid adoption of digital TV tuners into cellphones and cars in the portable TV chapter, and then look at how shopping and banking are evolving electronic cash, credit cards embedded to cellphones and digital connectivity is omnipresent. We discuss for example what many call the biggest change in consumer behavior, 2D Barcodes - also first introduced in South Korea and now becoming such a big hit in Japan and global giants like Google and Nokia betting on this as the next big breakthrough. We offer 2D Barcodes as one of our twelve case studies for you in this book.

We look at healthcare, schools, law enforcement and such matters in the government chapter - for example that the opportunities for cybercrime have caused every South Korean police department to set up a unit for cybercrime. We look at telematics, in particular as it relates to automobiles. In addition, we survey the music industry in Digital Korea, to see why 45% of all music sold in South Korea is already delivered to cellphones or so-called musicphones, which were invented in South Korea with the first commercial launch in 2003. For contrast, the Apple iPod has existed twice as long as, yet even in America, at the birthplace of the iPod by end of 2006 only 10% of American music was sold online. The iPod was indeed revolutionary, but it had to thrive in isolation. The musicphones in South Korea benefited from the whole society being digital and connected, including the record labels and the very musicians themselves.

We continue by examining pervasive computing, multiplayer gaming, and finally perhaps the most amazing of them all: the South Korean intention to make consumer robots equally ubiquitous. Where most other countries cautiously consider bringing robots in touch with humans, in South Korea the government is certain it will have a robot in every Korean home in ten years! So the robotics industry is rapidly developing the human interactivity know-how in what guiding might a robot help with at a shopping mall, or how a household robot could also double as the robotic nanny to help the children finish their homework. We end the book with a discussion about convergence from technical, industry and device points-of-view before giving our summary and concluding thoughts.

Like looking at a still image of a movie

In some ways, our task to describe the continuously connected Digital Korea is nearly impossible. It is like attempting to describe a great movie by showing still images of the movie. Yes, these are the actors in these kinds of scenes, but the real impact comes out of the whole coming together, from the script to the actors to the scenery to the music, lighting, etc. We have strived to cover all of the most relevant points so that at least a fair view can be made. South Korea is not "only" the most connected country in broadband internet user, or in 3G cellphones, etc. We hope to give you a context.

For our book, we had the privilege of visiting with numerous South Korean pioneering companies and interviewing dozens of leaders in this space. Some of those discussions have turned into case studies but others have their thoughts woven into the text and provide more of the detail in the book.

Inevitably, with a society changing as fast as the bleeding edge of technology, many of the statistics in this book will become obsolete soon after we have gone to print. With that, we have attempted to give context of the statistics, comparing South Korea to the world average for example, or to use leading countries like Japan, USA, Canada, UK etc to provide comparisons and contrasts.

We hope these help to illustrate that it is not only one or two areas where South Korea has "sneaked" ahead; it is in just about every possible measure of a digital country or information society.

For you as the reader, please do not contrast our stated statistic with the latest data you find in your country when you read this book. Consider rather, how far ahead South Korea was in 2006 at the time of our research and writing of this book, and please take it as a given that South Korean industry leadership will have moved on further since we wrote this book.

How will it impact our lives?

What will happen in this kind of environment, is a "virtuous cycle" of technical leadership. As the technical infrastructure is ahead of the world, it enables newest handsets and computers to be deployed, which in turn enables programmers to exploit to the fullest the abilities of the technologies, which in turn give the consumers choices that are innovative. This then results in customers who are familiar with the new, and thus become very sophisticated and demanding of ever more. They are willing to pay for cutting edge solutions, which again fuels further investments in faster technologies, etc. This is why so many usage numbers seem mind-boggling to Westerners.

For example, picture messaging from camera phones. In most Western countries the usage of "MMS" (Multimedia Messaging) is a severe disappointment at most networks. In the UK, with about 72 million mobile phones of, which about 60% are cameraphones and 15% are 3G high speed phones, picture messaging traffic is under a million picture messages per month. In South Korea, with high resolution cameraphones,

Tomi T Ahonen

near 100% cameraphone penetration, high speed 3G networks, and services serving the picture sharing needs of its customers, like Cyworld, out of a population of 40 million mobile phone owners, they send 6 million picture messages per month. A user population of nearly half, sends six times as many.

Why is this? Part of it is that everybody has the devices, and they all have high-speed access. That is only part of the story. The bigger part is the benefit from new, related innovations, only possible in that environment. A staggering statistic is that 90% of the picture messaging transfers are in fact cameraphone pictures uploaded to Cyworld. (For a Western context, imagine uploading directly from cameraphones to picture sharing online sites like Flickr or videos to YouTube).

Cyworld in South Korea is the world's most advanced digital online environment, which we discuss in several chapters and its own case study in this book. The virtuous cycle of devices, users, high-speed networks and most importantly the new services such as Cyworld, cause both a "push" and a "pull" effect, dramatically accelerating the usage, and improving service development.

Society needs to change

While technology allows new ways to do things, it invariably brings new problems with it. The same cellphone that allows us to contact our spouse urgently on the road, is also causing many drivers to shift focus from the road and causing accidents. The efficiency of rapid broadband access to social networking websites is good for publishing blogs and journals and joining in discussion groups. However, that same technology allows unscrupulous predators and sex offenders to target young innocent users and make untoward advances.

Issues of privacy arise, as do those of content ownership. The girl dancing in a video shot on her friend's cameraphone and uploaded on a video sharing site, may be original creative expressive art, but if she is dancing to a tune by Madonna - without permission - then it is likely an infringement on Madonna's rights to the song. New technologies bring with them new opportunities but also new threats.

South Korea has been at this frontier as well. Its society has been learning and adjusting, to issues ranging from students cheating in class by sending text messages during exams, to teenagers sending or receiving pornographic images on cameraphones, to privacy issues around tracking the locations of people by their phones, etc. Typical problems include the use of cameraphones in public baths, swimming pools, gyms etc. Some of the solutions around these kinds of problems can be technical - such as creating a sound to a cameraphone that it cannot be used to secretly take photos - to regulatory, such as forbidding the use of cameraphones at public baths and swimming pools - to behavioral, such as the guidelines for considerate phone usage that have been published in South Korea. We discuss these issues as well in this book.

Attitude to technology

South Koreans today can be said to be immersed in information. The amount of information available to South Koreans at any time of any day from anywhere can be overwhelming. Smart phones, internet cafes, gaming halls, and restaurants with broadband access all entice South Koreans to keep access information and refresh their contacts. This vast access to data seems to fit naturally with the "bballi bballi" culture of hurry-hurry we discussed earlier.

Yes, everything is a rush. South Koreans want to be ever more productive. And, to save time and money in the process. Data and telecoms networks both those in use, and their higher speed siblings being deployed, have indeed expanded productivity. However, bballi bballi also has some drawbacks. In Digital Korea, people often will not take time to relax and to disconnect. In the rapid pace life in South Korea, even leisure activities, such as gaming, happen at a high speeds.

As the environment changes, we also change with it. The consumer in South Korea has been pampered with the world's widest range of digital services and choices. With it comes a maturity to such options and services. In our interviews for this book, Harry Lee, Vice President at In Wireless of South Korea, said:

> *"The South Korean customer is not satisfied with voice communications only anymore. The customer wants life to be made easier. They are not satisfied with basic services such as text based data communications either, now they demand multimedia functions."*
> Harry Lee, Vice President, In Wireless

We can see how this increasing awareness of what is possible results in ever more demanding customers, who then push the providers to supply ever better services.

A mirror into your own future

We hope you will enjoy this journey with us to Digital Korea. We are convinced that these changes will happen in all industrialized countries. With that, this book can serve as your digital guide into the next five years or so of our life, your career and employment opportunities, your family and home, etc.

If you work in the digitally converging industries like telecoms, internet, media, banking etc, we strongly recommend visiting South Korea to see it for yourself. Even to us, who discuss South Korean inventions and industries in our daily technology expert lives, we are still continuously surprized and amazed at the latest innovations and developments. The synchronized simultaneous lead in all of the digital industries is a virtuous cycle, which currently perpetuates an ongoing leadership in all areas of digital life.

To understand our digital future, understand Digital Korea.

Chapter 2 - Digital Youth
Generation C in South Korea

Generation-C as the Community Generation was introduced in the book *Communities Dominate Brands* (Ahonen & Moore, 2005). The defining characteristic of Gen-C is that for the first time in mankind's history a new generation is growing up with permanent, 24-hour support of the friends, colleagues, community. The umbilical cord or the "lifeline" for Gen-C is the cellphone and the secretive cryptic connection...   (continued)

Excerpt from Tomi T Ahonen fourth book
Communities Dominate Brands with Alan Moore
(published by futuretext)
2005 first hardcover edition
2008 paperback edition
ISBN: 0-9544327-3-8

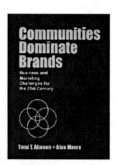

I - Introduction
On the Road to Engagement

If the last 10 years have caused disruption in your business, the next 10 years will cause much more so. Not driven by a controlled introduction of new technologies, but by an uncontrolled adoption of new, radical, unpredictable and even "unfair" methods by an emerging new element in consumption – the *digitally empowered community*. Digitalisation and the falling costline of technology have ripped through our business and social fabrics over the last five years, across all industries, across all countries, altering our economic and social landscapes forever. Yet what we have witnessed so far is only the beginning of a more profound, *seismic shift* in the very foundations of how business is conducted. We can imagine and do things, which were just not possible a few years ago. Life-threatening or life-enhancing? This is what this book is about; the Red pill or the Blue pill?, which one are you going to take? One thing is for sure: the structured order of our familiar industrial age has come to an end and it's dying as days do, gasping for every last ray of light.

All the rules are changing

Now, the Age of Connectedness and its newly active communities are altering the way all businesses will market, promote and sell their goods and services. The very first cases are emerging simultaneously around the world, and they clearly give an answer to what the marketing industry has expressed for several years already. Traditional methods of marketing, advertising and branding are increasingly ineffective. Something new is happening, only we could not put our fingers on it. Not yet. Not until this book.

Phillip Evans and Thomas S. Wurster state in their book *Blown to Bits* that digitalisation is "deconstructing" traditional industries such as home electronics, business, broadcast, retailing and banking, while at the same time creating new commercial opportunities such as Google and eBay, the low-cost airline industry, online banking, or Closed Audience Networks. These are trends echoed time and again by experts analysing the individual phenomena such as digital convergence and disruptive technologies.

Today, central to young people's discussions are music players, mobile phones, enhanced Bluetooth technology, digital cameras, robots, plasma screens and laptops. From Tokyo to New York this is the digital generation, brought up on generating their own content or consuming the content they want, digitally. So profound is their impact that the *Financial Times* writes that companies like Time Warner, Sony and Walt Disney are being forced to rethink their business models. Yes, we know the young are digital, but that is only half the story. There was a digital generation a decade ago, with Playstations, personal computers, digital calculators, portable CD players and Nintendo. *Digital* is *not* what is different this time; digital is not the key. The change is something deeper and more profound.

The new digital economics has removed the need to decide between whether one has richness or reach. Today, you can get both. This changes essentially everything. It changes the way customers can access information and changes the way they use it. It changes the way business can communicate with their customers and it also changes how a business might go to market. It changes the linking between channels that link businesses, customers, suppliers and employees. It offers opportunity and it offers your once helpless competitors the chance to radically rethink their business strategies and attack vital parts of your business model. New and hungry players are taking every opportunity to enter the value chain, hoping to disintermediate you and your brand promise.

We are still observing the very beginning of this, business guru Gary Hamel says: "The least appreciated effects of digitisation is the fragmentation of customer attention. Customers become harder to find and more difficult to keep."

From a Networked Age to the Connected Age

Much has been written about the digital age being the networked age; that we plug into and out of the network and get considerable benefits from being connected to the network. The network age was a good term for the 1990s, as it did describe how we as humans approached "the network" – i.e., the internet. We logged on, we accessed our email and we surfed seeking information. Much of what most readers will consider the digital world and digital convergence will consist of that networked model.

The first decade of the 21st century starts mankind's next evolution in delving deeper into the information age. We move beyond the networked age into the "connected age". Typical of the connected age is that we no longer have to physically log on and log off. We are not tied to any single physical place to find our connection. It is not the office or the home where we have our connection, and we do not have to connect at a hotspot. We are always connected and we can instantly access the network. We can be reached at any time, and typical of the connected age, we start to manage our connectedness when we deliberately disconnect ourselves for personal reasons.

The single most visible change from entering the Connected Age, is that we suddenly have permanent access to our peers, our friends, our colleagues and family members. We can start to live with a "lifeline" to those we trust. Our communities, which previously only existed at given points in time, now become ever-present. We are no longer alone. In the Connected Age modern people are able to draw on the community for assistance, information and support. We learn to search, share and interact in a new way.

In the Connected Age people will have public and private – and semi-private – personas, which coexist in the network and are connected independently. We may want to keep our public persona connected only during office hours. We may want our private connection always on, but always with the ringing sound turned off with all personal contacts knowing to use SMS text messaging to reach us. And we might connect and disconnect with our semi-private persona; for example, relating to our hobby or passion, be it football, car racing or opera.

In the Connected Age the intelligence and ability to customise our gadgets becomes ever more powerful. We will find that most of the novelty of surfing the net has worn off, and we rarely surf just for the sheer joy of discovering new websites. Our devices learn to adapt to our whims and preferences and quickly help us navigate to the sources of the information, entertainment and utility that we seek from the web. That kind of content and related applications will be increasingly consumed on mobile or cellular devices. When we use our cellular devices we will usually be in hurried states and need access fast. For that

Tomi T Ahonen

speed we are willing to pay something, and that payment in turn helps keep the content at our favored sites current and valuable.

But, with the greatest of threats comes also the greatest of opportunities. So, how do you navigate this newly converged world and what are the strategies that will enable you to do this successfully?

Brands in paralysis

We will show in the book how traditional advertising, marketing and branding are in crisis and how traditional marketing communications are becoming bottlenecks for growth. Brilliant marketing minds of a generation have been harnessed to deliver marketing from its despair, yet none have shown a sustainable method or tool for the marketing industry to deliver. All experts agree there is a problem, none of the solutions have been found to work. Foster and Kaplan state in a recent book entitled *Creative Destruction*:

> *Corporations are built on the assumption of continuity; their focus is on operations. Capital markets are built on the assumption of discontinuity; their focus is on creation and destruction. The data present a clear warning; unless companies open up their decision-making processes, relax conventional notions of control, and change at the scale and pace of the market, their performances will be drawn into an entropic slide into mediocrity.*
>
> Foster & Kaplan, *Creative Destruction, Currency 2001*

Technology changes the way we interact, the way we shop and consume. It creates new opportunities and destroys businesses that are unable to adapt to a sudden discontinuity with our past. We are moving from a production-driven to a consumption-led economy, where the nature of exchange is different, and this difference is exacerbated by the forces of digitalisation: the internet, e-commerce and the mobile phone.

Our recent history has been deeply affected by the increased speed of technological development plus the convergence and proliferation of the audio-visual, mobile, IT, and personal computing industries, increased internet and bandwidth penetration, and media choice. These developments have impacted on the businesses and the marketing community. As a result of these developments, business itself is faced with a tougher job when innovation and flexibility are the markers for competition, rather than efficiency being the fundamental driver of value.

We see creative destruction from disruptive effects to digitalisation to disintermediation by network effects in industry after industry. The music business, the movie business, television broadcasting, banking, the airline industry and travel, publishing, retail, utilities, government etc. The effects are seen everywhere. Michael Nutley, the editor of the *New Media Age,* says: "Industries, which try to dictate how their customers should transact with them are taking a huge risk in the digital age." As a consequence of the uptake of new technology and the way customers' habits are changing there is a lot of "creative destruction" happening across industries.

Enter the community

A key development that has been monitored and noted in numerous instances is the emergence of digitally connected communities. Mostly these have been seen in isolation, as a new "market space" opportunity to harness and harvest, to exploit if you will; to make money from. Communities like eBay's online auctions and shopping, or communities like online dating, music and movie file sharing, friend-finders and job recruitment, etc. These are significant developments by themselves. But they are the earliest visible symptoms of a massive development in human behaviour and change in society. Many more powerful and personal communities are also forming, and these are not limited by the shortcomings of the fixed internet.

Communities that use mobile phones to share, influence, connect and participate are spontaneously emerging in all countries in all areas of interest, from car shopping to birdwatching to anti-government revolt. Rather than the armchair networkers of fixed internet communities, those who connect on mobile phone communities are young, mobile and active. They can suddenly swarm and appear by literally the thousands on a moment's notice. These "smart mobs" as Howard Rheingold wrote in his book of the same title in 2003, can become activists either for or against any authority, politician, company, product or service.

With the first actual evidence of community activities on behalf of some product, services and companies, and of evidence of communities also against companies, we can formulate our thesis: that communities are the counterbalance to brand dominance in the 21st century. By examining what word of mouth, when enhanced by the powerful digital echoes of mobile phone communities and other networked communications such as IM Instant Messaging, email, and increasingly blogging, can do, we see that communities have been an undefined or underestimated barrier to recent marketing success. Furthermore, we establish that by harnessing community power and working with them, a modern marketer can succeed in delivering remarkably positive marketing effects to the intended target audience.

In our book we proceed logically by looking at the disruptive trends of technology, chance, digitalisation, disruption, convergence, and societal changes, then how businesses are changing. We examine how branding, marketing and advertising is in crisis. We establish the basis for understanding communities, both in the Networked Age of the past decade and the new Connected Age. We analyze the emerging new type of consumer. Still mostly under the age of 25, this Generation-C is the *Community* generation and we show how dramatically different it is from older generations, and how intuitively it already uses community power to its own gain. We then show how communities and brands interact, and why communities dominate brands. And finally, we show how businesses can thrive in this new marketing environment: they need to evolve from interruptive advertising to engagement marketing.

Bloggers, gamers or Gen-C?

We devote three chapters throughout the book to discuss in more detail the community behaviour of three groups of digitally-aware societies. In the virtual chapter we discuss videogamers. In the blogging chapter we discuss fixed internet bloggers of today, and the likely emerging mobile bloggers of the near tomorrow. And in the Gen-C chapter we discuss the young cellular-phone connected smart mobs. These are not the only digitally connected societies. There are countless more using the digital communication tools of choice most suitable for each community. We discuss gamers, bloggers and Gen-C because these three groups seem to have evolved furthest into discovering community power now, in 2005, and from a business point of view. We must emphasise that digital communities are inherently self-improving; they will evolve dramatically over the next few years. It is safe to assume that all of the power of the exceptionally successful community action that we describe in this book today will be totally commonplace with

Tomi T Ahonen

all communities a year or two down the line. Make no mistake about it: no matter what your business, your customers will behave like these communities.

Why us

We reveal a change to how all businesses need to interact, from the branding and advertising to all core marketing activities. The change is enormous, the biggest single change in business for the past 100 years. Why suddenly is it that the two of us would discover such a profound change?

We have been lucky to be involved in several strategic marketing projects in the earliest markets where this phenomenon has started to happen – the countries where mobile phone penetrations reached young teenagers first; Scandinavia in general and Finland in particular. We have also been lucky to work with those leading companies in those markets whose very core competence and deepest research happens to hit this area where our new Generation-C, with C for Community, has just emerged. We have supported companies that have specifically worked to understand Scandinavian youth and how it interacts with mobile phones. Our customers have included Nokia, Ericsson, TeliaSonera, Elisa, and numerous media companies, as well as support organisations with the deepest customer insights; such as specialist Xtract the user profiling company, or Fjord Networks, the User Interface company.

Even with exposure to the very earliest user patterns, it took us collaborative thinking and analysis and our own research to finally develop the theory that combines the counterbalancing forces of brands and communities. However, with every emerging new finding our conclusions become more firm. The facts solidly support our hypothesis and we can now already claim it to be true, the balance is in favor of the communities: communities dominate brands.

An American angle

Some of the issues in this book, particularly the early parts of digital convergence and disruptive technologies, are very familiar to American readers. The ideas of blogging and virtual environments are also not alien. And, as we all know, Americans tend to be world leaders in innovation in marketing, advertising and branding.

American readers should pay particularly close attention to the issues of the cellular phone, the Connected Age and Generation-C. Because of the early successes of various digital, internet and wireless data solutions, American businesses may be blinded to the "big picture" – the much more dramatic shift happening to communities activated by the cellular phone. It is not a "rival" technology to co-exist with email, e-commerce, IM Instant Messaging etc. No, cellular phone based communication is a *total cannibalization* of the digital space.

It is very easy to become impressed with the dramatic growth rates of the various digital delivery technologies from broadband internet to digital radio. Yet these all pale in comparison with the pervasiveness and power of the cellular phone. Do not become distracted, the analogy is not railroads vs. airplanes – both of, which still co-exist in the 21st century. The appropriate analogy is steam-powered cars vs. gasoline-powered cars. In 1890 over 90% of all motor driven vehicles were steam-powered. By 1920 less than 1% were so. Understand the shift from the Networked Age to the Connected Age. The future of every business depends on capturing the soul of Generation-C...   (continued)

Other books by futuretext

Mobile Web 2.0
by Ajit Jaokar & Tony Fish
futuretext 2006
ISBN : 978-0954432768
364 pages

"In their latest book, the authors make fresh challenges on the paradigms in Mobile data. You are not going to agree with it all, but it will challenge your own thinking."
- Jeremy Flynn, Head of Commercial Partnerships, **Vodafone** UK

Distraction
Being human in the digital age
by Mark Curtis
futuretext 2005
ISBN : 978-0954432744
248 pages

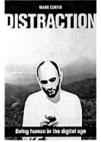

"This book is about us people surviving in a world that is becoming ever more intrusive in the various technologies. It is to computers and mobile phones what Charlie Chaplin's movie "Modern Times" was to the industrial revolution. Curtis puts it in very human terms and touching stories. I completely recommend it."
 - Tomi T Ahonen, Author and Consultant, Hong Kong

Riding the Russian Technology Boom
by Andrey Gidaspov
futuretext 2007
ISBN : 978-0955606915
420 pages

Mobile Strategies
Understanding Wireless Business Models, MVNOs and the Growth of Mobile Content
by Tom Weiss
futuretext 2006
ISBN : 978-0954432775
186 pages

Available now at major booksellers, Amazon and directly from www.futuretext.com

Printed in the United Kingdom
by Lightning Source UK Ltd.
134872UK00001B/196-237/P